W9-ADE-062

CHINA'S CHANGING MAP

CHINA'S CHANGING MAP

A Political and Economic Geography of The Chinese People's Republic

BY

THEODORE SHABAD

Author of
Geography of the U.S.S.R.

Maps by Vaughn S. Gray

FREDERICK A. PRAEGER
New York

BOOKS THAT MATTER

Library of Congress Catalog Number: 55-11530

Published in the United States of America in 1956
by FREDERICK A. PRAEGER, INC., PUBLISHERS
150 East 52 Street, New York 22, N. Y.

Printed in the United States of America

To

Leslie, Steven and Peter

PREFACE

The Chinese Communists established their present regime in Peking on October 1, 1949. During the more than six years since then a tremendous political, social and economic revolution has taken place in China. The Chinese People's Republic, still unrecognized by most of the nations outside the Soviet bloc, has emerged as a leading world power. The Chinese revolution has remolded society and set up one of the most centralized, regimented states that country has ever known. The aim of the Chinese Communists is to build a strong industrialized country modeled on the Soviet Union. Allied with the USSR and other nations of the Communist bloc, China has become the strongest power in Asia.

The impact of these developments on the world scene has been dramatic. There is little need to stress the importance both of the changes within China and of the new international role China has assumed. Many books published in recent years have sought to present and interpret the new facts about China. These volumes have dealt mainly with the political, social and economic transformation of the country. Most of these studies have dealt with institutions in the nation as a whole rather than with its component parts. Few have dealt systematically with the effect of the revolution on the landscape of China.

The author has attempted to fill this gap. The present volume seeks to focus attention on the areal changes that have taken place as a result of the Chinese revolution. Its approach is geographic to the extent that it marshals and arranges the known facts about China from the specific point of view of political and economic-geographic change. In the process of their revolution, the Chinese Communists have made over the political map of the country. Their concerted drive for all-out industrialization has left its imprint on the economic geography of the nation.

This volume does not purport to present a comprehensive treatment of the geography of China. The author has set himself a more limited and more specific objective. Political and economic changes since 1949 have been emphasized throughout the book. Historical background has been retained only where it was regarded essential. The author is aware that this orientation neglects to some extent the great weight of past

Chinese experience and focuses on the happenings of a few years. There is no question but that Communist institutions and transformations are still only a veneer on the massive bulk of China. But the author regards them as an ever thickening veneer that will increasingly penetrate into the core and affect the world around it.

In its aim, substance and methodology, the book has been conceived in the image of the author's "Geography of the USSR," published in 1951. It is designed to present in convenient form the essential political and economic-geographic facts of present China and to interpret their significance on the basis of Soviet experience. Similarities and differences between Soviet and Chinese institutions and developments are pointed out wherever such analysis sheds light on the Chinese scene.

Part I surveys China as a whole. The physical setting of the country is discussed to the extent that it is essential for an understanding of man's use of the land. The political geography of China is treated with specific reference to the new administrative structure, the present state of the population and the national autonomous areas of non-Chinese ethnic minorities. In the fields of industry, agriculture, transportation and foreign trade, the general survey summarizes institutional changes under the Communists, discusses the distribution of economic activities and presents the five-year plan and up-to-date production statistics of the major branches of the Chinese economy. These statistics, published for the first time in systematic form, have been derived by the author from scattered Chinese sources.

Part II is a regional treatment of the country. Here political and economic changes are discussed in detail province by province. As elsewhere in the book, stress is put on industrial construction, urbanization, and the setting up of new autonomous minority areas. Wherever possible, provinces are grouped into major natural regions, such as the North China plain, the loesslands or the Southeast coastal uplands. In that case, the provincial sections are preceded by a regional introduction stressing common physical and economic characteristics. In addition to a systematic survey of all minority areas, the provincial sections contain separate discussion of the 170 major cities of China. Following the Soviet pattern, many of these cities have been raised to that status because of new economic or industrial growth.

Vaughn Gray has prepared the maps for this book. They are designed as location maps and include most of the place names mentioned in the text. Places that could not be mapped because of space limitations are generally oriented in the text with reference to a more important center that does appear on the maps.

In the matter of place-name spellings, the author was confronted with a choice between the more common, though inconsistent Chinese post office names and the less popular, though more scientific Wade-Giles transliteration system. Because the reader is presumed to be more familiar with postal spellings, these have been used in the text and on the maps. However, both the postal names and the corresponding Wade-Giles transliteration forms are included in the index. Chinese words and names other than place names are given in the Wade-Giles form. With regard to non-Chinese place names, which occur mainly in Inner Mongolia, Sinkiang and Tibet, the Chinese name or the Chinese transcription of the indigenous name has been correlated whenever possible with the local designation. In a few cases, where the native name could not be identified from the Chinese characters, the Chinese transcription alone is given for identification of the place name.

The Chinese use generic territorial terms that can be variously translated in English as area, region, district, territory and so forth. In writing about the Soviet Union, whose terminology presents a similar problem, the author has consistently used the Russian generic terms to avoid confusion by ambiguous translation. Although this approach is novel in the Chinese field, the author has followed the same practice. Designations such as ch'ü, chou, hsien, hsiang have been retained in preference to ambiguous English equivalents. The meaning of these terms is explained in the discussion on the present administrative system. "Ch'ü" is a particularly imprecise generic term. It designates both an area of the size of Inner Mongolia (Inner Mongolian Autonomous Ch'ü) and an area such as the Yümen oilfield (Yümen Oil-Producing Ch'ü). Of the Chinese administrative terms, only the familiar "province" (Chinese *sheng*) and "city" (Chinese *shih*) have been retained in English.

With regard to the rendering of Chinese generic physical terms, such as "kiang," "ho," "shui" (all meaning "river") and "shan" (mountain), the following practice has been adopted. When the specific part of the place name is a single character, the Chinese generic has been used; for example: Han Kiang and Han Shui (two separate streams), instead of the ambiguous Han River. When the specific part of the name is made up of two or more characters, the English generic has been adopted; for example: Yungting River instead of Yungting Ho, the reasoning being that the specific name (Yungting) sufficiently identifies the stream in question. The Yangtze River, which the Chinese call Chang Kiang, the Yellow River (Hwang Ho) and the Sungari River (Sunghwa Kiang) have been used in their conventional English forms.

Communist China's isolation from the non-Soviet world has limited information available to outside observers. The material in the present volume has been assembled from a vast amount of scattered sources in the Chinese, Russian and Western languages. The most relevant information was gathered from the Chinese and Soviet press, recent Chinese maps and atlases, and a number of Soviet studies.

The territory covered in the followed discussion is mainland China under Communist control. Neither Outer Mongolia nor Formosa, each a separate de facto national unit, has been included.

In the effort to collect data for this book, the author had to overcome two major obstacles. One was Communist China's reluctance to export newspapers, periodicals, maps and other source materials. The other was the restrictions imposed by the United States on the importation of these materials. The author is hopeful that a progressive lessening of world tension will bring down the barriers interfering with the flow of ideas and information.

T. S.

New York
January, 1956

TABLE OF CONTENTS

MAPS

TABLES

PART I

Chapter 1

THE PHYSICAL SETTING

Location and Boundaries

China occupies a dominant position in Asia. Her 3,800,000 square miles cover a compact territory larger than that of the United States and second in the world only to that of the Soviet Union. Unlike her Soviet neighbor, which occupies the northern fringe of the Eurasian continent, China has a central location, bordering on virtually all the mainland nations of Asia except those of the Middle East.

The latitudinal position of China corresponds closely to that of the United States and both countries have the same east-west spread. If China were superimposed on North America, she would reach from Puerto Rico to Hudson Bay, and from the Atlantic to the Pacific. In terms of the geography of the Soviet Union, China extends from the longitude of Omsk (73 degrees E.) to Khabarovsk (135 degrees E.) over a distance of 3,000 miles. The country's north-south range is about 2,500 miles, from tropical Hainan Island to the subarctic Siberia.

In climatic terms, and thus in natural vegetation and soils, eastern China is the rough equivalent of the eastern United States. The industrial heart of China, in the Peking-Mukden-Dairen triangle, corresponds to the location of the urban belt extending from New York to Washington. However, the more important agricultural zones of China are somewhat farther south than the most populous parts of the United States.

The core areas of both the United States and China lie to the leeward of great continents in the battleground of polar and tropical airmasses. However, China extends westward and ends in the dry middle-latitude climate of arid central Asia, without the relief of the oceanic effects of a west coast. Moreover, China has much less level land than the United States, especially in the west and south. About one-half of China exceeds one mile in elevation. The inhospitable character of climate and topography is reflected particularly along China's international borders. Through the centuries, towering mountains or parched deserts have impeded China's intercourse with her neighbors.

China borders on eleven nations. They are North Korea, the Soviet Union, Outer Mongolia (Mongolian People's Republic), Afghanistan, Pakistan's section of Kashmir, India, Nepal, Bhutan, Burma, Laos and North Vietnam.

China's frontier with North Korea is neatly defined by the Yalu and Tumen rivers, whose combined courses cut across the base of the Korean peninsula between the Yellow Sea and the Sea of Japan. Traffic over the Yalu-Tumen frontier is among the most active along China's frontiers. The rivers are crossed by a number of rail lines linking the industrial areas of North Korea with adjacent Manchuria. The two main routes are the west-coast railroad, crossing the Yalu at Antung-Sinuiju and serving Pyongyang, and the east-coast line, which bridges the Tumen River and goes on to the Korean centers of Chongjin, Kim Chak, Hungnam and Wonsan.

The Soviet Union's frontier with China is interrupted by Outer Mongolia. Most of the eastern section of the Soviet-Chinese border is formed by the mighty Amur River and its tributaries, the Ussuri and the Argun. Little traffic passes this effective river barrier separating Manchuria and Siberia. While population is relatively concentrated along the Trans-Siberian Railroad on the Soviet side, the Chinese bank is sparsely settled. Border trade is restricted almost entirely to the Chinese Eastern railroad, a branch of the Trans-Siberian crossing Manchuria as a short cut to the Soviet Far East. The Chinese Eastern crosses the frontier at Manchouli, at its western end, and at Tungning (the former Suifenho) in the east. The latter handles the relatively limited trade between Manchuria and the Vladivostok-Khabarovsk area of the Soviet Far East. It is the Manchouli station, situated opposite the Soviet border stop of Otpor, that controls the most important transportation route linking China overland with the outside world. Here passes virtually all the economic aid supplied by the Soviet Union and the Eastern European countries for China's industrialization. In return, Manchouli is the chief overland outlet of China's exports.

Up to this point, the Chinese frontier follows river lines and its delineation is not disputed. The only areas in controversy are the Changpai Mountains on the Korean border and low-lying marshy islands at the Amur-Ussuri confluence on the Soviet line. On Chinese maps, both the entire Changpai massif and the Amur River islands are shown as part of China. Korean maps draw the international frontier through the peak of the Changpai Mountains and Soviet sources consider the Amur isles part of the Soviet Union.

Near Manchouli begins the 2,700-mile-long border with Outer Mongolia. Although this frontier is delineated in detail on Soviet maps, giving the impression of accurate survey, it is labeled on Chinese maps "still to be delimited" and is drawn in rough outline. The Outer Mongolian line crosses the steppe and desert of the Gobi, where occasional nomad herdsmen are the only elements of population. The only major trade route through this area has been the Peking-Ulan-Bator highway via Kalgan. Since 1954 this route is paralleled by the Peking-Tsining—Ulan-Bator railroad. The rail route, which cuts 721 miles from the Moscow-Peking run through Manchuria, is expected to replace the Manchouli gateway as the main transportation route between China and the Soviet Union.

West of Outer Mongolia, the Soviet-Chinese border continues from the Altai Mountains to the Tien Shan and the Pamir highlands. The frontier runs alternately along mountain ranges and across valleys that are the natural gateways in this western section of the Soviet-Chinese line. The main highway crossings north of the Tien Shan are at Tahcheng, on the way to Ayaguz on the Turksib Railroad, at in the Ili valley west of Kuldja, on the way to Alma-Ata. The Dzungarian Gates, a historic routeway, have not been used in modern times, but may carry the track of the planned Sinkiang railroad between China and the Soviet Union. In the Kashgar area, south of the Tien Shan, truck routes cross the Soviet frontier into the Kirghiz SSR in Torugart Pass and at Irkeshtam.

The western section of the Soviet-Chinese border is delimited by treaty, except for the Pamirs. Until 1953, some Chinese maps showed all of the Pamirs as part of China. Since that time, the Chinese have withdrawn the line to the eastern margins of the highlands, in accordance with Soviet maps, and labeled it "still to be delimited." The disputed frontier at the westernmost end of Chinese territory includes the Wakhan panhandle of Afghanistan and part of the Karakoram Mountains of Kashmir. Chinese maps show the frontier along the main watershed range of the Karakoram, while Indian sources advance the frontier to one of the front ranges in the north.

The border with India, Nepal and Bhutan continues along the formidable mountain barrier of the Himalayas, inaccessible to motorized traffic and crossed only by a few caravan routes. These are, in particular, the upper Indus valley route linking Tibet and Ladakh in Kashmir and the main India-Tibet route via Yatung and Kalimpong. However, at year-end of 1955, Tibetan highway construction crews advancing along the main route to India were approaching the border at Yatung. They were extending the newly built Tibetan truck road system to the very gates of India.

At the eastern end of the Himalayan barrier, the Chinese border is disputed with India and Burma. Along the Assam frontier of India, the Chinese claim jurisdiction over the Miri, Abor and Mishmi hill areas and advance their frontier (on maps) to the very edge of the Brahmaputra valley. In Burma, the Chinese have long considered the northernmost part of the country (north of Lat. 25 degrees 30 minutes N.) part of Yünnan Province. On the basis of maps published since 1953, the Peking regime appears to have relinquished its claim to part of northern Burma, including the upper reaches of the Chindwin River and the Hukawng Valley (traversed by the war-famed Ledo Road). The maps still show Chinese jurisdiction over the upper reaches of the Irrawaddy River, north of Myitkyina.

The Burmese-Chinese frontier appears to be relatively well defined south of Myitkyina. In this area it is crossed by the Burma Road, a key transportation link through China's backdoor. Farther south, Chinese and Burmese maps disagree on the alignment of the border, each nation laying claim to the remote Wa (Kawa) States on the east bank of the Salween River.

The border continues through mountainous terrain shared with Laos and North Vietnam to the Gulf of Tonkin. The Vietnamese frontier is crossed by two major transportation routes. They are the Hanoi-Kunming railroad at the border stations of Hokow-Laokay and the Liuchow-Hanoi line at the border stations of Munankwan-Dongdang. The Liuchow railroad, completed in 1952, for the first time connected North Vietnam with the Chinese rail system. The Kunming line, which is the natural outlet for Yünnan Province, was partly dismantled during the Second World War and subsequent civil warfare. Its reconstruction was begun in 1955.

Geologic Structure

In general terms, the geologic history of China can be discussed in terms of the Chinese platform, a stable, rigid section of the earth's crust, and a series of enclosing unstable zones or geosynclines that have produced the great Himalayan, Kunlun and Tien Shan uplifts in the west and the oceanic trough and island arc off the eastern coast.

Two areas of somewhat differing geologic history make up the Chinese platform. They are, on the one hand, the Sinian shield, covering almost all of North China and Manchuria and a large part of the Northwest, and the South China massif, which includes the Szechwan basin and China south of the Yangtze River.

The Sinian shield dates from Pre-Cambrian times. It is a part of the Chinese platform that has been a region of emergence through most of its history and its formations are largely of nonmarine origin. Continental development occurred in the Proterozoic era, the Upper Cambrian, Devonian and Lower Carboniferous periods and since the Upper Permian. Marine invasions, dated from the end of the Proterozoic, the Lower Cambrian, Ordovician, and Upper Paleozoic, left limestone and shale formations. The sedimentary cover is generally thin and discontinuous. Rocks of the ancient metamorphic basement outcrop over large areas, consisting of Archeozoic gneisses and crystalline schists and of Early Proterozoic micaceous schists, phyllite and quartzite.

The South China massif, in contrast to its northern counterpart, has generally been a region of subsidence and has been subjected to marine invasions over a longer period of time. Sediments show a fairly complete stratigraphic record, with all marine systems from the Upper Proterozoic to the Triassic represented. The southern massif finally became emergent in the Late Triassic. Basement rocks are of Proterozoic origin, except along the coast where Archeozoic formations outcrop.

The northern and southern parts of the Chinese platform are separated by a narrow folded zone that gave rise to the Tsin Ling mountain system in the Hercynian revolution (Upper Paleozoic) and the Kilien Mountains of the Nan Shan system in the earlier Caledonian revolution (Lower Paleozoic).

In the Cretaceous period occurred the greatest mountain-building period of the Chinese platform. It is known as the Yen Shan revolution, for its type locality at the northern edge of the North China plain. In the course of the Yen Shan upheaval, the platform was broken into a series of separate blocs that continued to maintain their rigidity. These blocs are Shantung-Liaotung, Manchuria, Ordos, Szechwan and Tarim. The mountains formed in the Yen Shan revolution trend typically NE-SW and are especially developed in the South China massif.

After the Yen Shan period, which incidentally corresponds to the Laramide revolution that gave birth to the Rocky Mountains in North America, deposition of the products of continental erosion continued on the rigid blocs. They began to subside, except for the Shantung-Liaotung massif, which continued to retain its mountain characteristics. The subsiding blocs of the Chinese platform were covered with Mesozoic-Cenozoic redbeds of fluvial and lacustrine origin. The largest accumulation occurred in the foothills of the western Kunlun (Yarkand depression), the central Tien Shan (Kucha depression) and the Nan Shan

(Kansu depression). The total thickness of sediments reached 25,000 to 30,000 feet.

Among relatively recent formations are the Manchurian and North China plains, which subsided along fairly clearly defined fault lines. However, while the present rolling topography of the Manchurian plain is largely of erosional origin, the North China lowland is entirely the product of the accumulation of sediments of the Yellow River.

Volcanic activity related to the Yen Shan revolution produced rhyolite and andesite lava flows in the Great Khingan, the Peking hills, Shantung and the southeast coast. Among intrusive rocks, granite predominates, forming large masses near the southeast coast and smaller bodies in the Yin Shan of Inner Mongolia, the Peking hills and the Lüliang Mountains of Shansi. Tertiary and Pleistocene basalt flows underlie large areas in the Great Khingan and the East Manchurian uplands, the Alashan Mountains, the Luichow peninsula and northern Hainan.

The Tien Shan-Altai tectonic zone of China includes the central and eastern sections of the Tien Shan, the Dzungarian massif, the Tarbagatai and Saur Mountains, the Zaisan depression and the Mongolian Altai.

The Tien Shan penetrates into China from the Soviet Union and tapers off gradually both in width and in elevation. It consists of a number of parallel ranges of varying geologic ages. A central zone, including the Narat Range, is made up of Pre-Cambrian formations (crystalline schist, slate, phyllite). Adjoining it on the north (Borokhoro Range) and south (Kokshaal-Tau) are thick sandstone, shale and limestone formations of Cambrian-Ordovician and Lower Devonian age. Finally, the outer zones consist of Upper Paleozoic sandstone and shale.

The Dzungarian massif consists essentially of undisturbed horizontal sedimentary strata ranging from Lower Carboniferous marine formations through Middle and Upper Carboniferous volcanic deposits, Lower Permian sandstone and shale, and coal-bearing sandstone and argillite of the Upper Triassic and Jurassic, to continental deposits of Cretaceous and Tertiary origin.

The Tarbagatai and Saur Mountains on the Soviet border are made up of strongly warped Silurian shale and sandstone overlain unformably by Middle Paleozoic volcanic materials. The Zaisan depression, which is occupied by the upper Irtysh River, is filled with unconsolidated marine sediments of the Middle and Upper Paleozoic era. The Mongolian Altai consists of two geologic zones. The northern high-elevation zone consists of Lower Paleozoic shale and sandstone, while the southern foothill belt is made up in large part by outcrops of the Pre-Cambian basement.

It would thus appear that the Tien Shan-Altai geosyncline filled with sediments during the Lower Paleozoic era. These sediments were uplifted during the Middle and Upper Paleozoic into the original mountain system. The Dzungarian massif, which had passed through a continental period while the geosyncline was being filled with marine sediments, subsided at the time of the mountain making. Dzungaria then passed through a marine invasion, followed by lacustrine deposition.

The Kunlun-Himalaya zone is made up of the mountain systems of the Kunlun and the Himalaya, separated by the high plateau of Tibet. The Kunlun system, formed in the Lower and Middle Paleozoic era, has the following geologic make-up. Its northern ranges consist of phyllitized shale and sandstone of Proterozoic age. Gneisses and schists of Archeozoic age and granite intrusions characterize the middle section. The southern slopes, facing Tibet, are made up of intensely warped sandstone and shale of the Lower Paleozoic.

The Himalayan branch arose during the Alpine revolution. The axis of the system consists of Pre-Cambrian gneiss and schist. Thin strata of Upper Paleozoic, Triassic and Jurassic age cover the flanks. Igneous rocks are represented by post-Cretaceous granite intrusions and rhyolite and andesite lava flows of the same period. The geologic history of the Tibetan plateau is only sketchily known. Scattered data indicate a wide development of Upper Paleozoic, Jurassic, Cretaceous and Tertiary deposits.

Topographic Forms

The topography of China reflects the tectonic history of the region. The mountains produced by the Yen Shan revolution of the Cretaceous period trend characteristically NE-SW. Other mountain ranges, formed predominantly during the earlier Caledonian and Hercynian revolutions of the Paleozoic era typically strike E-W. These two intersecting patterns have formed a checkerboard-like configuration that can be traced with relative ease through most of China.

The easternmost of the Yen Shan tectonic lines is evident in the Southeast uplands of the coastal provinces of Chekiang and Fukien. This massif, consisting of several parallel ranges, rises to 3,500-5,000 feet in the Wuyi and Tienmu Mountains along the western margins. It is adjoined by a synclinal zone, also following the NE-SW trend, occupied by the lowlands of the Hwai Ho and the lower Yangtze River and the valleys of the Kan Kiang in Kiangsi Province and the Tung Kiang and

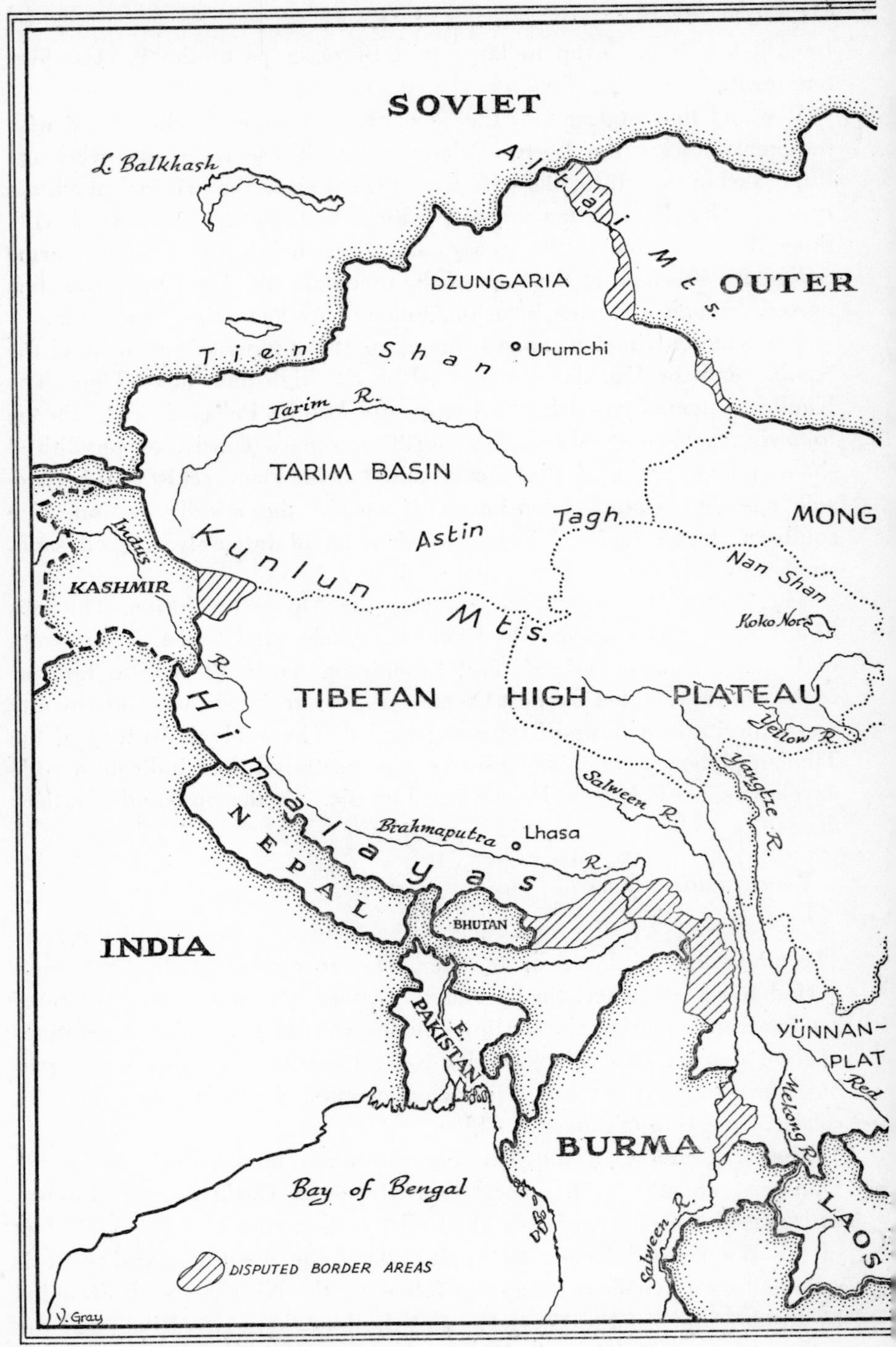

Physical Features of China

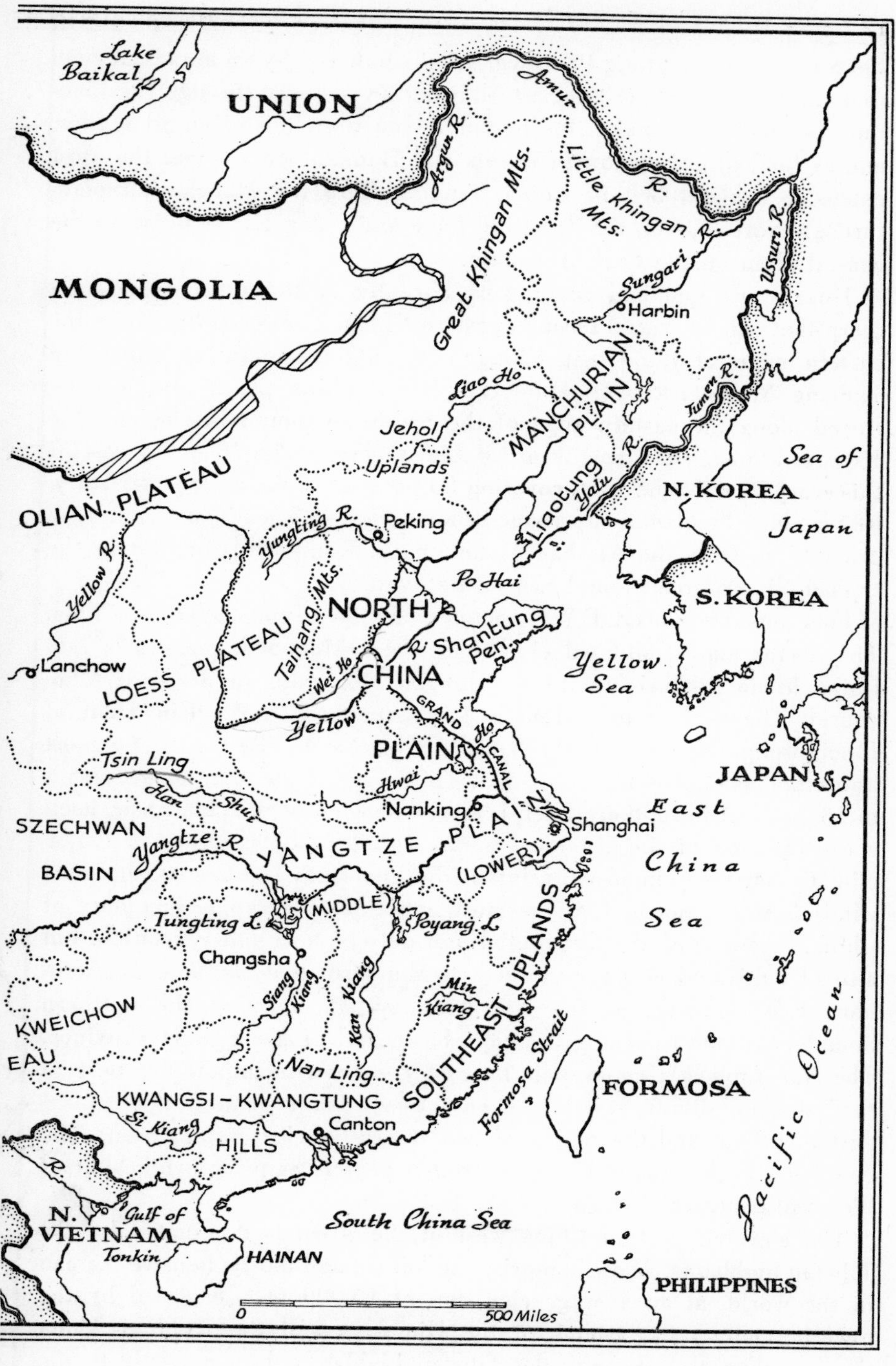
Lake Baikal
UNION
Amur
Argun R.
Great Khingan Mts.
Little Khingan Mts.
R.
Ussuri R.
Sungari R.
Harbin
MONGOLIA
MANCHURIAN PLAIN
Liao Ho
Tumen R.
Jehol Uplands
Yalu R.
Liaotung
Sea of Japan
N. KOREA
OLIAN PLATEAU
Yungting R.
Peking
Yellow R.
Po Hai
S. KOREA
Taihang Mts.
NORTH CHINA PLAIN
Shantung Pen.
Lanchow
LOESS PLATEAU
Wei Ho
R.
Yellow Sea
Yellow
GRAND CANAL
Ho
Tsin Ling
Hwai
JAPAN
Han Shui
Nanking
East China Sea
SZECHWAN BASIN
Shanghai
Yangtze R.
YANGTZE PLAIN
(LOWER)
(MIDDLE)
Tungting L.
Poyang L.
Changsha
SOUTHEAST UPLANDS
Siang Kiang
Kan Kiang
Min Kiang
KWEICHOW
EAU
Formosa Strait
Pacific Ocean
Nan Ling
FORMOSA
KWANGSI - KWANGTUNG HILLS
Si Kiang
Canton
R.
N. VIETNAM
Gulf of Tonkin
South China Sea
HAINAN
PHILIPPINES
0
500 Miles

Pei Kiang in Kwangtung Province. This is followed by an anticlinal zone that can be traced from the East Manchurian uplands, through the Liaotung peninsula, Shantung, the mountains on the Hunan-Kiangsi border, and as far as the Luichow peninsula and Hainan. Then comes the most extensive lowland belt of China, ranging from the Manchurian plain through North China, the Tungting Lake and Siang Kiang plain, to the coastal plain on the Gulf of Tonkin.

This broad synclinal zone stops abruptly at the great continental scarp that can be traced through eastern China. The scarp lies along the eastern edge of the Great Khingan Mountains, continues along the Taihang Mountains overlooking the North China plain, and can be traced along the eastern edge of the Szechwan mountain rim and the Kweichow plateau. Virtually all of China below 1,500 feet lies east of this scarp line. To the west, covering 85 per cent of the nation's territory, lie plateaus, highlands and rugged mountains, with a predominant E-W orientation. Only the Alashan Mountains in Kansu Province retain the typical NE-SW trend found east of the scarp.

Four equally spaced E-W structures can be distinguished in China. The northernmost, situated chiefly in Outer Mongolia, penetrates into China in the Ilkhuri and Little Khingan Mountains of northern Manchuria. The next tectonic line is best expressed in the Yin Shan of Inner Mongolia, north of the Yellow River bend. The third, and most important, system is the Tsin Ling. This rugged mountain range, rising to 13,500 feet in southern Shensi, is an extension of the Nan Shan, itself a continuation of the Kunlun system. The Tsin Ling acts as a major climatic barrier to monsoon rainfall from the south and dust-laden desert winds from the north. It is the most important geographic boundary of China, determining the distribution not only of soils and vegetation, but also of cultivated crops, customs and Mandarin dialects. The southernmost E-W structure is the Nan Ling system, forming the northern boundary of the Si Kiang drainage basin and of Kwangtung Province. The Nan Ling is a geographic boundary, second in importance only to the Tsin Ling divide. It defines the Cantonese language area, the tropical part of China, and the region of two successive rice crops a year. The Nan Ling is the only E-W structure that penetrates prominently east of the great continental scarp.

The elevated part of China west of the scarp is dominated by the Tibetan highlands. These comprise the loftiest and most extensive plateau in the world, at an average elevation of 15,000 feet, enclosed by the towering mountain systems of the Himalaya and the Kunlun. Along their northwestern margin, the Tibetan highlands drop abruptly to the

2,500-foot-high Tarim basin. This desert-filled depression, in turn, is separated by the Tien Shan mountain system from the Dzungarian steppe basin farther north. The two depressions and the intervening mountain barrier constitute the Chinese political unit of Sinkiang. Northeast of the Tibetan highlands extends the vast 3,000-foot-high Mongolian plateau. This desert and steppe peneplain is the dominant topographic feature of the province of Kansu and Inner Mongolia. Between the Mongolian plateau and the Tsin Ling divide is the dissected loess plateau, a region where fine silt blown from the desert to the north forms a veneer over the entire landscape.

East of the Tibetan highlands and south of the Tsin Ling divide, the Cretaceous-Tertiary lake basin of Szechwan drops to an elevation of 900 feet. The Szechwan basin, now filled with buff, red and purple sandstone and shale, is frequently called the Red basin. It is the only major population and agricultural center west of the continental scarp.

Southeast of the Tibetan highlands and south of the Szechwan basin is the plateau region of Kweichow and Yünnan. The Kweichow plateau at 4,000 feet and the Yünnan plateau at 6,000 feet rise in a sort of step-like formation from the eastern lowlands to the western highlands. The western part of Yünnan is a continuation of the canyon country of eastern Tibet, from where Southeast Asia's great streams and intervening high ranges fan out into the Indochinese peninsula.

Coasts

China's coastline of 7,000 miles touches on three seas of the Pacific Ocean: the Yellow Sea, the East China Sea and the South China Sea. With the exception of parts of the South China Sea, these bodies of water are on the continental shelf separated from the deeper reaches of the Pacific proper by the East Asian island arc. China's coast extends from Antung, at the mouth of the Yalu River on the Korean border, in the north, to Tunghing, on the North Vietnamese border, in the south. It is shared by the provinces of Liaoning, Hopei, Shantung, Kiangsu, Chekiang, Fukien and Kwangtung.

In the north, the Yellow Sea penetrates westward between the rocky peninsulas of Liaotung and Shantung and forms the large embayment of Po Hai, formerly called Gulf of Chihli. The Po Hai receives major rivers of North China, including the Liao Ho, the Hai Ho and the Yellow River. The bayshore is generally shallow and smooth and offers few good harbors. The old port of Yingkow at the mouth of the Liao Ho has been silting up. The principal ports along this part of the coast are Chinwangtao, an outlet for the Kailan coal mines, and the new outer port of Tientsin at Tangku. The development of Hulutao, much discussed shortly after the Second World War, has not materialized. The best natural Yellow Sea harbors are situated on the rocky peninsulas. They are Dairen and the naval base of Port Arthur on the Liaotung peninsula, and the ports of Chefoo, Weihai, and especially Tsingtao on the Shantung peninsula. South of Shantung and as far as the Yangtze River mouth, the coast is again characterized by shallow water and an evenness of shoreline. The only port is Lienyünkang, eastern terminus of the Lunghai railroad.

South of the Yangtze River mouth, the coast of China is rocky and indented, with numerous islets and inlets. The East China Sea extends from the Yangtze mouth to the Formosa Strait. Its chief ports are Shanghai, China's foremost metropolis, Ningpo, Wenchow and Foochow. South of the strait is the South China Sea, with the ports of Amoy, Swatow, Canton, Britain's Hong Kong, and Tsamkong (Chankiang). Hainan is the largest Chinese island under control of the Peking regime. The Government also claims jurisdiction over the islands of the South China Sea extending as far as Lat. 4 degrees N.

Climate

China's climate is dominated by airmass movements known collectively as the winter and summer monsoons. In winter excessive radiation over the Asian continent chills the air and creates a stationary high-pressure area known as the Siberian High. In January the center of this high is situated south of Lake Baikal in Outer Mongolia. At that time of the year a region of low pressure forms over the northern Pacific in the area of the Aleutian Islands. Cold dry air masses of Polar Continental origin move successively from the area of the Siberian High toward the Pacific, forming what is known as the winter monsoon. Strong northerly winds accompanying these air flows carry a negligible amount of precipitation, but bring dust storms that are common throughout North China during the winter months.

During the summer, the continental interior is overheated and becomes warmer than the ocean. The expanding and rising continental air creates a low-pressure system in the area of the winter high. At the same time a region of high pressure forms over the relatively cooler Pacific in the area of the Hawaiian Islands. A succession of hot moist air masses invades China from the southeast. When this air is lifted, either by mountains or cold-front wedges in its path, abundant precipitation results.

China's climate is thus alternately continental and dry in winter and maritime and wet in summer. The seasonal shifts in air circulation take place in April and September. The winter and summer monsoons vary in strength and permanence. In winter the opposing high and low pressure cells are situated relatively close to each other. As a result, the pressure gradient is strong and the cold dry northerlies blow steadily and with considerable force. During the summer, the pressure cells are much farther apart, the pressure gradients are weaker and winds associated with the summer monsoon are variable both in strength and in direction. The relative strength of the winter and summer monsoons explains why the cold dry Polar Continental air affects a much greater area of China during a longer period of time than the warm moist invasions of Tropical Maritime air.

Superimposed on the basic to-and-fro seasonal circulation are lesser airmass movements, middle-latitude cyclones and tropical cyclones (typhoons). The middle-latitude cyclones, many of which are believed to be of European origin, follow a number of paths from west to east across China. Most of them pass eastward through the Yangtze valley and across the North China plain. These cyclones, formed by the interaction of opposing warm and cold airmasses, produce most of the precipitation throughout China. A considerable amount of precipitation, especially along the southeast coast, is related to the passage of typhoons. These tropical cyclones arise in the area of the Marshall Islands of the Pacific and follow more or less regular paths to the northwest. They either strike the China coast or recurve northeastward toward Japan, by-passing the mainland. Typhoons are most common between June and August. Their passage produces heavy rain squalls, contrasting with the usual gentle drizzles associated with the westerly cyclonic storms.

As might be expected from the monsoonal circulation pattern, seasonal temperatures are sharply differentiated through most of China. The greatest annual temperature range is found in northern Manchuria where the January average drops to —13° F (—25° C) while in July the mercury climbs to 70° F (20° C) as a monthly average. The annual temperature range decreases gradually toward the south. In tropical Hainan it is only 15 degrees compared with the more than 80 degrees in northern Manchuria. As a result of the regular increase of average January temperatures from north to south, the winter isotherms are all aligned from east to west. The January isotherm of 32° F follows the Hwai Ho valley, the Tsin Ling divide and curves around the west rim of the Szechwan basin into southern Tibet. During July, temperatures are more uniform, with an average of 70° to 85° F (29° C). The highest summer temperatures are found in the lowlands of eastern China and the South China hills, as well as in the Tarim basin of Sinkiang. The lowest average July readings occur in the Tibetan highlands, the Altai Mountains and the northern Khingan of Manchuria.

Precipitation shows even greater regional contrasts than temperature. It is the chief climatic factor differentiating North China and South China. South of the Tsin Ling divide and the Hwai Ho valley, annual rainfall is from 40 to more than 80 inches. Precipitation decreases rapidly toward the north and west. It is 25 inches in the North China plain and Manchuria and less than four inches in the Mongolian desert plateau and the Tarim basin. Most of China's rainfall occurs during the summer monsoon. But while South China receives some rain throughout the year, North China has virtually no precipitation in winter under the influence of the cold dry air of the northerly monsoon.

River Patterns and Projects

The pattern of China's major rivers is determined by the east-west structural trend of the nation's topography. As a result, these streams all flow eastward to the Pacific. Tributaries are in part defined by the NE-SW trend of the Yen Shan structures. This is especially true in South China where many tributaries join the eastward flowing streams at right angles.

The northernmost river system is that of the Sungari, which flows through Manchuria to the Amur River on the Soviet-Chinese border. The Sungari receives the Nun Kiang (Nonni) and is navigable for river steamers during the six-month icefree season. It serves the cities of Kirin, Harbin and Kiamusze, in addition to Tsitsihar on the Nun Kiang. The large Fengman hydroelectric station is just above Kirin.

Southern Manchuria is drained by the Liao Ho, which enters the Po Hai at Yingkow. Unlike the mountain-fed Sungari, the Liao Ho rises in the semi-arid Mongolian plateau and is navigable only for flat-bottomed junks in its lower reaches. The Yalu and Tumen rivers on the Korean-Chinese border, are used chiefly for timber floating and are of limited importance for navigation. The Shuifeng (Supung) hydroelectric station on the Yalu is shared by China and North Korea.

Southwest of the Liao Ho system, beyond the small coastal drainage basin of the Lwan Ho, is the complex system of the Hai Ho. The Hai Ho itself is only a short stream flowing 30 miles from Tientsin to the sea. It is the outlet of five major tributaries that drain the North China plain and converge fanlike at Tientsin. On the northernmost of these tributaries, the Yungting River, the multi-purpose Kwanting reservoir was completed in 1954. Another flood-control measure has been the construction of a second seaward outlet, by-passing the Hai Ho south of Tientsin.

The great river of North China is the Yellow River, known in Chinese as the Hwang Ho. The basin of this 2,900-mile-long stream is bounded on the north by the Yin Shan and on the south by the Tsin Ling divide. The Yellow River rises at an elevation of 15,000 feet in the Tibetan highlands. Its rapid upper course cuts gorges through easily eroded loess formations as the stream describes the great bend around the resistant Ordos plateau. After the Yellow River enters the North China plain, its gradient is greatly reduced and the silt-laden stream is no longer able to carry its load at reduced velocity. Extensive deposition follows. Over the years the river aggraded its lower course to such an extent that the channel was built up above the level of the surrounding countryside. The river's natural levees had to be heightened by artificially constructed embankments to prevent flooding.

The Yellow River has repeatedly broken through its containing dikes and changed course, spreading its alluvium over the North China plain. There have been nine major course changes in the history of the Yellow River. Until 1194, the river reached the sea at various points of the Po Hai north of the Shantung peninsula. In that year, one arm entered the sea south of Shantung through the valley of the Hwai Ho. After nearly seven centuries of southeasterly flow, the Yellow River resumed its northeasterly course about 1855 in what is essentially its present channel. Once again, the river was diverted toward the Hwai Ho basin in June, 1938, but this time its dike was broken intentionally to slow the Japanese advance in China. The breach was sealed in March, 1947, and the Yellow River returned to its old course.

The Communists have given renewed attention to the problem of flood control along the Yellow River. The solution of the problem requires a complex system of flood-detention reservoirs in the upper reaches. As a stop-gap measure, the Peking regime has strengthened the dikes along the lower course and provided spillways, particularly at Litsing, near the mouth, where ice jams frequently cause flooding in the spring. The People's Victory Canal, completed in 1953, diverts some of the water of the Yellow River into the Wei Ho at Sinsiang.

In July, 1955, an over-all water resource development program for the Yellow River was made public. The plan, covering half a century of work, calls for the construction of a number of multi-purpose dams and reservoirs along the Yellow River, soil conservation and irrigation projects. Smaller reservoirs on upstream tributaries will be designed to prevent the silting of the main-stream installations. The first phase of the program is scheduled for the first three five-year plans, ending 1967. Large multi-purpose reservoirs will be built at the Sanmen gorge on the Honan-Shansi border during the second five-year plan (1958-62) and at the Liukia gorge on the Kansu-Tsinghai line during the third plan period. Each reservoir will provide the head for a hydroelectric station of 1,000,000 kilowatt capacity. Also included in the first phase is the construction of three irrigation dams in Kansu, Inner Mongolia and Honan. When the first phase is completed, a 435-mile section of the Yellow River will become navigable from its mouth to Taohwayu in Honan, and a 525-mile section below Yinchwan in Kansu.

The principal tributaries of the Yellow River are the Wei Ho in Shensi and the Fen Ho in Shansi. No tributaries enter the elevated channel of the river in its lower course. Because of its lack of navigability and the ever-present flood danger, few large cities have developed along the Yellow River. The stream flows past Lanchow and Yinchwan in Kansu, Paotow in Inner Mongolia, Kaifeng in Honan and Tsinan in Shantung.

The Hwai Ho is the largest river between the Yellow River and the Yangtze and drains the southeastern margin of the North China plain. A relatively short river—675 miles long—the Hwai Ho is subject to severe summer flooding. When the Yellow River usurped the channel of the Hwai Ho before 1855, and again from 1938 to 1947, the invading stream deposited vast amounts of sediment in the Hwai Ho channel, disrupting its natural course to the sea. The Hwai Ho discharged its water into the fluctuating lakes Hungtse and Kaoyu, which enlarged in times of flood over vast areas. Part of the water from the naturally mouthless Hwai Ho followed the Grand Canal to the Yangtze; another part made its way through shifting channels to the sea.

In 1950, the Peking regime embarked upon an ambitious program of Hwai Ho flood control. The plan called for the construction of detention reservoirs (some with power-generating capacity) on the upstream tributaries, the dredging of the main channel and strengthening of dikes, flood-diversion dams and reservoirs in mid-course and the digging of a new outlet to the Yellow Sea. By 1955, seven major reservoirs had been completed on upstream tributaries, including five in Honan and two in Anhwei. The flood-control program is also designed to improve navigation on the Hwai Ho, which serves the coal center of Hwainan and the city of Pengpu.

The Yangtze River, 3,400 miles long, is the longest river of China and by far its most important waterway. Rising in the Tibetan highlands, the Yangtze traverses central China from west to east, linking the interior of the country with the maritime routes of the Pacific. Navigation starts at the western edge of the Szechwan basin and proceeds past Chungking, Hankow and Nanking to the sea near Shanghai. Hankow is accessible to ocean-going vessels, but difficult gorges above Ichang restrict upstream navigation to 500-ton steamers. The chief tributaries are the Min Kiang and Kialing River in Szechwan, the Han Shui in Hupei, the Siang Kiang in Hunan and the Kan Kiang in Kiangsi. The latter two flow through the Tungting and Poyang lakes, natural flood reservoirs for the surplus waters of the Yangtze. Although the Yangtze carries less sediment than the Yellow River—600 million tons a year compared with 4,000 million tons—and aggrades its channel to a lesser extent, it nevertheless presents a summer flood threat. As a partial measure against floods in the Tungting Lake area, the Peking regime constructed the Kingkiang flood-detention basin. This basin, named for a local section of the Yangtze River, covers an area of 350 square miles and can accommodate up to 6 billion cubic meters of water. It was built in 1952-53 south of the city of Shasi. The drainage basin of the Yangtze River, between the Tsin Ling divide and the Nan Ling in the south, covers about one-fifth of China. It is moreover the most populated and economically the most important fifth of the nation.

South of the mouth of the Yangtze River are a number of coastal stream basins draining the provinces of Chekiang, Fukien and easternmost Kwangtung. Each of the principal streams is associated with a rivermouth city. They are the Tsientang River with Hangchow (which is not a seaport), the Wu Kiang with Wenchow, the Min Kiang with Foochow, the Lung Kiang with Amoy and the Han Kiang with Swatow.

In southern China, south of the Nan Ling divide, three rivers converge on the Canton delta. They are the Tung Kiang, the Pei Kiang and the Si Kiang. The Si Kiang, the most important of the three from the point of view of navigation, rises in the Yünnan plateau and traverses Kwangsi and western Kwangtung from west to east.

Except for the upper reaches of the great rivers of Southeast Asia, the rest of China is occupied by internal drainage basins. These are the arid parts of the country, including Inner Mongolia, Kansu, Sinkiang and most of Tsinghai and Tibet. The upper Irtysh River, which leaves China through a backdoor, ultimately finds its way to the Arctic Ocean.

Soils and Vegetation

A combination of climate and natural vegetation acting on a variety of parent materials have produced an infinite complexity of soils in China. The effect of the vegetation cover plays a secondary role in many parts of the country, particularly in densely settled areas where virtually the entire land has been put under cultivation and little of the original vegetation remains.

Just as China can be divided into North and South in discussions of other aspects of physical geography, the country falls conveniently into northern and southern soil groups. In North China, where rainfall is limited and grassland vegetation prevails in uncultivated areas, soils tend to be rich in lime and soluble plant nutrients. They are called pedocals, or soils with an excess of calcium-carbonate (lime). In South China, where rainfall is more abundant and forest vegetation predominates, soils tend to be leached and poor in humus. They are called pedalfers because the excessive leaching leaves behind aluminum and iron hydroxides.

Pedocals occur in the arid, semi-arid and subhumid climatic regions of China. They range from subhumid chernozems (black earths) through chestnut and brown soils to arid desert soils. Chernozems are among the most fertile in the world, but in China they are restricted to northern Manchuria and Inner Mongolia. Most of them are cultivated in soybeans and wheat and other grains. Their original vegetation cover is tall-grass steppe. Chestnut and brown soils occupy the arid side of the chernozem belt. They contain less humus and are consequently lighter in color, lightness increasing with aridity. These soils make up a large part of central Manchuria and Inner Mongolia, as well as the northeastern margins of the Tibetan highlands and the moister parts of Sinkiang. Short-grass steppe is the typical vegetation. The very light-colored, high-lime soils of the loesslands of Shansi, Shensi and southeastern Kansu are related to the chestnut soils. Gray desert soils, the most arid phase of the pedocal series, extend through the great inner Asian desert belt from the Taklamakan desert in Sinkiang through northern Kansu into the border area between Inner and Outer Mongolia. Here short grass and brush is the natural vegetation. Agriculture is limited to irrigated oases.

Deciduous and coniferous upland forests are found in North China in the mountains enclosing the Manchurian plain, the Taihang Mountains, the Yen Shan and the hills of the Shantung and Liaotung peninsulas. The Manchurian forests, which crown the Great and Little Khingan ranges and the East Manchurian uplands, are developed on podzol soils characterized by an ash-colored horizon below the top soil layer. The upland forests enclosing the North China plain are associated with brown soils that are very much like the podzols though less intensely leached. These brown forest soils are found in Liaotung, Shantung, the Taihang scarp, as well as in the Tsin Ling divide, which separates the North China and South China soil groups.

Perhaps the most important agricultural soil of North China is the calcareous alluvium developed on the floodplain of the North China lowland. Unlike the foregoing zonal soils, which have been developed through the prolonged action of climate and vegetation zonation, the alluvium is called intrazonal because it has been formed mainly through the depositional action of streams within zones. The texture of the alluvium ranges from coarse sand close to the streams to silt at greater distances from the rivers. The coarse sand, often accumulated in the form of natural levees, is a poor soil, while silt is highly productive. Century-long cultivation of these soils has left virtually no trace of the original vegetation. Wheat and cotton are cultivated in silty soils, while tobacco and peanuts are favored by the sandy soils. A special type of alluvial soil is the so-called shakiang soil. This type is characterized by lime concretions in its lower horizons. The concretions are believed to come from the ground water that has been saturated with calcium carbonate. The shakiang soils are developed in the flat topography of central Honan and northwest Anhwei, as well as in western Shantung.

In South China, intrazonal alluvial soils are found immediately south of the major soil divide. Unlike their northern counterpart, the southern alluvial soils are leached under the increasingly humid conditions and are noncalcareous. They are ideally suited for rice cultivation. Periodic flooding of the rice fields has developed a dense impervious clay horizon, which in turn has become an asset in keeping the fields flooded. These rice paddy soils are best developed in the middle and lower Yangtze valley.

The most important zonal soils in South China are lateritic red and yellow soils. They are characterized by advanced chemical and mechanical decomposition of the parent rock under humid, sub-tropical conditions, accumulation of hydroxides giving the soils their characteristic color, low humus content and hence low fertility. Both red and yellow soils are associated with subtropical forests. Red soils predominate in the hill country south of the Yangtze, the Southeast coastal uplands, the Kwangtung-Kwangsi hills and Yünnan. Yellow soils are associated chiefly with the Kweichow plateau. A distinctive purple-brown soil found in the Szechwan basin is derived from the highly colored shales and sandstones of Cretaceous and Triassic age.

Most of South China's red and yellow soils are associated with subtropical evergreen broadleaf forest (pine, fir, bamboo). Cultivators have used these soils for tea, tung trees and, to some extent, for rice. In general the soils are of little agricultural value. The distinctive purplish soils of the Szechwan basin are largely cultivated. Rice is the dominant crop, but there is also a diversified production of corn, sweet potatoes and tobacco. Pine, cypress, bamboo and oak are found on the uncultivated slopes.

The southeastern margins of the Tibetan highlands have relatively high precipitation (about 40 inches a year). Here coniferous forest is developed on predominantly podzolic soils. Farther northwest, on the Tibetan plateau, soils and vegetation vary frequently in accordance with slope insolation. Northward-facing slopes, which receive less sunshine and are consequently cooler and moister, are generally forested or covered with tall grass. Southward-facing slopes, which are more exposed to the sun, are drier and display predominantly short and tall-grass associations. In the desolate central part of Tibet, soils are poorly developed and vegetation extremely meager.

Chapter 2

THE POLITICAL FRAMEWORK

Provincial Changes Since 1949

By an act of the Nationalist Government on June 5, 1947, China was divided into 34 provinces (excluding Formosa), one territory (Tibet), over which the Chinese then had no effective control, and 12 cities under the direct jurisdiction of the central Government. The 12 cities were Nanking, Shanghai, Peiping, Tsingtao, Tientsin, Chungking, Dairen, Harbin, Hankow, Canton, Sian and Mukden.

According to the China Handbook, 1950, the provinces were further divided into 2,023 hsien and 55 cities under the direct jurisdiction of the provincial governments. As some of the provinces were considered to be too extensive for effective administration, the Nanking regime established the intermediate level of administrative ch'ü (hsing-cheng ch'ü). The hsien of 23 provinces were grouped in administrative ch'ü instead of being directly subordinated to the provincial Government. (According to later Communist sources, the provinces under the Nationalists were divided into 2,016 hsien, 57 provincially administered cities and 209 administrative ch'ü.)

This was the administrative pattern inherited by the Communists at the time of the proclamation of the Chinese People's Republic on October 1, 1949. The Peking regime proceeded to reorganize the administration in accordance with existing conditions and the program of political consolidation. The nation was divided into six greater administrative ch'ü (ta hsing-cheng ch'ü). These major regional divisions, each in turn subdivided into a number of provinces, represented various stages of Communist power consolidation in China. In 1950, when the greater administrative ch'ü were established, the Northeast (Manchurian) region, for example, was completely consolidated, while agrarian reform was in progress in the East and Center-South and counterrevolutionary activity was still a major factor in the Southwest. The division of China into six major regions made it possible for the Peking regime to adopt specific regional measures. The greater administrative ch'ü and their provinces and regionally administered cities were:

(1) North China (Hua-pei), with the provinces of Hopei, Chahar, Pingyüan, Shansi and Suiyüan, and the cities of Peking and Tientsin. The North China ch'ü was at first directly under the Central Government, where a special Ministry for North China was set up for its administration. A regional administrative committee was set up as late as August, 1952.

(2) Northeast (Tung-pei), with the provinces of Liaotung, Liaosi, Kirin, Sungkiang, Heilungkiang and Jehol, and the cities of Mukden, Fushun, Anshan, Penki and Port-Arthur—Dairen. After the end of the Second World War, the Nationalist Government divided Manchuria into nine provinces (Liaoning, Antung, Liaopei, Kirin, Sungkiang, Hokiang, Heilungkiang, Nunkiang and Hsingan) plus Jehol. This administrative pattern was never put into effect because the Nationalists failed to gain full control of Manchuria. The Nationalist set-up was superseded by five Communist provinces plus Jehol, which made up the Northeast ch'ü. Because Manchuria was the most advanced region from the point of view of Communist power consolidation, a so-called Northeast People's Government functioned there from August, 1949, to November, 1952. This regional government had greater powers than the bodies set up in the other greater administrative ch'ü.

(3) East China (Hua-tung), with the provinces of Shantung, Kiangsu, Anhwei, Chekiang, Fukien, and the cities of Shanghai and Nanking (in 1952, Nanking was placed under the provincial jurisdiction of Kiangsu.) The East China ch'ü was supposed to include Formosa in case of the island's occupation by the Communists. Kiangsu and Anhwei were each administered after 1949 as two separated provincial units, situated north and south of the Yangtze River, to conform with varying stages of Communist consolidation. North and South Anhwei was recombined in August, 1952, and North and South Kiangsu in the following November.

(4) Center-South (Chung-nan), with the provinces of Honan, Hupei, Hunan, Kiangsi, Kwangtung, Kwangsi, and the cities of Wuhan (Hankow, Hanyang, Wuchang) and Canton.

(5) Southwest (Hsi-nan), with the provinces of Szechwan, Kweichow, Yünnan, Sikang, Tibet, and the city of Chungking. Szechwan was administered in four sections until 1952.

(6) Northwest (Hsi-pei), with the provinces of Shensi, Kansu, Ningsia, Tsinghai, Sinkiang, and the city of Sian.

The Inner Mongolian Autonomous Ch'ü (set up in 1947) was independent of the system of greater administrative ch'ü.

In November, 1952, occurred the first major reorganization of the political-administrative system. The six major regional authorities, which until that time had wielded considerable powers, were reduced to mere supervisory bodies. This measure was designed to strengthen Communist consolidation at the provincial level, looking toward ultimate abolition of the supra-provincial structure. The provinces of Chahar and Pingyüan in North China were abolished. Chahar had been greatly reduced in area because of territorial transfers to Inner Mongolia and the rump was considered to be too small to function as a province. The rest of Chahar was divided between Shansi and Hopei. Pingyüan had been created in 1949 out of the Communist Shansi-Honan-Hopei border region that existed during the civil war. The new province, made up largely of parts of Honan and Shantung, failed to achieve provincial unity. No provincial center arose, with the former Shantung section gravitating toward Tsining and the Honan portion toward Sinsiang. Short-lived Pingyüan was dissolved in 1952 and the previous provincial borders were approximately restored. The temporary divisions of Kiangsu, Anhwei and Szechwan were terminated at this time and Nanking was placed under provincial rule.

After November, 1952, mainland China had 31 provinces, including Inner Mongolia and Tibet (now independent of the Southwest ch'ü), and 12 regionally administered cities. Two more such cities—Changchun and Harbin—were added late in 1953 in Manchuria.

A second major administrative reorganization was announced June 19, 1954. This time the greater administrative ch'ü were abolished altogether and the provinces placed directly under the central Government. Several provinces were eliminated and combined. In Manchuria, Sungkiang was incorporated into Heilungkiang, and Liaotung and Liaosi were combined to form Liaoning. In the Northwest, Ningsia was incorporated into Kansu. The province of Suiyüan was merged with the Inner Mongolian Autonomous Ch'ü. Eleven of the 14 cities that had been regionally administered were placed under provincial jurisdiction. Only Peking, Tientsin and Shanghai remained under central administration.

The changes of June, 1954, left China with 27 mainland provinces, including Tibet and Inner Mongolia, and three centrally administered cities.

The most recent provincial shift was announced in July, 1955. The provinces of Sikang and Jehol were abolished. Sikang proper (east of the upper Yangtze River) was merged with Szechwan, while preparations were made to incorporate the Chamdo area (west of the upper

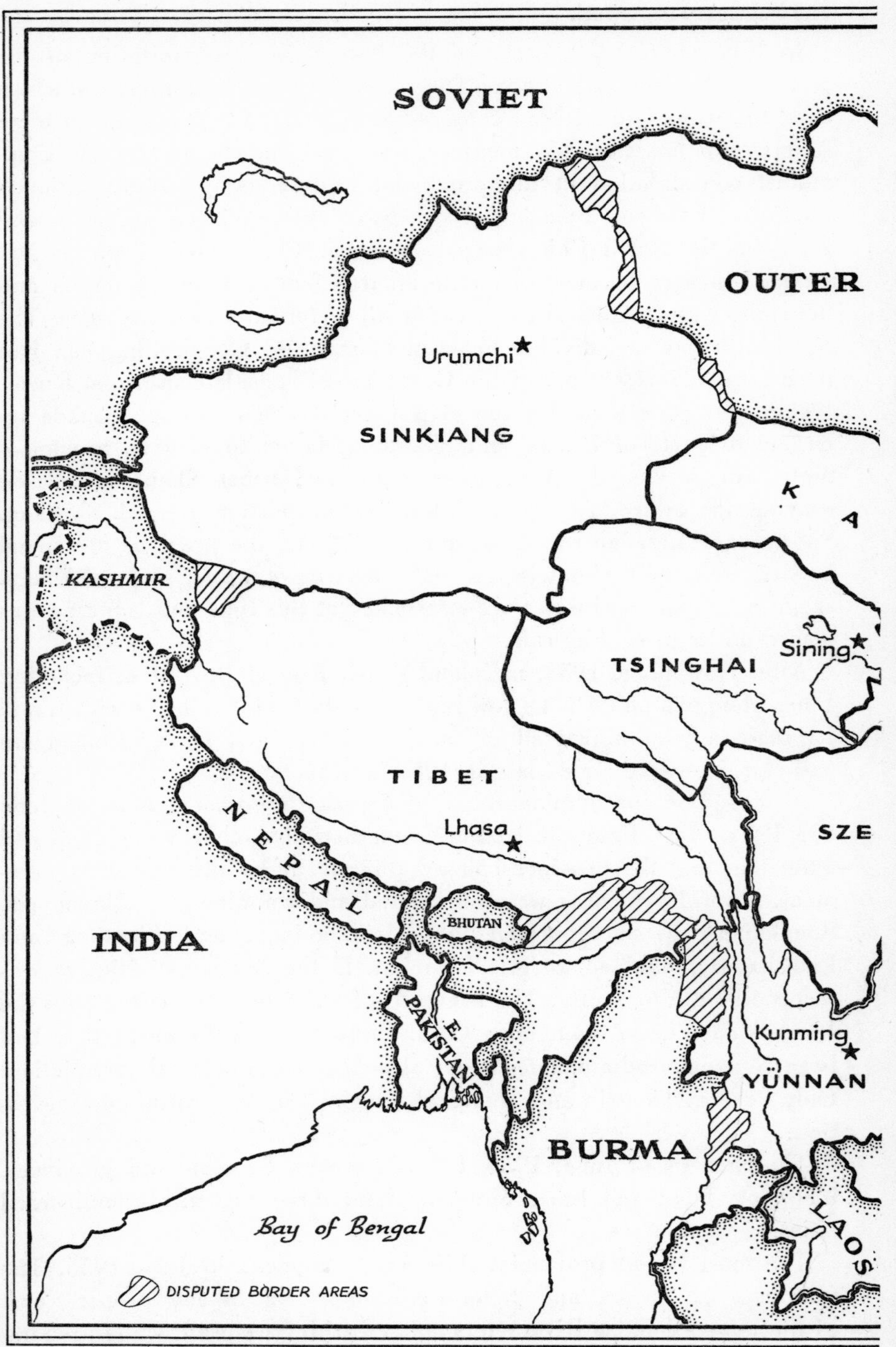

Political Divisions of China

UNION
MONGOLIA
INNER MONGOLIA
HEILUNGKIANG
Harbin
Changchun
KIRIN
Mukden
LIAONING
N. KOREA
S. KOREA
HOPEI
PEKING
TIENTSIN
Paoting
Huhehot
SHANSI
Taiyüan
Tsinan
SHANTUNG
KANSU
Lanchow
SHENSI
Sian
Chengchow
HONAN
KIANGSU
Nanking
ANHWEI
Hofei
SHANGHAI
JAPAN
East China Sea
SZECHWAN
Chengtu
HUPEI
Wuchang
Hangchow
CHEKIANG
Nanchang
Changsha
HUNAN
KIANGSI
Kweiyang
KWEICHOW
Foochow
FUKIEN
FORMOSA
Pacific Ocean
KWANGSI
Nanning
KWANGTUNG
Canton
N. VIETNAM
South China Sea
HAINAN
PHILIPPINES
0
500 Miles

Yangtze) into autonomous Tibet. Jehol, like Chahar, had lost considerable territory to Inner Mongolia and was evidently judged to be too small to function as a province. It was divided among Inner Mongolia, Liaoning and Hopei. The latest shift reduced the number of Chinese mainland provinces to 25, including Tibet and Inner Mongolia.

The Present Administrative System

The framework of the present system is set by Article 53 of the Constitution adopted in September, 1954. According to this article, the administrative division of China is as follows:

(1) The country is divided into provinces *(sheng)*, autonomous ch'ü and cities *(shih)* directly under the central authority.

(2) Provinces and autonomous ch'ü are divided into autonomous chou, hsien, autonomous hsien and cities.

(3) Hsien and autonomous hsien are divided into hsiang, nationality hsiang and towns.

Cities directly under the central authority and other large cities are divided into boroughs. Autonomous chou are divided into hsien, autonomous hsien and cities.

Autonomous ch'ü, autonomous chou and autonomous hsien are areas of national autonomy.

As of the end of 1955, China had 22 ordinary provinces, the autonomous ch'ü of Inner Mongolia, Sinkiang, and Tibet (in preparation) and the centrally administered cities of Peking, Tientsin and Shanghai. The provinces and autonomous ch'ü, in turn, were divided into 25 autonomous chou, 2,100 hsien and equivalent units, about 50 autonomous hsien and about 170 cities under provincial jurisdiction. Inasmuch as national autonomous units will be treated in detail in a later section, the following discussion is restricted to non-autonomous administrative units.

Comparison of the Communist administrative pattern as of the end of 1955 and the Nationalist political map of 1947 reveals a number of interesting changes. As has become evident from the preceding discussion, the number of divisions at the provincial level has been reduced from 34 (excluding Formosa) in 1947 to 25 at the end of 1955. The territorial mergers that led to the reduction in the number of provinces took place generally in the outlying parts of China, including Manchuria. The resulting increase in the average size of the provinces calls to mind the territorial consolidation in the Soviet Union in the early stages of industrialization. Through the 1920's, the Soviet Government combined the pre-revolutionary divisions known as guberniyas into a few very large administrative units designed for economic planning. To be sure, the Tsarist guberniyas were far more numerous than the provinces of Nationalist China as of 1947. Moreover, the Chinese provincial consolidation has been justified by administrative considerations, and not economic planning needs. But similar trends at parallel stages of Soviet and Chinese development are worthy of note.

Although not provided by the 1954 Constitution, an intermediate level has continued to exist between the province and the hsien. This is the administrative ch'ü (hsing-cheng ch'ü) of the Nationalists, which under the Communists has been called special ch'ü (chuan ch'ü). These special ch'ü existed in 21 provinces as late as 1955, combining groups of hsien under special administrations within provinces.

While the number of provinces has been considerably reduced under the Communists, the number of hsien has remained remarkably stable, having fluctuated around 2,100. Provinces (or their special ch'ü), autonomous chou and autonomous ch'ü are all divided into hsien or comparable units. The hsien compares in size and population to a county in the United States. The average number of hsien per province is about 80 or 90, and the average population between 200,000 and 300,000. In areas populated by Mongols, the unit comparable to the hsien is the banner (Chinese *ch'i*). Banners are grouped in larger units known as leagues (Chinese *meng*). In Tibet, the unit comparable to the hsien is the tsung (Chinese phonetic rendering of Tibetan *dzong*).

In connection with the hsien, Soviet experience is also of interest. The number of Soviet rayons (units corresponding to the hsien) remained fairly stable during the early stages of industrialization in the late 1920's and early 1930's. They numbered about 2,000. It was only with the advent of agricultural collectivization and the introduction of machine-tractor stations in the 1930's that the number of Soviet rayons began to increase. This in turn led to the compartmentalization of the large divisions at the provincial level. In China, the collectivization of agriculture is proceeding at a far more leisurely pace than was the case in the Soviet Union. Chinese mechanization is still insignificant. As both collectivization and mechanization gather speed during the next two decades, it is likely that administration at the hsien level will become more important just as the rayon became a major unit with the coming of Government control over agriculture. In that case we may see a subdivision of the existing large Chinese provinces into smaller units similar to those established in the Soviet Union before the Second World War.

The Chinese hsien is further subdivided into hsiang, the basic rural administrative unit, and towns (*chen*). There are about 220,000 hsiang and 5,000 towns. These towns owe their urban status largely to a local market rather than modern industry. The hsien seat, for example, is usually a market town. In this connection a frustrating aspect of Chinese place names might be mentioned. In many instances, the hsien bears a name that differs from the name of its seat. In that case, the name of the hsien is applied to the administrative seat as long as the local administrative machinery has its headquarters there. If, as often happens, the hsien shifts its seat to another market town, the name of the hsien is applied to its new seat, while the former headquarters reverts to its original name or is simply called Old X Hsien. This explains why Chinese maps of different dates often show the same hsien name in different locations.

In the Soviet Union, political-administrative divisions are regarded as areal units having also economic functions. In particular, the Soviet administrative unit is visualized as an economic region of greater or lesser versatility in which all resources are to be developed to the utmost of local capabilities. In China, up to now, no such considerations appear to be guiding the nation's administrative evolution.

Economic-administrative factors also determine the classification of Soviet urban centers. Populated points owe their administrative status almost entirely to economic criteria, specifically the presence of industry. A large rural town of, say, 20,000 persons with primarily farming interests is classified as a village, while a mining town with a few thousand persons is classified as a city. The economic importance of any given urban center can be gauged by its administrative status. A place with developing industry can rise through the Soviet urban hierarchy, consisting of the so-called workers' settlement and cities of varying grade. No such systematic urban classes with all their refinements have yet been set up in China. But the beginnings of an urban classification based on economic (industrial) factors are apparent. In contrast to the four-level urban classification of the Soviet Union, two levels are in operation in China. The lower level (corresponding to hsien) is the so-called industrial-mining ch'ü (kung-k'uang ch'ü), which was first established about 1951. It usually designates a small industrial center slated for expansion. Once the urban population has reached the neighborhood of 50,000, the industrial-mining ch'ü is promoted to the status of city under provincial authority. No more than fifteen industrial-mining districts have thus far been created in China, but a few have already risen through the ranks to the status of provincial city. Fengfeng, expanding coking coal center in southern Hopei, was among the first places to be designated a mining ch'ü (k'uang ch'ü) about 1951. Having grown to the required size, Fengfeng was converted into a provincial city in 1954. The lower population limit for cities under provincial jurisdiction is 50,000. Cities of unusual economic importance may be promoted before that limit is reached.

The National Autonomous Structure

Like the Soviet Union, China is a multi-national state. However, the Chinese majority is by far more predominant in China than the Russian or Slavic group is in the Soviet Union. Russians make up about one-half of the Soviet population; including the Ukrainians and Belorussians, the proportion rises to nearly 75 per cent. In China, the Chinese account for 94 per cent of the total population. This difference in the relative predominance of the basic ethnic groups has determined the basic political structure of the two nations. The Soviet Union is juridically a union of 16 republics. According to Article 17 of the 1936 Constitution, this union is voluntary and the republics reserve the right of free secession. It is unlikely that any republic will ever raise the issue of secession, but juridically it has that right. China, on the other hand, is a unified, multi-national state. According to Article 3 of the 1954 Constitution, national autonomous units are inalienable parts of the People's Republic of China.

The primary doctrinal basis of Chinese Communist policy with respect to national minorities was originally set forth in the Common Program of the Chinese People's Political Consultative Conference, promulgated in September, 1949. Articles 50-53 assert the equality of the nationalities and the need for regional autonomy based on the preservation of language, customs or religious beliefs.

The first autonomous region was set up even before the promulgation of the Common Program. It was Inner Mongolia, declared to be autonomous as early as May, 1947. The next important national unit was the Kantse Tibetan area, founded in November, 1950. Thereafter, national autonomous units were created at a rapidly increasing rate. Most of the areas were established in the course of 1953 and 1954. These autonomous areas varied greatly in size and population. They ranged from the Inner Mongolian region, which initially had an area of 255,000 square miles and a population of 2,500,000 to national units at the hsiang (village) level. Despite the evident disparity in size and importance, all areas bore the uniform designation of "autonomous ch'ü" (tzu-chih ch'ü).

It was only with the proclamation of the 1954 Constitution that a system of gradations was set up. The highest level is the autonomous ch'ü. This type of unit, now corresponding to a province, can be related to an autonomous Soviet Socialist republic in the Soviet Union. Three autonomous ch'ü have been established or are being established. They are Inner Mongolia, Sinkiang, and Tibet, areas that are associated with the three most important non-Chinese nationalities in terms of cultural development. The Mongols, Uigurs (ethnic group of Sinkiang) and Tibetans occupy a dominant position among the minorities. The bank-notes of China, for example, now bear inscriptions in Mongol, Uigur and Tibetan, in addition to Chinese.

The next lowest national level is the autonomous chou. It appears to apply to all autonomous units that include two or more hsien, irrespective of area or population. As of January, 1956, there were 25 autonomous chou. The most populous autonomous chou is that of the Chuang nationality in western Kwangsi. It has a population of 8,400,000, exceeding even that of the Inner Mongolian Autonomous Ch'ü (about 7,000,000). At the same time, the autonomous chou category includes Mongol areas in Sinkiang, with a population of only 50,000. Autonomous chou are subordinated to the provincial administration and are thus in a sense equivalent to the special ch'ü (chuan ch'ü), which also include groups of hsien.

At the hsien level, the Chinese have set up the rank of autonomous hsien for national minorities whose area of concentration does not extend beyond the limits of a hsien. As of January, 1956, there were 50 such units. The lowest grade is the nationality hsiang, which is of only local significance and is not discussed here.

The national autonomous areas of China are listed in Table 1.

The 1953 Population Census of China

The total population of China has long been a matter of confusion and controversy. When the Communists came to power in 1949, they used the figure of 475,000,000. This population total was based on a count made by the Nationalist Government after its establishment in 1928. The enumeration, conducted over a period of two years and published in 1931, yielded the figure of 474,787,386. Nationalist figures published in subsequent years generally lay between 450,000,000 and 500,000,000. The last Nationalist enumeration, based in part on estimates by local officials, yielded the figure of 463,493,418 for June, 1948.

Table 1

NATIONAL AUTONOMOUS AREAS

Ethnic Group (Population)	*Name of Area*	*Type of Area*	*Administrative Seat*	*Provincial Location*
Chuang (6,611,455)	West Kwangsi	Chou	Nanning	W Kwangsi
Uigur (3,640,125)	Sinkiang	Ch'ü	Urumchi	Sinkiang
Chinese Moslem* (3,559,350)	Sihaiku	Chou	Kuyüan	E Kansu
	Wuchung	Chou	Wuchung	E Kansu
	Changki	Chou	Changki	N Sinkiang
	Changkiachwan	Hsien	Changkiachwan	SE Kansu
	Kingyüan	Hsien	Kingyüan	SE Kansu
	Kwangtung	Hsien	Kwangtung	SE Kansu
	Yenki	Hsien	Yenki	central Sinkiang
	Hwalung	Hsien	Hwalung	NE Tsinghai
	Weiyüan	Hsien	Weiyüan	NE Tsinghai
Yi* (3,254,269)	Liangshan	Chou	Chaochüeh	W Szechwan
	Milo	Hsien	Milo	E Yünnan
	Oshan	Hsien	Oshan	E Yünnan
Tibetan* (2,775,622)	Tibet	Ch'ü	Lhasa	Tibet
	South Kansu	Chou	Heitso	SE Kansu
	Kantse	Chou	Kangting	W Szechwan
	Ahpa	Chou	Shwakingsze	NW Szechwan
	Golog (Kuo-lo)	Chou	Chimai	SE Tsinghai
	Hainan	Chou	Kungho	NE Tsinghai
	Haipei	Chou	Weiyüan	NE Tsinghai
	Hwangnan	Chou	Tungjen	E Tsinghai
	Yüshu	Chou	Yüshu	S Tsinghai
	Tienchu	Hsien	Anyüanyi	SE Kansu
	Muli	Hsien	Muli	W Szechwan
	Tehtsin	Hsien	Tehtsin	NW Yünnan
Miao* (2,511,339)	West Hunan	Chou	Kishow	NW Hunan
	Tamiaoshan	Hsien	Jungshui	N Kwangsi
	Leishan	Hsien	Leishan	SE Kweichow
	Lushan	Hsien	Lushan	SE Kweichow
	Taikiang	Hsien	Taikiang	SE Kweichow
	Tanchai	Hsien	Tanchai	SE Kweichow
Manchu (2,418,931)	(none)			
Mongol* (1,462,956)	Inner Mongolia	Ch'ü	Huhehot	Inner Mongolia
	Kansu (Alashan)	Chou	Bayinhot	NE Kansu
	Bayin Gol	Chou	Yenki	central Sinkiang
	Borotala	Chou	Bulak	NW Sinkiang
	Durbet	Banner	Taikang	W Heilungkiang

Ethnic Group (Population)	*Name of Area*	*Type of Area*	*Administrative Seat*	*Provincial Location*
Mongol (cont.)	North Gorlos	Banner	Chaoyüan	W Heilungkiang
	Edsin	Banner	Hsi-miao	N Kansu
	North Kansu	Banner	near Tunhwang	NW Kansu
	South Gorlos	Banner	near Fuyü	W Kirin
	Tumet	Banner	Fusin	W Liaoning
	Khobuk-Saur	Banner	Hofeng	N Sinkiang
	Honan	Banner	unidentified	E Tsinghai
Puyi* (1,247,883)	Lotien	Hsien	Lotien	S Kweichow
Korean (1,120,405)	Yenpien	Chou	Yenki	E Kirin
Tung (690,000)	Tungtao	Hsien	Tungtao	SW Hunan
	Sankiang	Hsien	Sankiang	N Kwangsi
Yao (640,000)	Nama	Hsien	Nama	W Kwangsi
	Tayaoshan	Hsien	Kinsiu	E Kwangsi
	Tuan	Hsien	Tuan	W Kwangsi
	Linnam	Hsien	Linnam	NW Kwangtung
	Kianghwa	Hsien	Kianghwa	SW Hunan
Thai* (580,000)	Hsi-shuang-pan-na	Chou	Yünkinghung	S Yünnan
Minchia (480,000)	(no area)			
Kazakh* (470,000)	Ili	Chou	Kuldja	N Sinkiang
	Aksai	Hsien	unidentified	NW Kansu
	Barkol	Hsien	Barkol	E Sinkiang
	Mulei	Hsien	Mulei	E Sinkiang
Li* (330,000)	(see below)			
Kawa* (280,000)	(see below)			
Hani* (270,000)	Hungho	Chou	Yüanyang	SE Yünnan
Lisu (180,000)	Nu Kiang	Chou	Pikiang	NW Yünnan
Nung (170,000)	(no area)			
Lahu* (170,000)	Lantsang	Hsien	Lantsang	SW Yünnan
Nasi (170,000)	(no area)			
Shuichia (150,000)	(no area)			
Tunghsiang (140,000)	Tunghsiang	Hsien	Sonanpa	SE Kansu
Chingpo* (110,000)	(see below)			

Ethnic Group (Population)	*Name of Area*	*Type of Area*	*Administrative Seat*	*Provincial Location*
Kirghiz (80,000)	Kizil Su	Chou	Artush	SW Sinkiang
Chiang (70,000)	(no area)			
Tujen (60,000)	Huchu	Hsien	Huchu	NE Tsinghai
Salar (30,000)	Shunhwa	Hsien	Shunhwa	NE Tsinghai
Tadzhik (15,000)	Tash Kurghan	Hsien	Tash Kurghan	SW Sinkiang
Sibo (20,000)	Chapchal	Hsien	Chapchal	NW Sinkiang
Yüku (3,000)	South Kansu	Hsien	Hungwansze	central Kansu
Orochon (2,000)	Orochon	Banner	unidentified	N Inner Mongolia

*Ethnic groups designated with an asterisk are also part of the following joint autonomous areas.

Miao-Li	Hainan	Chou	Tungshek	S Kwangtung (Hainan)
Mongol-Tibetan-Kazakh	Haisi	Chou	Tsagan Usu	NW Tsinghai
Thai-Chingpo	Tehung	Chou	Lusi	W Yünnan
Yi-Chinese Moslem-Miao	Weining	Hsien	Weining	NW Kweichow
Puyi-Miao	Hweishui	Hsien	Hweishui	S Kweichow
Hani-Yi	Kiangcheng	Hsien	Kiangcheng	S Yünnan
Thai-Kawa	Kengma	Hsien	Kengma	W Yünnan
Thai-Lahu-Kawa	Menglien	Hsien	Menglien	SW Yünnan
several unidentified ethnic groups	Lunglin	Hsien	Lunglin	W Kwangsi
	Lungsheng	Hsien	Lungsheng	N Kwangsi

The 475,000,000 figure appeared in Communist publications from 1949 to 1954. During the same period, six other figures ranging from 483,000,000 to 575,000,000 were also published by Peking at one time or another.

In connection with the general election, the Chinese Communists conducted a population census as of June 30, 1953. The census included a direct population survey and an indirect registration. The direct survey, which covered 98.5 per cent of the population, was effected in all areas included in the general election. It involved essentially a count of the population by heads of households, who reported to census and election officials. The indirect registration, which was used in remote areas not covered by the election, was based on reports from local governments.

The first results of the census were published June 20, 1954. The China mainland population was listed as 582,584,839, including 8,708,169 indirectly registered. Following a sample check of 9 per cent of the population, the Peking regime issued final figures on November 1, 1954. The revised mainland population figure was 582,603,417, including 8,397,477 indirectly registered. It will be noted that the total population remained virtually the same and that 300,000 persons indirectly registered were shifted to the direct survey category.

The census report issued in November, 1954, included only summary figures. These included a sample survey of population growth, age distribution, sex composition, ethnic composition, rural-urban distribution and distribution by provinces.

The sample survey of population growth was based on a sample of 30,180,000 in 29 provincial cities, the former province of Ningsia, ten other hsien and smaller administrative units. It showed births at a rate of 37 per 1,000 and deaths at a rate of 17 per 1,000, a natural increase of 20 per 1,000 a year. If this rate is applied to the whole of China, the population would rise as shown in Table 2.

TABLE 2

POPULATION GROWTH AFTER 1953

June 30, 1953	582,600,000
Jan. 1, 1954	587,800,000
Jan. 1, 1955	599,600,000
Jan. 1, 1956	611,600,000

A rough age-group breakdown showed that China's was a young population. About 15.6 per cent of the total was under 4 years old, compared with 8.7 per cent in the United States at the same date, and 41.1 per cent was less than 18 years old, compared with 32.6 per cent in the United States. Men outnumbered women by 107.5 to 100. The predominance of males has been typical of China's population.

The 1953 census classified about 35 million persons, or 6 per cent of the population, as national minorities. According to the census instructions, the determination of linguistic or other ethnic affiliation was to be left to each household head. He was expected to list the national minority of which he considered himself to be a member. The census summary contained total numbers for the ten minority groups exceeding one million in population. The data for smaller groups were disclosed in other sources. A detailed discussion of ethnic groups and their distribution appears in the following section.

The population classified as urban in June, 1953, was 77,257,282, or 13.26 per cent of the total. This population included the towns (*chen*) within hsien, the industrial and mining ch'ü and cities under provincial and central authority. Information released in connection with the census disclosed that the urban population had risen 40 per cent since 1950. This gives an urban share of 55.2 million persons for the earlier year. On the basis of Soviet experience, it can be assumed that the increase resulted not only from natural increase and migration from rural areas, but also from the redefinition of rural places as urban places. Speeches by Chinese leaders in July and August, 1955, referred to urban population figures of more than 90 million and of 100 million persons. A mean of 95 million persons indicates the rough trend of urbanization from 1950 to 1955 (Table 3).

TABLE 3

TREND OF URBANIZATION

	Urban Population	*Per Cent of Total*
1950	55,200,000	10
1953	77,300,000	13.3
1955	95,000,000	15

The rush to the cities is a corollary of the forced industrialization program. It corresponds to an identical phenomenon in the Soviet Union, where the criteria for urban population are similar to those used in China. The Soviet urban share rose from 17.9 per cent in 1926 to 32.8 per cent in 1939, increasing about one per cent a year as in the case of China.

China has twenty-five cities with a population of more than 500,000, approximately the same number as the Soviet Union. However, the more industrialized northern neighbor has more medium-size urban centers—about 300 cities of more than 50,000, compared with about 170 in China. The bulk of the Chinese urban population is concentrated in the hsien market towns, which cannot be termed industrial urban centers in the modern sense. It is to be expected that the number of cities in the medium class will increase rapidly as China's industrialization progresses, filling the gap between the great metropolitan centers and the small market towns.

The census summary disclosed exact figures only for the three cities under central authority: Shanghai, Peking and Tientsin. The population of other cities with more than 500,000 persons could be computed from election data or appeared in scattered sources. A list of available population data for the twenty-five cities of 500,000 persons or more appears in Table 4.

TABLE 4

CITIES WITH 500,000 OR MORE POPULATION
June, 1953

City	*Population*	*City*	*Population*
Shanghai	6,204,417	Sian	760,000
Peking	2,768,417	Fushun	700,000
Tientsin	2,693,831	Hangchow	700,000
Mukden	2,213,000	Tangshan	700,000
Chungking	1,620,000	Tsinan	680,000
Canton	1,600,000	Anshan	600,000
Wuhan	1,500,000	Taiyüan	600,000
Harbin	1,200,000	Wusih	581,000
Port-Arthur—Dairen	1,200,000	Foochow	553,000
Nanking	1,000,000	Changsha	500,000
Tsingtao	917,000	Kunming	500,000
Changchun	800,000	Penki	500,000
Chengtu	800,000		

Note: Figures rounded to the nearest 100,000 are subject to a margin of error of plus or minus 50,000.

About 75 per cent of China's population lives in 15 per cent of the nation's territory. This is the eastern lowland and hills area situated east of the great continental scarp formed by the Khingan-Taihang-Kweichow plateau line. The only major population concentration west of that line is in Szechwan, which is the country's most populous province.

The greatest density is found in the middle and lower reaches of the Yangtze River. There a density of 2,000 to 2,500 persons to the square mile is not uncommon. although the over-all average in the lowlands is more nearly 1,000 to 1,200. Similar densities occur in the Canton delta and in the coastal plains of Kwangtung and Fukien. More than one-fifth of the nation's population is found in the North China plain, one of the original Chinese settlement areas. There the average density is 650 per square mile.

Outside of the areas of greatest concentration, major densities are found in the Szechwan basin (500 per square mile) and in southern Manchuria (400). Beyond that, settlement decreases rapidly toward the western mountains and deserts, which are virtually devoid of settlement.

The distribution of China's population by provinces is shown in Table 5.

Ethnic Groups

In the following discussion, China's ethnic groups are classified insofar as possible on the basis of language affiliation. Two major language families include virtually all the languages spoken in China. They are the Indo-Chinese family, also known as Sino-Tibetan, and the Altaic family, formerly regarded as part of a greater Ural-Altaic family. Among the ethnic groups outside of these two families are the Koreans, sometimes regarded as linked to the Altaic family or as a separate family with the Japanese, the Tadzhiks of Sinkiang, who are an Indo-European group, and the Kawa of Yünnan, members of the Mon-Khmer group of the Austro-Asiatic family. As of 1955, forty-four ethnic groups were officially recognized at the local government level. Of these, twenty-nine were represented in the National People's Congress.

The Chinese are of course the dominant ethnic group of China, numbering 546,283,057 according to the June, 1953, census, or 94 per cent of the total population. The Chinese call the Chinese ethnic group Han or Han-tsu (Han nationality) for the Han dynasty (206 B.C.-220 A.D.). The Chinese use the term Chung-hua jen-min or Chung-kuo jen-min to designate the Chinese people in the sense of the "people of China."

Chinese, a major group of the Indo-Chinese language family, is a monosyllabic tone language written by means of characters representing words. While the script is used throughout the Chinese language area, the spoken language has regional phonetic differences. Spoken Chinese can be divided into two major groups, separated roughly by a NE-SW line joining the mouth of the Yangtze River and the Chinese-North Vietnamese border. North of this line are the so-called Mandarin dialects, spoken by about 400 million persons. There are three major Mandarin dialects: the Peking dialect, spoken throughout North China, Northwest China and Manchuria north of a line formed by the Tsin Ling divide and the Hwai Ho; the Chengtu or Upper Yangtze dialect in Southwest China,

TABLE 5

POPULATION BY MAJOR ADMINISTRATIVE DIVISIONS

June, 1953

Provinces	*Population*
Anhwei	30,343,637
Chekiang	22,865,747
Fukien	13,142,721
Heilungkiang	11,897,309
Honan	44,214,594
Hopei	35,984,644
(including part of Jehol)	39,000,000*
Hunan	33,226,954
Hupei	27,789,693
Kansu	12,928,102
Kiangsi	16,772,865
Kiangsu	41,252,192
Kirin	11,290,073
Kwangsi	19,560,822
(excluding Pakhoi area)	19,000,000†
Kwangtung	34,770,059
(including Pakhoi area)	35,000,000†
Kweichow	15,037,310
Liaoning	18,545,147
(including part of Jehol)	20,000,000*
Shansi	14,314,485
Shantung	48,876,548
Shensi	15,881,281
Szechwan	62,303,999
(including Sikang)	65,685,063
Tsinghai	1,676,534
Yünnan	17,472,737
Autonomous Ch'ü	
Inner Mongolia	6,100,104
(including part of Jehol)	7,000,000*
Sinkiang	4,873,608
Tibet (including Chamdo area)	1,273,969
Independent Cities	
Peking	2,768,149
Shanghai	6,204,417
Tientsin	2,693,831
Total	582,603,417

*Estimated population following partition of Jehol Province in 1956.

†Estimated following return of Pakhoi area by Kwangsi to Kwangtung in June, 1955.

and the Nanking or Lower Yangtze dialect in Kiangsi, southern Anhwei and northern Kiangsu. Efforts are being made to transform the Peking dialect into China's national language. Associated with the Mandarin dialects is Hunanese, in central and southern Hunan, with about 20 million speakers, and the Hweichow dialect, in the Tunki region of southernmost Anhwei, with about 7 million speakers.

The most important Chinese language south of the linguistic divide is the Shanghai or Wu dialect, spoken in southern Kiangsu and Chekiang by about 45 million persons. This is followed along the coast by the Foochow or Min dialect, spoken by about 10 million persons in the Min Kiang basin of Fukien. It is adjoined in the south by the Amoy-Swatow dialect, about 15 million strong. Next comes the Hakka language, spoken by another 15 million persons in northeastern Kwangtung and southernmost Kiangsi. Another major southern Chinese language, second only to the Shanghai dialect, is Cantonese, spoken by about 40 million persons. Cantonese is the vernacular of central and western Kwangtung and southern Kwangsi. The Amoy-Swatow, Hakka and Cantonese dialects are spoken by most overseas Chinese, numbering about 12 million, who emigrated from these parts of China.

The Chinese Communists distinguish two national minorities that are also Chinese-speaking. They are the Chinese Moslems and the Manchus.

The Chinese Moslems are known as Hui (Hwei) in the Chinese literature and Dungan in the Russian sources. They began to arrive in Northwest China from Central Asia in the 7th century and became assimilated with the Chinese population, preserving their religious beliefs. There were 3,559,350 Chinese Moslems in 1953, the majority in Kansu, Tsinghai and Sinkiang. Moslem colonies are found in virtually all provinces of northern and western China. National autonomous areas have been set up in regions of greatest concentration, but these account for at most 1,000,000 Moslems. They include three autonomous chou: Wuchung and Sihaiku in Kansu and Changki in Sinkiang; and six autonomous hsien: Kingyüan, Changkiachwan and Kwangtung in Kansu, Hwalung and Weiyüan in Tsinghai, and Yenki in Sinkiang. The Chinese Moslems are also associated with the Yi and Miao in the triple-nationality hsien of Weining, in Kweichow.

The criteria used by the Chinese Communists in determining the Manchu classification are not entirely clear. The 1953 census reported 2,418,931 persons of the Manchu nationality. Language as a criterion is excluded because Manchu is virtually a dead language. The reported Manchus most likely regard themselves as the descendants of the Manchus of Manchuria who conquered China in the course of the 17th century and founded the Manchu dynasty (1644-1912). They are virtually indistinguishable from the Chinese and are scattered throughout Manchuria and North China. They have no autonomous territorial units.

In addition to the Chinese language group, the Indo-Chinese family includes the Kam-Thai, Miao-Yao and Tibetan-Burman groups, all of which are represented in China.

The Kam-Thai group includes the lesser Kam-Sui branch and the more important Thai branch. The only major member of the Kam-Sui branch appears to be the Shuichia nationality. The Shuichia, numbering 150,000, are settled in the karst region of southeastern Kweichow, around Tuhshan, Lipo and Santu. As of January, 1956, this minority had no major autonomous area.

The Thai language branch is about 10 million strong in southwest China. It includes the Chuang, Puyi, Tung, Thai and Nung nationalities, all engaged in agriculture.

The Chuang, numbering 6,611,455, are the most populous minority in China. About 5,400,000 of them live in the Chuang Autonomous Chou of western Kwangsi, which is their only autonomous area.

Adjoining the Chuang settlement area in the north is the Puyi nationality of southwestern Kweichow. The Puyi, formerly known as the Chungchia, number 1,247,883 and live chiefly in the valley of the Peipan Kiang (northern branch of the Pan Kiang). Puyi autonomous areas have been set up in southern Kweichow. They are the Lotien hsien of the Puyi nationality and the Hweishui hsien, which the Puyi share with the Miao.

The Tung group is settled in the border region of southwest Hunan, northern Kwangsi and southeastern Kweichow. They number about 690,000. There are two autonomous hsien: the Sankiang hsien in northern Kwangsi and the Tungtao hsien in southwestern Hunan.

The Thai proper are related to the Shans of Burma, the Siamese of Thailand and the Lao of Indochina. The Chinese segment of the Thai ethnic group is settled in Yünnan Province, where it numbers 580,000. It constitutes the Hsi-shuang-pan-na Autonomous Chou in the southern part of the province and shares the Tehung Autonomous Chou in the west with the Chingpo (Kachin). The Thai of the Hsi-shuang-pan-na Chou speak the Lü dialect, those of the Tehung Chou are more closely related to the Shans of northern Burma. Lü-speaking Thai elements are also associated with the Kawa and Lahu in the triple-nationality Menglien hsien and with the Kawa in the Kengma hsien.

The Nung, numbering 170,000, are settled in southeasternmost Yünnan, at the junction of the Kwangsi and North Vietnamese borders.

The Chinese segment of the Nung, who are also settled in North Vietnam, has no autonomous district.

Also related to the Kam-Thai language group is the Li language spoken by the indigenous population of Hainan Island. The Li nationality, 330,000 strong, shares an autonomous chou with the Miao of Hainan, who are only one-tenth as numerous as the Li on the island.

In 1954, Latinized scripts were said to be in preparation for the Chuang, Puyi and Li nationalities. The Thai written language was to be improved, but it was not stated whether the modern Siamese alphabet or a Latinized form would serve as its basis.

The Miao-Yao branch of the Indo-Chinese language family numbers more than 3 million persons, including 2,511,339 of the Miao nationality and 640,000 of the Yao. These two related minorities are scattered throughout South and Southwest China, the Yao being generally east of the Miao.

About two-thirds of the Miao nationality lives in Kweichow Province. There it is organized in four autonomous hsien (Lushan, Taikiang, Tanchai, and Leishan) and shares the Hweishui hsien with the Puyi and the Weining hsien with the Yi and Chinese Moslems. In Kwangsi, the Miao are organized in the Tamiaoshan hsien; in Hunan, they form the West Hunan Autonomous Chou. About 30,000 Miao on Hainan share an autonomous chou with the Li people.

Most of the Yao are found in the Kwangsi-Kwangtung-Hunan border region, around Kianghwa in Hunan, Linnam in Kwangtung and Tayaoshan, Tuan and Nama in Kwangsi. Before the Communists, the Miao and Yao had used scripts derived from Chinese characters. Missionaries had moreover developed a syllabic system for the Miao people. A Latinized Miao script was reported in preparation in 1954.

The Tibetan-Burman group includes three major branches: the Yi (formerly called Lolo), the Kachin, and the Tibetan. The group is associated areally with the Tibetan highlands and the canyon country adjoining in the southeast. It includes about 7.5 million persons.

The Yi and associated tribes (Minchia, Hani, Lisu, Nasi, Lahu) are numerically the most important branch with 4.5 million persons. They are found in Yünnan, Kweichow, Szechwan and the former Sikang province. The Yi proper, who number 3,254,269, have their home in the Liang Shan, mountain range on the former Szechwan-Sikang border. There they are organized in the Liangshan Autonomous Chou, inhabited by about 700,000 Yi. In Yünnan, where the Yi are found in the mountains on both sides of the upper Red River, the nationality forms the autonomous hsien of Milo and Oshan and shares Kiangcheng hsien with the related Hani people. The Yi also share Weining hsien in Kweichow with the Miao and Chinese Moslems. Like other tribes in Southwest China, the Yi formerly used a script adapted from Chinese characters. A Latinized system was developed by the Chinese Communists, and a newspaper in the new script appeared in Sichang in September, 1952.

The Minchia, related to the Yi ethnic group, have been much assimilated with the Chinese in the Tali region of Yünnan. Because of their lack of ethnic individuality, they have not been set up as a national autonomous area. They number about 480,000.

Another associated people are the Hani, who are settled on the right bank of the Red River, on the border between Yünnan and North Vietnam. Numbering 270,000 persons, the group is set up in the Hungho Autonomous Chou and shares the adjoining Kiangcheng hsien with the Yi people.

The Lisu people, 180,000 strong, are settled in the canyon country of the Salween and Mekong rivers in northwestern Yünnan. On Chinese maps, the Lisu Autonomous Chou extends westward into the headwaters of the Irrawaddy disputed between Burma and China.

The Nasi people, reported to number 170,000, are settled in the Likiang area adjoining the Lisu in the east. Formerly called Moso, the Nasi had not been constituted in an autonomous unit as of January, 1956.

The Lahu people, numbering 170,000, are settled in southwest Yünnan. Their territory extends northwest of the Hsi-shuang-pan-na Thai area and east of the Kawa area. They are set up in the Lantsang autonomous hsien and share the Menglien hsien with the Thai and the Kawa.

The Kachin language branch is represented in China by the Chingpo people of western Yünnan. Chingpo is the Chinese phonetic rendering of the self-designation of these people. The Chingpo are associated with the Thai in the Tehung autonomous chou. They number about 110,000.

The Tibetan language branch is areally the most widespread of the non-Chinese minority languages. Its 2,775,622 speakers, according to the 1953 census, are found throughout the Tibetan highlands. The Tibetans have one of the best developed cultures among the minorities of China, with a distinctive alphabet dating from the 7th century. They are essentially nomadic herders. The Tibetan ethnic group is distributed as follows: 1,250,000 in Tibet, 800,000 in Szechwan (including abolished Sikang Province), 450,000 in Tsinghai and 200,000 in Kansu. In Tibet, which includes the Chamdo area, the Tibetans are set up as an autonomous ch'ü, the highest type of national minority unit. In Szechwan, the

Tibetans are organized in two autonomous chou, each with a Tibetan population of about 400,000, and the Muli autonomous hsien. In Tsinghai, there are five Tibetan autonomous chou (Haipei, Hainan, Hwangnan, Golog, and Yüshu). In addition, the Tibetan Tienchün hsien is associated in Tsinghai with a Mongol and a Kazakh hsien in a joint autonomous chou. In Kansu, the Tibetans have an autonomous chou, with a Tibetan population of 150,000, and the Tienchu autonomous hsien. Finally, there is the Tehtsin autonomous hsien in northern Yünnan.

The Chiang, a nationality closely related to the Tibetans, lives in the Mowhsien-Wenchwan-Lihsien territory of the Ahpa Tibetan Autonomous Chou. The Chiang number about 70,000.

The only other important national group in Southwest China are the Kawa, a member of the Mon-Khmer group of the Austro-Asiatic language family. The Kawa (known as the Wa in Burma) are settled astride the Burma-Yünnan frontier. In Kengma hsien they are associated with the Thai and in Menglien hsien with the Thai and Lahu nationalities. The June, 1953, census set the number of Kawa at 280,000.

The Altaic language family is represented in China by its three branches—Tungus-Manchu, Mongolian and Turkic. The Tungus-Manchu branch is represented in Manchuria, Inner Mongolia and, oddly enough, in Sinkiang. It includes several small tribes, each numbering between 5,000 and 10,000 persons. They are the Orochon and Solon, classified as Tungusic, and the Sibo and Hoche, classified as Manchurian. The Orochon and Solon tribes are hunters and herders in the northern part of the Great Khingan mountains. The Orochon (known in Chinese as Olunchun) have an autonomous banner in Inner Mongolia. Both the Orochon and the Solon are related to the Tungusic Evenki of the Soviet Union.

The Hoche, or Hochih, are settled in northeasternmost Manchuria at the confluence of the Amur and Ussuri rivers. Their Western designation is Fishskin Tatars and they are related to the Gold or Nanay of the Soviet Union. The Sibo, who are settled in the Ili valley of Sinkiang, are descendants of Manchu tribesmen who participated in Chinese military expeditions in Sinkiang in the 18th century and settled there.

The Mongolian branch of Altaic has 1,462,956 speakers in China. It falls into four major dialect groups, of which Buryat is spoken largely in the USSR and Khalkha chiefly in Outer Mongolia. The two Chinese groups are the Ordos-Chahar dialects of Inner Mongolia and the Kalmyk dialects (Derbet and Torgut) found in Kansu and Sinkiang. A branch of Buryat is also spoken in the Barga region of northern Inner Mongolia. The distribution of the Mongols in China is as follows: The Mongol population of Inner Mongolia was 800,000 until 1954. It rose to 1,000,000 with the annexation of Suiyüan Province in 1954 and to 1,200,000 with the incorporation of northern Jehol in 1956. There are about 150,000 Mongols in the present three provinces of Manchuria and another 150,000 in the northwestern provinces of Kansu, Tsinghai and Sinkiang.

Administratively, the Mongols of China are now set up in one autonomous ch'ü (Inner Mongolia), four autonomous chou, one of which is shared with Kazakhs and Tibetans, and nine autonomous banners outside of preceding units. Two autonomous chou are in Sinkiang (Borotala and Bayin Gol), one is in Kansu, and the combined chou is in the Tsaidam basin of Tsinghai. The autonomous banners are distributed as follows: Khobuk-Saur in Sinkiang, Honan in Tsinghai, Supei and Edsin banners in Kansu, and in Manchuria one Tumet banner at Fusin, the North and South Gorlos banners in the Chaoyüan-Fuyü area and a Durbet banner at Taikang.

Until 1955, the Mongols of China made use of the traditional Mongol alphabet, based on the old Uigur script and adopted in the 13th century. After the establishment of Communist rule, preparations were made to introduce a new alphabet in Inner Mongolia based on the Cyrillic and a final decision was reached in 1955. The Cyrillic alphabet was introduced in Outer Mongolia starting in 1946. It may be assumed that the use of a common literary language based on the Khalkha dialect will strengthen ties between the populations of Outer Mongolia and Inner Mongolia.

The language of the Daur (Dahur), a Manchu group that has been largely Mongolized, is often classified with Mongolian. The Daur, who number only a few thousand, are settled around Hailar in northern Inner Mongolia and Tsitsihar in Manchuria. They have no major autonomous areas.

The Turkic language branch is represented by about 4.3 million speakers in China. There are three sub-groupings: Uigur-Uzbek, Kazakh-Kirghiz, and Salar-Yüku. The Uigur group is by far the most important Turkic unit in China. It numbers 3,640,125 persons, virtually all of whom are settled in the Tarim basin of Sinkiang. Sinkiang has in effect been made an autonomous ch'ü based on the Uigur nationality. The related Uzbeks, whose main settlement area is in the Soviet Union, are found in China largely in the Ili valley. They number about 13,000 and have no autonomous unit. Both the Uigurs and the Uzbeks are irrigation farmers.

Nomadic herding is the principal economic activity of the Kazakh-Kirghiz group. The Kazakhs, numbering 470,000 in China, and the Kirghiz, 80,000 strong, also have their main settlement in the Soviet Union. Virtually all the Kazakhs in China are concentrated in the Dzungarian basin of Sinkiang, where they are set up in the Ili Autonomous Chou. Small groups of Kazakhs are organized as the Mulei and Barkol autonomous hsien in Sinkiang and as the Aksai autonomous hsien in Kansu. Finally, the Kazakhs also share an autonomous chou with the Tibetans and Mongols in Tsinghai. The Kirghiz ethnic group is set up in the Kizil Su Autonomous Chou of Sinkiang.

The easternmost representatives of the Turkic group are the Salar and Yüku ethnic groups. The Salar, who number about 30,000, have an autonomous hsien at Shunhwa in Tsinghai. The Yüku, whose name is the Chinese phonetic rendering of Yugur, number about 3,000 and are settled in the Sunan autonomous hsien of Kansu. With the exception of the Yüku, who are Lamaists, all the Turkic-speaking groups are Moslem.

In the Kansu-Tsinghai frontier area are a number of groups of mixed cultural characteristics. They are the Tunghsiang, the Tujen and the Paoan. The Tunghsiang, the most numerous of these groups with 140,000 persons, have an autonomous hsien southwest of Lanchow in Kansu. They are Moslems and speak Mongor, a form of ancient Mongolian. The Tujen, whose population is 60,000, are settled in the Huchu autonomous hsien northeast of Sining in Tsinghai. They also speak Mongor, but are Lamaists in religion. The Paoan, 4,000 strong, are found in the area of Tungjen in Tsinghai. They have no major autonomous unit. The Paoan are Tibetan-speaking Moslems.

The Iranic Tadzhiks of Sinkiang number about 15,000 in the outliers of the Pamir highlands. Sometimes known as the Sarikoli, they speak one of the large number of Iranic dialects of the Pamir region. They constitute the Tash Kurghan autonomous hsien with headquarters at Tash Kurghan, known in Chinese as Puli.

Finally, the Koreans of China are settled in eastern Kirin Province of Manchuria, adjoining their Korean homeland. The Chinese segment of the Korean population numbers 1,120,405 and is settled predominantly in a region historically known as Chientao. There the Chinese Communists have set up the Yenpien Autonomous Chou, which contains about half the Korean population of China.

In summary, China's ethnic minorities belong to two major language families: the Indo-Chinese and the Altaic, with the former found in the southwestern quadrant of the country and the latter in the northwestern. Economically, most of these ethnic minorities are farmers like the basic Chinese population. The total nomadic herding population is about 3.5 million, including chiefly Tibetans, Mongols, Kazakhs. Certain small tribes, such as the Orochon of Manchuria, making hunting their chief source of livelihood. In religion, 8 million minority people are Moslems. They include the Uigurs and the Chinese Moslems, each with about 3.6 million persons, Kazakhs, Tunghsiang, Kirghiz, Salar and others. Tibetans and Mongols, the Tujen and Yüku are Lamaists, and the Thai peoples of Southwest China are predominantly Hinayana Buddhists. Other groups engage in various shamanistic practices.

Chapter 3

THE ECONOMIC PATTERN

The Chinese Communists are determined to transform their country into a Socialist state and a world power in the image of the Soviet Union. This seems to be a utopian aim at their present stage of development and the rulers of China have no illusions on that score. According to their present estimates it will take fifteen years, or three five-year plans, to collectivize agriculture, complete nationalization of industry and establish a Socialist society. And, they say, it will require fifty years, or the second half of this century, to achieve a high degree of industrialization and transform China into a world economic power.

The Soviet Union collectivized its agriculture in early 1930 in one of the most tempestuous periods of world economic history. It carried out its industrialization drive of the 1930's at the cost of great deprivations for the consumer. Partly out of economic necessity, partly out of choice, the Chinese Communists have adopted a more leisurely pace. But the goal to be attained by this gradual approach is no less specific than was the Soviet objective. Essentially it involves the all-out mobilization of the nation's resources for economic development. The cornerstone of Communist economic development is industrialization and the emphasis is on heavy industry. For only through the development of their fuel and power resources, an iron and steel industry, machinery and chemicals do the Chinese Communists expect to be able to achieve their aim of becoming one of the world's leading economic powers.

The following discussion of Chinese economic progress is based largely on the provisions of the first five-year plan (1953-1957), disclosed in July, 1955.

Industry

For statistical purposes, the Chinese Communists divide the total output of industry and agriculture into four segments. They are: (1) modern industry, using machinery and operating on a factory scale; (2)

handicraft workshops, using little machinery but operating on a factory scale; (3) individual handicraftsmen and handicraft producer cooperatives, and (4) agriculture and subsidiary peasant occupations. Individual and cooperative handicrafts are generally excluded from the total output value of industry.

Estimated figures in Table 6 give the output value of the four segments of industry and agriculture in billions of new-currency yüan in terms of constant prices of 1952. (The yüan was revalued in early 1955). These monetary values have been estimated from scattered sources and are subject to correction as further data become available.

TABLE 6

GROSS OUTPUT OF INDUSTRY AND AGRICULTURE

(in billions of new-currency yüan)

	1949	*1952*	*1953*	*1954*	*1955**	*1957 Plan*
All industry	11	27.01	36	42	44	53.56
Modern sector	8	22.08	28	34	36	45
Handicraft sector	3	4.93	7	7	8	8.6
Individual and cooperative handicrafts	3	7.31	9	10	11	11.77
Agriculture and subsidiary production	33	48.39	50	52	55	59.66
Total gross output	47	82.71	95	104	111	124.99

*Data for 1955 are provisional estimates.
(Some columns do not add up because of rounding)

In their industrialization drive, the Chinese are fostering the development of modern industry over the traditional handicraft production. One of the Communist industrial indices expresses the output of modern industry as a percentage of the total output of industry and agriculture.

TABLE 7

GROSS OUTPUT OF MODERN INDUSTRY

	in billion yüan	*in per cent of total output*
1949	8	17
1952	22.08	26.7
1953	28	30
1954	34	33
1955 Estimate	36	33
1957 Plan	45	36

This index does not reveal the share of modern industry in industrial output alone. Analysis of Chinese data shows that handicraft factory industry has been growing at virtually the same rate as modern industry. The five-year plan calls for an increase in the gross output of modern industry of 104.1 per cent from 1952 to 1957. However, the gross output of all industry (including handicraft factories) is slated to rise by 98.3 per cent, only a few percentage points less. The share of modern industry in total industrial output through the first five-year plan period is slightly less than 80 per cent.

The major institutional change under the Communists has been the gradual transfer of industry to state control. The Peking regime inherited a sizable state enterprise sector from the Nationalists. This has been gradually enlarged partly through outright expropriation, partly through the establishment of joint state-private enterprises, and partly through the fostering of cooperatives. At the present stage of economic development, Chinese industry consists institutionally of four sectors. Three of these—the state, joint state-private and cooperative sectors—are under direct governmental control and supervision and fall under the jurisdiction of industrial ministries. The fourth sector, which includes the remaining private enterprises, is not under ministry jurisdiction. In practice, however, the state extends its control to the private sector through allocations of raw materials, the placing of government orders and other administrative measures.

The following table illustrates the increase of the share of industry under government control. It shows the percentage of industrial output of state, joint state-private and cooperative enterprises in the total output of industry, the balance being the output of the private sector.

TABLE 8

INSTITUTIONAL STRUCTURE OF INDUSTRY

	Total industrial output (in billion yüan)	*State sector (in per cent)*	*Private sector (in per cent)*
1949	10.8	36.7	63.3
1952	27.0	61	39
1953	35.5	63.2	36.8
1954	41.5	75.1	24.9
1955 Estimate	43.7	82	18
1957 Plan	53.6	87.8	12.2

In 1954, the last year for which statistics have been issued, the 75.1 per cent of industry under governmental control included 59 per cent state-owned industry, 12.3 joint state-private enterprises and 3.8 per cent cooperatives. The continuing existence of the private sector is demonstrated by the fact that in 1957 the private share of industrial output is still expected to be 12.2 per cent.

In the course of 1955, it became evident that the elimination of the private sector of industry was proceeding at a more rapid pace than originally planned. The institution of joint state-private management was no longer pressed merely on an individual plant basis. Entire branches of industry were being converted to joint management. The 1955 plan called for a reduction of private industrial output to 21 per cent of the total output. Toward the end of the year, however, the forecast was that the percentage would be lowered to 18 per cent. Final economic results for 1955 may disclose an even smaller percentage.

It has already been pointed out that in the Chinese drive for industrialization the stress is on heavy industry. This means production of producer goods in contrast to light industry or consumer goods. One of the Chinese industrial indices charts the output value of producer goods in terms of total industrial output.

TABLE 9

OUTPUT SHARE OF PRODUCER GOODS

(in per cent of total industrial output)

1949	28.8 per cent
1952	39.7
1953	41.1
1954	42.3
1955 Plan	45.1
1957 Plan	45.4

Table 9 reflects rather sensitively the rapid rate of increase during the reconstruction period 1949-52 and the slower rates in subsequent years. As in the case of modern industry, the producer goods program is likely to be achieved by 1957. The great emphasis given to heavy industry is borne out by the allocation of capital investments during the five-year plan. Out of an industrial capital construction budget of 24.85 billion yüan, 88.8 per cent are being allocated to producer goods and 11.2 per cent to consumer goods.

The basis of heavy industry are fuel and power industries and these have received a good deal of attention. China's coal output in 1949 was only one-half of the pre-war peak, but the previous high was surpassed in 1952. After a relatively small rise in 1953, production advanced rapidly in 1954 and 1955 and may reach the 113 million tons set for the end of the five-year plan in 1957.

TABLE 10

COAL PRODUCTION
(in million metric tons)

Pre-1949 Peak	62.0
1949	31.0
1950	40.9
1951	50.8
1952	63.528
1953	69.4
1954	79.928
1955 Estimate	92.75
1957 Plan	112.985

This increase in production under the first five-year plan is to be achieved through the expansion of old mines and the building of new ones. According to the plan, work is to be started on the construction of 93.1 million tons of additional coal-mining capacity, of which 53.85 million tons are to be completed during the five-year plan and the rest after 1957. In the first three years of the plan, 26 million tons of new coal-mining capacity were commissioned.

As a result of this expansion of the coal industry, 31 mines are expected to produce more than one million tons each. The productions planned for the five largest mines by 1957 are shown in Table 11.

TABLE 11

1957 GOALS OF MAJOR COAL BASINS
(in million tons)

Kailan	9.68
Fushun	9.3
Fusin	8.45
Hwainan	6.85
Tatung	6.45

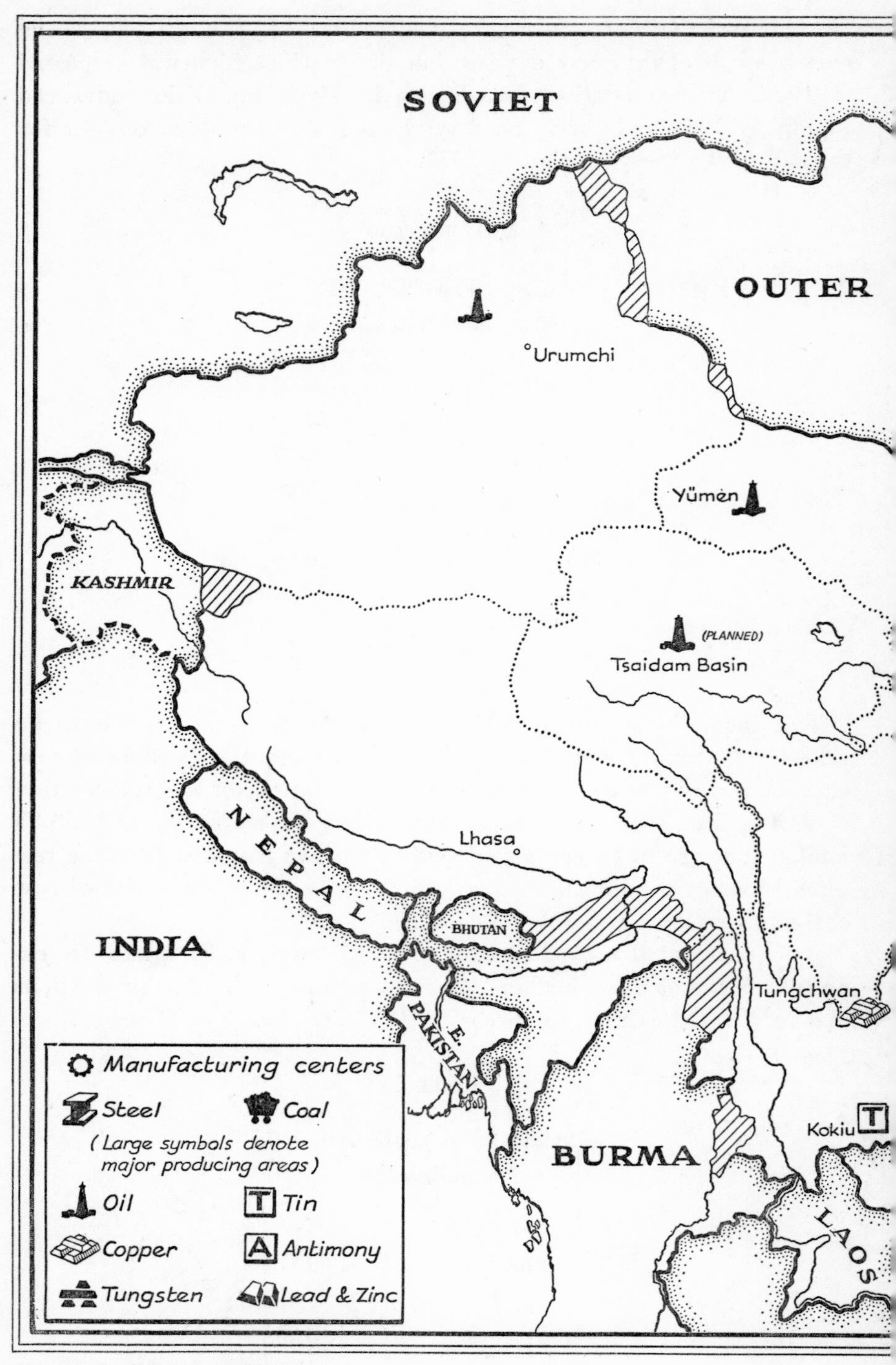

Economic Centers of China

UNION
MONGOLIA
Hokang
Harbin
Changchun
Fusin
Fushun
Mukden
Anshan
N. KOREA
Paotow
(PLANNED)
Peking
Kailan
Tatung
Shihkingshan
Tientsin
Dairen
S. KOREA
Taiyüan
Tsinan
Tzepo
Tsingtao
Lanchow
Tsiaotso
Tsaochwang
Sian
Chengchow
Hwainan
JAPAN
East
China
Sea
Wusih
Shanghai
Chengtu
Wuhan
Hwangshih
(PLANNED)
Chungking
A
Pingsiang
Pacific Ocean
FORMOSA
Canton
N. VIETNAM
South China Sea
HAINAN
PHILIPPINES
0
500 Miles

It will be noted that the three leading mines are in northern Hopei and in southern Manchuria, the industrial heart of China. They will continue to operate at or near output levels achieved by the Japanese during the war. On the other hand, Hwainan in northern Anhwei and Tatung in northern Shansi are in areas of new industrial development and are being considerably expanded above previous levels. The fact that the five leading mining centers account for only 35 per cent of China's total coal output and that thirty-one mines are scheduled to exceed the one-million level indicates remarkable decentralization of the Chinese coal industry.

Outside of the five leading areas, China's major coal-mining centers are: Penki and Pehpiao in Liaoning, Liaoyüan (Sian) in Kirin, and Hokang, Shwangyashan and Kisi in Heilungkiang, all in Manchuria; Fengfeng in Hopei, Tsaochwang (1957 goal: 1,750,000 tons), Tzepo and Weifang in Shantung, Tsiaotso (1957 goal: 2,300,000 tons) in Honan, and Pingsiang in Kiangsi.

In terms of reserves, China has the capacity of becoming one of the leading coal nations. A Communist estimate of 1954 put the reserves at depths up to 1,500 feet at 445 billion tons. Mining has been increasingly modernized. In 1954, 33.6 per cent of all coal was obtained by mechanized methods compared with 4 per cent in 1950. Increasing use has been made of the more efficient longwall mining system, which in 1954 was applied to almost 80 per cent of the coal mined compared with 13 per cent in 1949.

Petroleum, another major world fuel, has until now played an insignificant role in China. However, the Communists are confident that an intensive exploration campaign in the Northwest, notably in Sinkiang and the Tsaidam basin of Tsinghai, will uncover considerably resources. Until now 150 favorable structures are said to have been found in China, including about seventy in Sinkiang and more than twenty in the Tsaidam basin. The Communists plan to make an intensive exploration effort in the next decade. Compared with total exploratory drilling of 212,000 meters from 1907 to 1954, they propose to drill 300,000 meters alone in 1956, 500,000 meters in 1957 and 6 million meters during the second five-year plan (1958-62). For the time being, crude oil production proceeds in three areas of China. They are the Yenchang field of Shensi, the oldest and least important of the producing areas, opened in 1907; the Yümen field in Kansu, the most important present producer, and the Tushantze field near Wusu in Sinkiang. Although the Communists have reported a nine-fold increase from 1949 to 1955, actual production is still extremely small.

TABLE 12
CRUDE OIL PRODUCTION
(in thousand metric tons)

1944	116
1945	115
1946	120
1947	91
1948	132
1949	122
1950	202
1951	306
1952	436
1953	649
1954	824
1955 Estimate	1050
1956 Plan	1320
1957 Plan	2012

It is evident from the timing of the exploration program that major production results, if any, cannot be expected before the second five-year plan.

In the absence of any significant petroleum production, the Chinese have been stressing the extraction of shale oil at Fushun, where synthetic fuel is also being produced through the hydrogenation of coal. The Peking regime is confident that as a result of its contemplated intensive drilling program and the development of a synthetic fuels industry China will be able to meet its consumption requirements within ten to fifteen years.

When the Soviet Union planned its industrialization, it formulated the so-called Goelro plan, a nation-wide electrification program that was to lay the basis for further progress. The Chinese have not promulgated a special electrification plan, but are nonetheless devoting much of their attention to expansion and construction of electric power plants. China surpassed in 1952 the pre-1949 level of electric power generation and the five-year plan calls for more than a doubling of electric power output from 7.26 billion kilowatt-hours in 1952 to 15.9 billions in 1957.

This substantial increase in output is to be achieved through the installation of additional power-generating capacity. The five-year plan calls for work to be started on the construction of 4,060,000 kilowatt of additional capacity, of which about one-half, or 2,050,000 kilowatt is to be completed by 1957. During the first 3 years of the plan, 900,000 kilowatt of new capacity was commissioned, raising installed capacity from 1.96 million kilowatt in 1952 to 2.9 millions in 1955. The 1957 plan is 4.01 million kilowatt of generating capacity.

The five-year plan contemplates the construction of ninety-two power plants, of which twenty-four major items are to be built with Soviet aid. The program includes fifteen thermal power stations with a capacity of 50,000 kilowatt or more. These include plants at Taiyüan, Sian and Lanchow, growing industrial centers of the Northwest; Fushun and Fusin, Manchurian coal producers, and the future steel centers of Hwangshih (near Tayeh) and Paotow.

Power development during the five-year plan calls for the construction of sixteen hydroelectric plants. Foremost among these is the Fengman station on the upper Sungari River in Manchuria, built by the Japanese during the Second World War and partly dismantled by the Soviet Army in 1946. When fully reconstructed by the Peking regime in 1959, the station will have a capacity of 567,000 kilowatt. The Chinese are also participating in the reconstruction of the Shuifeng (Supung) hydroelectric station on the Yalu River (Korean border). The station, scheduled to reach its full capacity of 600,000 kilowatt in 1956, supplies power to both North Korea and Manchuria. Other hydroelectric projects are the Kwanting dam northwest of Peking and the Lungki River station northeast of Chungking. The Sanmen station on the Yellow River is due in 1961. As a result of construction, the share of hydroelectric stations in the total installed power capacity is expected to rise from 9.3 per cent in 1952 to 17.1 per cent in 1957.

TABLE 13

ELECTRIC POWER PRODUCTION

	Installed Capacity (in million kilowatt)		*Power Output (in billion kilowatt-hours)*
	Total	*Hydroelectric*	*Total*
Pre-1949 Peak	2.5		6.00
1949	1.0		4.32
1950			4.58
1951			5.79
1952	1.96	0.19	7.26
1953	2.2		9.2
1954	2.5		10.9
1955 Estimate	2.9		12.56
1957 Plan	4.01	0.68	15.9

Next to adequate fuel and power resources, a nation's heavy industry must be based on iron and steel production. Iron ore is mined predominantly in southern Manchuria near Anshan, Penki and on the Korean border. On the basis of China's pig iron output and assuming no long-haul iron ore shipments, Manchuria's share in the total iron ore production was about 60 per cent in 1954. Other major iron ore mines are in the Lungyen district at Süanhwa (Hopei) and along the Yangtze River near Chungking, Hwangshih (Hupei) and Maanshan (Anhwei). Major operations on Hainan Island have been dormant since the end of the Second World War. A large deposit in Inner Mongolia is expected to be developed in connection with the construction of a steel plant at Paotow. The five-year iron ore plan calls for a 3.7-fold increase over 1952.

The Communists have been able to raise China's iron and steel output from the rock-bottom level of the industry in 1949. Soviet dismantling of major installations at Anshan, keystone of the industry, had brought the once thriving steel center to a virtual standstill. Through gradual restoration of the Japanese-built facilities and their more intensive utilization, the Peking regime was able to surpass pre-war output levels of steel in 1951 and pig iron in 1952.

In 1943, at the peak of Japanese production, the nine blast furnaces then in operation at Anshan produced 1.3 million tons of pig iron. In 1954, five blast furnaces had been rehabilitated. But because of more intensive utilization, these five furnaces produced 1.5 million tons of pig iron in 1954, or 200,000 tons more than was smelted by nine furnaces in 1943. The capacities of the original nine blast furnaces of Anshan and their dates of initial construction and post-war restoration are given in Table 14.

TABLE 14
BLAST FURNACES OF ANSHAN

Number	*Initial Capacity (in tons)*	*Date of Initial Construction*	*Date of Post-War Restoration*
No. 1	400	1919	1949-1952
No. 2	400	1919	1949-1952
No. 3	550	1930	1949-1952
No. 4	600	1937	incomplete
No. 5	700	1938	July, 1955
No. 6	700	1938	Oct., 1954
No. 7	700	1938	late 1953
No. 8	700	1938	March, 1953
No. 9	700	1943	1956

Note: Nos. 4-9 are modern, automatic furnaces.

It is possible that Communist rated capacity of these blast furnaces exceeds the initial Japanese capacity in some cases. The Communists announced that the opening of the two blast furnaces (Nos. 7 and 8) in 1953 increased the rated capacity by 80 per cent. Since the two furnaces had a combined capacity of 1,400 tons, it could be calculated that the capacity previously in operation was about 1,750 tons. However, as appears from the table, the total initial capacity of the Japanese furnaces Nos. 1, 2 and 3 was 1,350 tons. It could be presumed that either the height or shape of the furnaces was modified in the course of restoration to expand their capacity. This hypothesis was supported by the fact that while the Japanese rated capacity of all nine furnaces in 1943 was 1,950,000 (actual output was only 68 per cent of capacity), the Communists proposed to produce 2,500,000 tons at Anshan when reconstruction was completed by 1960.

Intensive utilization of partly restored pre-war installations also accounted for the rapid steel output increase at Anshan. In 1943, two open-hearth plants operated by the Japanese produced a peak steel output of 843,000 tons. The older of these two open-hearth plants, originally built in 1935, was not dismantled by the Soviet Army and could be placed into operation by the Communists in 1949. In 1954, this single plant produced 1,000,000 tons. The Chinese propose to rebuild the second open-hearth plant by 1960. After the completion of all reconstruction in that year, Anshan is expected to produce 3,220,000 tons of steel. It is evident that during the present five-year plan and the early part of the second plan Anshan will supply the lion's share of the Chinese steel output.

Outside of Anshan, pig iron is produced in Manchuria at Penki and steel at Penki, Fushun, Mukden and Dairen. Penki, which made about 200,000 tons of pig iron in 1954, specializes in the production of low-phosphorus iron for use in Bessemer converters. In contrast to Anshan's bulk production, Penki also makes smaller amounts of special steels. The steel-making facilities at Mukden, Fushun and Dairen are associated with the machinery industries in those cities.

Elsewhere in China, pig iron is produced at Süanhwa and Shihkingshan (Peking) from Süanhwa ore. The pig iron is shipped to steel plants at Tientsin and Tangshan or converted into steel at the Shihkingshan plant itself. All these installations form part of the North China iron and steel complex based on Süanhwa ore and Fengfeng coke.

In the Yangtze River valley, iron and steel are produced at Chungking on the basis of local ore and coke. The metallurgical industry of Chungking was founded in 1940, largely on the basis of equipment dismantled at Hanyang and Hwangshih in the path of the Japanese advance. At Hwangshih, the Chinese Communists propose to build a new integrated iron and steel mill on the site of the dismantled installation. The raw material basis would be local high-grade iron ore and Pingsiang (Kiangsi) coke. In the lower Yangtze Valley is the Maanshan-Shanghai iron and steel complex. A battery of small blast furnaces at Maanshan processes local iron ore with long-haul coke and is able to satisfy about one-half of the pig iron requirements of the Shanghai steel mills.

In the northwest, the Communists have expanded the iron and steel industry of Taiyüan and propose to create a new metallurgical base at Paotow. The Taiyüan plant operates on Shansi coke and iron ore and receives some pig iron from a small blast furnace at Yangchüan. The projected Paotow plant will apparently receive coking coal from near-by Shihkwaikow and iron ore from Paiyünopo to the north. The first phase of the new Hwangshih and Paotow steel centers is due for completion in 1961-62.

TABLE 15

PIG IRON AND STEEL PRODUCTION

(in million metric tons)

	Pig Iron	*Crude Steel*	*Rolled Steel*
Pre-1949 Peak	1.9	.9	.59
1949	.246	.158	.121
1950	.97	.74	.36
1951	1.41	.90	.69
1952	1.90	1.35	1.11
1953	2.24	1.77	1.48
1954	2.96	2.22	1.73
1955 Estimate	3.7	2.7	2.36
1957 Plan	4.674	4.12	3.045
1962 Plan	9.0	10.0	

The former predominance of the blast furnaces of Manchuria in pig iron output has been considerably reduced. In 1954, the northeastern region accounted for only 60 per cent of China's total production. This has been achieved through maximum utilization of existing and rehabilitated blast furnace capacity outside of Manchuria. Steel production is still concentrated in the Northeast and is likely to remain so pending the completion of the Hwangshih and Paotow projects during the second five-year plan.

According to the first five-year plan, work is to be started before 1957 on the construction of additional pig iron capacity of 5,750,000 tons and steel capacity of 6,100,000 tons. However, only 2,800,000 tons of the added blast furnace capacity and 2,530,000 tons of open-hearth capacity are scheduled to be completed by 1957. Steel capacity added in the first three years of the plan amounted to 740,000 tons.

Turning to the nonferrous field, we find that China is one of the leading world producers of tungsten and antimony. It is also a major supplier of tin and molybdenum to the Soviet Union and the Eastern European countries. However, its production of the key base metals—copper, lead and zinc—is negligible for the time being.

Tungsten production, in which China leads the world, is concentrated in the Tayü area of southern Kiangsi and adjacent parts of southern Hunan and northern Kwangtung. The greater part of China's antimony output comes from the Sikwangshan area of central Hunan. The leading tin center is Kokiu in Yünnan, whose natural outlet is through the North Vietnamese port of Haiphong. Tin is also associated with the tungsten of southern Kiangsi. The principal molybdenum site, developed by the Japanese in Manchuria, is near Chinsi in Liaoning Province. Mercury, another Chinese export item, is mined in the Kweichow-Hunan border area, notably at Fenghwang.

Among the major base metals, copper, lead and zinc are mined in several small deposits in Manchuria, some of the lead being associated with the molybdenum deposit near Chinsi. Outside of Manchuria, complex argentiferous lead-zinc ores are mined at Shuikowshan in central Hunan and copper at Tungchwan in Yünnan. Aluminum was produced by the Japanese at Fushun during the Second World War on the basis of alunite and aluminous shale found in southern Manchuria. The plant was restored by the Communists and its first phase went into operation in 1954. The five-year plan calls for a 70 per cent increase in copper production. Mines are being developed at Showwangfen in former Jehol Province (not located on available maps) and at Tungkwanshan on the Yangtze River in Anhwei Province. Other developments are scheduled for the Southwest, presumably in the Tungchwan area, and the Northwest. A major impetus is to be given to the mining of lead and zinc ores, notably in the Hweitseh-Tungchwan area of the Southwest. The five-year plan calls for 230 per cent increase of lead and a 210 per cent increase of zinc over the 1952 level. Planned increases are also listed for tungsten (50 per cent) and tin (80 per cent).

Other major minerals include salt, which is obtained both from coastal salines in Hopei, Kiangsu and Chekiang and from brine wells, notably in Szechwan. Salt lakes in Inner Mongolia, Kansu and southern Shansi also yield a small output. Chinese salt production is to rise from 4.94 million tons in 1952 to 7.55 million in 1957. Gold is obtained chiefly in placer deposits of the Amur River valley of northern Manchuria and along the borders of the Tibetan highlands.

Machinery industries are being pushed by the Chinese Communists as the basis for further industrialization. The leading machinery centers are Mukden in Manchuria, which is near raw steel sources and specializes in heavy and bulky machinery, and Shanghai, whose skilled labor force makes precision goods. Other engineering cities are Harbin, Changchun, Fushun and Dairen in Manchuria, Tsinan and Tsingtao in Shantung, Peking and Tientsin in Hopei, and Taiyüan in Shansi.

The five-year plan calls for the construction of two heavy machinery plants to produce metallurgical equipment and mining machinery. When completed during the next five-year plan period, these two plants are supposed to be able to equip jointly an integrated 1.6-million-ton iron and steel plant every year. The present plan also calls for the construction of electrical generating machinery plants capable of producing a total of 800,000 kilowatt of power generating equipment a year. These plants will turn out 12,000-kilowatt, 25,000-kilowatt and 50,000-kilowatt units for the expanding electric power development.

For the first time an automobile and tractor industry is being created in China. Two truck factories are projected under the terms of the five-year plan. The No. 1 Automobile plant, now under construction at Changchun, is scheduled to produce 4,000 trucks a year by 1957 and 30,000 trucks a year when it reaches full capacity during the following five-year plan. Construction will also have started by 1957 on the No. 2 Automobile plant, situated somewhere in Central-South China. The No. 2 plant will have twice the capacity of the first one, or 60,000 trucks a year. The tractor plant, under construction at Loyang in Honan Province, will be the forerunner of China's mechanization of agriculture. When commissioned in 1959, it is due to produce 15,000 tractors of 54 horsepower a year. A second tractor plant is being established at Tientsin.

The beginnings of a chemical industry are found in the coke by-products plants of Anshan, Penki and other coking centers and in the soda ash factory of Tientsin and the fertilizer plants of Nanking and Chungking. The five-year plan calls for the construction of fertilizer plants with a capacity of 910,000 tons a year, of which 280,000 tons are to be commissioned by 1957.

During the five-year plan, five nitrate fertilizer plants are to be newly built or reconstructed in Manchuria, East China, the Northwest and the Southwest. They include two Soviet-designed plants, due for completion in 1958 and 1960, which will have a combined annual output of 210,000 tons of nitrate fertilizer. In addition, two phosphate plants are to be built in North and East China, with a combined output of 300,000 tons of phosphate fertilizer.

Total fertilizer production in 1952 was about 210,000 tons. The output of the main categories, ammonium sulphate and ammonium nitrate, is shown in Table 16.

TABLE 16
CHEMICAL FERTILIZER PRODUCTION
(in thousand metric tons)

	1951	*1952*	*1953*	*1954*	*1957 Plan*
Ammonium sulphate	129	181	226	298	504
Ammonium nitrate	4.9	7.5	22.5	27.0	44

During the five-year plan, four rubber factories in Manchuria, North China and East China are to be rebuilt and one factory is to be newly built. Rubber tire production is planned to rise from 417,000 in 1952 to 760,000 in 1957. It was 703,000 in 1954.

The ambitious industrial construction program undertaken by the Chinese places major demands on the building materials industry, in particular cement production. Having rehabilitated the war-destroyed cement plants, China achieved in 1951 the pre-1949 peak of cement output. The five-year plan calls for more than a doubling of production to 6 million tons. Work is to be started during the plan on a projected increase in annual capacity of 3.6 million tons, of which 2.36 million tons are to be put into operation by 1957. During the first two years of the plan, 650,000 tons were commissioned.

TABLE 17
CEMENT AND PLATE GLASS PRODUCTION

	Cement (in million metric tons)	*Plate Glass (in million square meters)*
Pre-1949 Peak	2.29	
1949	.66	
1950	1.41	
1951	2.48	18.07
1952	2.86	21.32
1953	3.87	24.30
1954	4.6	31.35
1957 Plan	6.00	40.00

The bulk of the cement production originates in North China and Manchuria, including plants at Liuliho (near Peking), Tangshan and Penki. Among factories built to supply cement to construction projects in the Northwest is a plant at Tatung.

Timber, another major building material, is gaining in importance. Output was expected to rise from 10 million cubic meters in 1952 to 20 million in 1957. The five-year plan was exceeded already in 1954, when timber production reached 21.1 million cubic meters. Expansion of timber-felling enterprises was notable in the Great Khingan Mountains of Inner Mongolia and in the Little Khingan of Manchuria. New lumber centers, such as Tuliho in Inner Mongolia and Ichun in Manchuria, have sprung up. The plan called for the laying of 3,049 kilometers of lumber railroads in the newly developed areas.

Chinese statistics include a time series for the production of machine-processed paper, as opposed to the fine Chinese paper made by traditional handicraft methods. The 1957 plan calls for a fourfold increase of factory paper production over the pre-1949 peak level. In 1957, 154,000 tons, or 25 per cent of the total, are due to be newsprint. The increase reflects the growing stress on cultural and educational work required to transform China into an educated, industrial society. The five-year plan calls for an increase in annual capacity of 186,000 tons of paper, of which 95,000 tons are to be put into operation by 1957. Of this amount, 40,000 tons were commissioned during 1953 and 1954.

TABLE 18
FACTORY PAPER PRODUCTION
(in thousand metric tons)

Pre-1949 Peak	165
1949	108
1950	140
1951	241
1952	372
1953	428
1954	556
1957 Plan	655

(In addition, handicraft paper production is due to rise from 167,000 tons in 1952 to 237,000 tons in 1957.)

It will have been evident from the preceding discussion that the Chinese Communists are stressing producer goods production at the expense of consumer items. While the output value of producer goods was expected to grow by 126.5 per cent in the course of the five-year plan, the value of consumer goods was scheduled for only a 79.7 per cent rise. It appeared in 1955 that consumer goods might fall short even of that goal. Underfulfilment of the consumer goods schedule has been typical of the performance of Soviet five-year plans where limited resources have generally been directed into the field of heavy industry at the expense of light industry.

TABLE 19

OUTPUT SHARE OF CONSUMER GOODS

	Total industrial output	*Share of Consumer Goods*	
	(in billion yüan)	*(in billion yüan)*	*(in per cent)*
1949	10.8	7.7	71.2
1952	27.0	16.3	60.3
1953	35.5	20.9	58.9
1954	41.5	23.9	57.7
1955 Estimate	43.7	24.0	54.9
1957 Plan	53.6	29.3	54.6

A leading branch of light industry has been the manufacture of cotton yarn and cloth. China's cotton crop is grown predominantly in the North China plain and in the Wei Ho valley of southern Shensi. The great cotton mill centers are situated along the eastern seaboard at Tientsin, Tsingtao and Shanghai, which alone had almost 50 per cent of the nation's cotton spindles. As a result 75 to 80 per cent of the cotton crop had to be shipped over considerable distances to the coastal mills. Motivated by the Communist principle of bringing industry closer to sources of raw material, the Peking regime proceeded to build cotton mills in the cotton-growing areas, in part with equipment dismantled in the coastal centers. New cotton mills were thus established in the North China plain at Peking, Shihkiachwang, Hantan and Chengchow, and in the Wei Ho valley at Sian and Sienyang. In Peking alone, three mills were erected with a total of 230,000 spindles and 7,000 weaving looms.

China's peak spindle inventory before the Second World War was about 5.2 million. In 1949, the first year of Communist production, about 4 million spindles were believed to have been in operation. By 1952, the base year of the five-year plan, 5.66 million spindles were operating. The five-year plan calls for the addition of 1.89 million spindles. Of these, 1.65 million are to be put into operation by 1957, bringing the total to 7.31 million. About 700,000 spindles were commissioned in 1953 and 1954, the first two years of the plan.

Table 20

COTTON TEXTILE PRODUCTION*

	Cotton Yarn (in million bales) (one bale = 400 pounds)	*Cotton Cloth (in million bolts) (one bolt = 40 yards)*
Pre-1949 Peak	2.4	54.5
1949	1.8	36.5
1950	2.4	56.2
1951	2.6	71.9
1952	3.618	111.634
1953	4.0	135.3
1954	4.5	152.9
1957 Plan	5.0	163.721

* The table does not include locally hand-made yarn and cloth. In 1957, hand-made cloth was expected to amount to 15 million bolts.

In spite of Communist efforts to bring the textile industry closer to raw material sources, the bulk of China's cotton, wool and silk mills remained concentrated along the eastern coast, in particular in the Shanghai-Nanking-Hangchow triangle. Shanghai itself not only has the largest number of cotton spindles, but also leads in the milling of woolens and silk goods. A new linen industry is being created at Harbin in Manchuria.

Table 21

OTHER TEXTILE PRODUCTION
(in million meters)

	1952	*1957 Plan*
Silk fabrics	38.83	69.294
Linen	0.29	18.3
Wool fabrics	3.7	7.5
Gunny bags	67.35*	68.0*

* Million bags.

In the past, virtually all the sugar produced in China was obtained from cane grown in Fukien, Kwangtung, Kwangsi and Szechwan. Only an insignificant amount was obtained from beets in northern Manchuria. The Chinese Communists are taking steps to expand beet production in northern Manchuria and introduce the growing of sugar beets in Inner Mongolia under irrigated conditions. While cane sugar output is scheduled to double in the course of the five-year plan, nearly a fivefold increase has been slated for beet sugar production. Sugar beets are processed entirely in modern refineries. In the case of cane sugar, on the other hand, only 50 to 55 per cent is produced by mills, the rest being extracted by low-yield handicraft methods.

The five-year plan calls for an increase in modern sugar milling capacity of 560,000, of which 428,000 tons are to be commissioned by 1957. During the first two years of the plan, 109,000 tons of additional capacity were put into operation.

TABLE 22

PROCESSED FOODS AND OTHER CONSUMER GOODS

(in million tons)

	Pre-1949 Peak	*1949*	*1952*	*1953*	*1954*	*1957 Plan*
Flour	2.48	1.28	2.99	3.44	3.75	4.67
Fish and meat			.346			.921
Vegetable oil			.983			1.794
Factory			.724	.89	.94	1.552
Handicraft			.259			.242
Sugar			.451	.6		1.10
Factory	.222	.106	.249	.268	.329	.686
Handicraft			.202	.3		.414
Salt			4.943			7.554
Factory			3.46			5.932
Handicraft			1.48			1.62
Cigarettes *(in million crates of 50,000 cigarettes)*	2.4	1.6	2.65	3.6	3.78	4.70
Matches *(in million cases of 1,000 boxes)*		6.75	9.11	8.0	10.3	12.70

Other consumer products such as wheat flour, edible oils and cigarettes are produced almost entirely in the coastal industrial centers of southern Manchuria, the North China plain and the Shanghai area. In assessing the production of consumer goods in China, it must be borne in mind that processed foods and other products are intended essentially for the urban segment of the population.

Before ending the discussion of industry, a few words must be said about the matter of geographical redistribution of industrial enterprises. Following the example set by the Soviet Union in its eastward movement of industry, the Chinese propose to build up the economy of their western regions to achieve a more balanced distribution of industry. They are concerned with placing new industries near sources of fuel and raw materials to eliminate excessively long hauls from raw material producers to processing centers.

China's industry as of 1952 was concentrated in Manchuria and the coastal provinces of Hopei, Shantung and Kiangsu. The value of the gross industrial output of these areas was 70 per cent of the national industrial output, with almost one-fourth originating in Shanghai alone. Manchuria and the coastal provinces accounted for about 80 per cent of the output of the iron and steel and metal-fabricating industries and more than 90 per cent of China's cotton looms. The great industrial centers of Tientsin, Mukden, Anshan, Dairen, Tsingtao and Shanghai accounted for nearly 50 per cent of the nation's total industrial output.

By contrast, the western areas of China—Inner Mongolia, the Northwest and the Southwest—with 24 per cent of the nation's population and 69 per cent of its area accounted for only 8 per cent of the total industrial production, half of it coming from Szechwan Province. The western areas were essentially raw material producers with few processing enterprises.

As a result of this distribution of economic functions, long transportation hauls were required to bring raw materials to the coastal processing centers and, in many cases, to return the finished product to the consumers in outlying areas. Let us consider the case of Shanghai. This dominant textile center had more than 40 per cent of the country's cotton spindles. To keep these machines in operation, 60 to 70 per cent of the raw cotton requirements had to be transported from the main cotton-growing areas of Honan, Shantung and Hopei. (The balance of the raw cotton was grown in the Shanghai region itself.) Similarly, East China, which as of 1952 accounted for 35 per cent of the total machinery output, produced only 1.1 per cent of the country's pig iron and 17 per cent of the rolled steel. Hundreds of thousands of tons of metal had to be brought in for fabrication.

The first five-year plan is intended to lay the basis for the more "rational" distribution of industry, to use a Communist term. Out of 694 major industrial construction projects, 472 are to be placed in the interior. However, inasmuch as most of these projects will not be completed until the second five-year plan, the effect of the redistribution will not be felt until that time. In the meantime, the Chinese propose to strengthen the existing industrial bases in Manchuria and the coastal regions as a sort of supporting bridgehead for the planned westward expansion. At the same time, railroad construction is being pressed in the western regions to provide transportation lines for the contemplated industrial build-up.

Specifically, the Chinese contemplate the creation of new industrial complexes around the projected steel centers of Paotow and Hwangshih. These complexes will include, for example, new centers for the production of heavy machinery. The Communists consider it "rational" to locate such plants near metal producers to eliminate long hauls of bulk metal shipments. As a result of these measures, the distribution of the machinery industry is expected to change radically. In 1952, 80 per cent of the machinery output originated in the coastal regions and 20 per cent in the interior. When enterprises scheduled for construction during the first five-year plan have been completed, the ratio is expected to change to 38 per cent on the coast and 62 per cent in the interior. Similar plans for redistribution are taking shape in other industries.

Agriculture

Lest the detailed industrial description give the reader a misleading impression, it must be strongly emphasized at this point that China is still essentially an agricultural country. About 84 per cent of the population is classified as rural and of these 500 million persons more than 400 million are engaged in the growing of food crops. Agricultural produce moreover provides the raw material for more than 50 per cent of China's industrial production. And it is the export of agricultural products that is expected to supply most of the foreign exchange needed for the import of industrial equipment and construction materials.

To be sure, industry is now the dynamic sector of the Chinese economy and is advancing at a far more rapid rate than agriculture. Under the terms of the five-year plan, the value of China's gross industrial output is due to rise by 98.3 per cent from 1952 to 1957. By contrast, the total value of production of agriculture and subsidiary rural occupations is scheduled to rise by only 23.3 per cent, from 48.4 billion yüan in 1952 to 59.7 billion yüan in 1957. It was 32.6 billion yüan in 1949.

The agriculture of China has been characterized by intensive cultivation with high yields per acre and low output per man. Out of the nation's total area of 950 million hectares only about 11.5 per cent, or 108 million hectares were under cultivation in 1952. There are slightly less than 120 million peasant households in China. The average household, accordingly, has a farm of the size of about one hectare (2.5 acres). By comparison, the average household in the United States has a farm of about sixty hectares (155 acres).

The Communists inherited the institutional framework of traditional rural China in which land was privately held and unequally distributed. According to a Communist classification, 10 per cent of the peasants owning 75 per cent of the land were landlords, who did not work their own land, and rich peasants, who depended only in part on their own labor; 20 per cent were middle peasants, who worked their own land, and 70 per cent were poor peasants, who were largely tenants.

From 1950 to 1952, the Chinese Communists carried out their land reform, which consisted essentially of confiscation and redistribution. About one-third of the population had already been affected by land reform on a piecemeal basis before the law was published in June, 1950. The reform had been carried out in the so-called old liberated areas—Manchuria and parts of North China—which had a rural population of about 150 million persons. During 1951 and 1952 the reform was basically completed in the rest of China. As a result of the redistribution of land, the average size of a family farm was not substantially changed. The net effect of the reform was to eliminate landlords and virtually eliminate rich peasants as a class and to reduce the acreage owned per family toward a common standard. As a result, more than 70 per cent of the peasants were classified as "middle" and more than 20 per cent as "poor," efforts being made to reduce the number of poor peasants.

The land reform program was associated with institutional changes trending toward the collectivization of agriculture. This proceeded in two stages: the establishment of mutual-aid teams, a rudimentary form of agricultural cooperation, and the creation of agricultural producer cooperatives, which were to be converted into true collective farms as they are known in the Soviet Union. For the time being, Chinese producer cooperatives represent only partial collective ownership and are termed semi-Socialist in character. They involve essentially the pooling of land and equipment under unified management, for which each household receives a proportionate number of shares in the cooperative.

At first it appeared that Chinese farm collectivization would be a gradual process, certainly more so than the abrupt upheaval that took place in Soviet agriculture in 1930. In general terms, Chinese leaders had set fifteen years as the over-all period required to complete collectivization on the Soviet pattern. By the end of the first five-year plan, that is in the spring of 1958, only half of the 120 million households of China were to be merged in cooperatives of the semi-Socialist type. However, in October, 1955, Mao Tse-tung reaffirmed the policy of farm collectivization and called for greater efforts in implementing that policy. In the wake of that speech, in the second half of 1955, the formation of cooperatives was greatly speeded. By the end of January, 1956, 92,810,000 households, or 78 per cent of China's total number of rural households, had been joined in cooperatives. Of these, as many as 24,590,000 families were already constituted in full-fledged collectives of the Soviet type.

In view of the rapid progress achieved in the second half of 1955, Mao Tse-tung said in January, 1956, that the cooperativization movement might be completed 85 per cent in 1956 and Soviet-type farms would be instituted throughout China by 1959 or 1960.

TABLE 23

COOPERATIVIZATION OF AGRICULTURE

At End of Year	*Number of Cooperatives*	*Households in Cooperatives Number*	*Per Cent*
1951	300		
1952	3,663	58,500	0.05
1953	14,900	275,000	0.25
1954	490,000	12,700,000	11.5
1955 (August)	650,000	16,900,000	15
1955	1,900,000	70,000,000	60
1956 (Plan)		100,000,000	85

In addition to various forms of agricultural cooperation, the Chinese Communist institutional structure includes state farms and machine-tractor stations. The state farms include small local enterprises that serve as experimental and seed-selection stations and large mechanized farms on the Soviet model that operate chiefly in the new sparsely settled lands of northern Manchuria. At the end of 1954, there were more than 2,000 local state farms, and 97 large mechanized farms with a total of 185,000 hectares. There were also 89 tractor stations, with a tractor pool of 778 machines (in 15-horsepower units). The Soviet Union, by contrast, has 8,950 machine-tractor stations with a total tractor pool of 1,260,000 15-horsepower units.

Two major grain areas stand out in China. The North is a dry dust-blown land of wheat, millet and kaoliang. The South is green and humid and devoted almost entirely to rice as the predominant food crop. Chinese Communist grain (food crop) statistics include not only rice, wheat and the lesser grains, but also soybeans and potatoes.

TABLE 24

FOOD CROP PRODUCTION

	Output (in million tons)	Area (in million hectares)
Pre-1949 Peak	150	
1949	113	
1950	132	
1951	145	
1952	163.915	122.739
1953	166.8	126
1954	169.5	129
1955 Estimate	182.5	
1956 Plan	199	
1957 Original Plan	192.81	126.376

China is the world's leading rice producer, accounting for 40 to 45 per cent of the total world output. Rice is the nation's most important grain and makes up about 40 per cent of the total food crop. It is cultivated almost entirely south of the Tsin Ling divide and the Hwai Ho, where it is favored by the warm humid climate and the impervious clay-pan soils that retain irrigation water. The major rice-surplus regions are the Red basin of Szechwan and the "rice bowls" of the middle and lower Yangtze Valley. Rice is a summer crop and is usually alternated with wheat, a winter crop, in the Yangtze Valley. In the double-cropping rice region of southernmost China, the paddy fields yield two harvests a year. The average yield is three tons per hectare. In 1955, 4.6 million hectares were double-cropped.

TABLE 25

RICE PRODUCTION

	Output (in million tons)	Area (in million hectares)
Pre-1949 Peak	52.5	
1949	38.3	
1950	50	
1951	59.0	
1952	68.425	28.098
1953	70.4	
1954	69.7	
1955 Estimate	75	
1957 Plan	81.77	29.361

Wheat is the characteristic food grain of North China. The country is the world's third wheat producer, after the Soviet Union and the United States. Wheat is cultivated mainly in the so-called Winter Wheat-Kaoliang region of Hopei, Honan and Shantung, where it is favored by the calcareous alluvial soils and the moderate rainfall. About 15 per cent of China's wheat is grown in the dry northwestern margins beyond the Great Wall, where it is a summer crop. In 1954, out of a total wheat area of 27.2 million hectares, about 24 million were sown in winter wheat. The over-all yield of Chinese wheat is a little less than one ton per hectare.

TABLE 26

WHEAT PRODUCTION

	Output (in million tons)	*Area (in million hectares)*
Pre-1949 Peak	23	
1949	13.0	
1950	15	
1951	16.8	
1952	18.125	24.53
1953	18.1	
1954	23.2	27.2
1957 Plan	23.725	26.417

Lesser cereals grown in China in addition to rice and wheat are barley, corn, kaoliang and millet. Barley, like wheat, is a winter crop, cultivated predominantly in the Yangtze Valley. In hilly districts where rice is not cultivated, barley is grown as the main food crop in the summer. Barley occupies a special position among the cereals of the Tibetan highlands, where it is the staple food of the Tibetan population in a roasted and ground form known as tsamba.

Corn is found in a belt extending from Yünnan northeast to southern Manchuria where loamy soils and warm, moist summers favor its cultivation. To the northwest of this zone, the climate is too dry and the growing season too short. To the southeast, corn generally gives way before rice and sweet potatoes.

Kaoliang, a sorghum, is an important secondary grain. It is associated as a summer crop with winter wheat in the North China plain and with soybeans in Manchuria. The term "kaoliang," which means "tall millet," is used by the Chinese only in North China. Elsewhere it is called "shu-shu," meaning "millet from Shu," ancient name of Szechwan.

Millet, another of the lesser grains, is in general more drought-resistant than kaoliang and is grown farther west. It is associated with wheat in the Winter Wheat-Millet region of the loesslands of Shansi, Shensi and southeastern Kansu.

The production of coarse grains, according to the five-year plan, is scheduled to rise from 51.52 million tons in 1952 to 54.795 million tons in 1957. During the same period, the sown area is due to be cut back from 49.95 million hectares to 48.33 million hectares.

Also included among the food crops are sweet potatoes and Irish potatoes. Sweet potatoes are produced chiefly in southern China. They are a hillside crop that can be grown on sandy and stony soils unsuitable for more demanding crops. Irish potatoes are relatively new in China and are found mainly in the vicinity of urban, industrial areas of North China and Manchuria.

The production of all tubers, including sweet potatoes and Irish potatoes, is scheduled to increase from 16.325 million tons in 1952 to 21.6 million tons in 1957. During the same period, the area sown to these crops is expected to rise from 8.6 million to 9.715 million hectares. Potato production figures are in terms of "grain-equivalents." The ratio of actual potato output to grain-equivalents is 4:1.

Soybeans are a distinctive crop of Manchuria, but are also grown in eastern China, notably Shantung. They are a leading export crop. Peanuts grow best on sandy soils found in Shantung, northern Kiangsu and Anhwei. China's annual production, exceeded only by India, is 2 to 3 million tons.

TABLE 27

SOYBEAN PRODUCTION

	Output (in million tons)	*Area (in million hectares)*
Pre-1949 Peak	10	
1952	9.52	11.57
1953	10.09	
1954	9.18	
1957 Plan	11.22	12.56

In keeping with Soviet experience, the Chinese are stressing the expansion of industrial crops. The area under such crops is planned to increase by 27.1 per cent during the five-year plan, from 11.78 million hectares in 1952 to 14.97 millions in 1957. Food crops, by contrast, are expected to rise only 3 per cent in terms of sown area. The leading industrial crops of China are cotton and other fibers, such as jute and hemp; tobacco, sugar cane, sugar beets and oilseeds.

China's principal natural fiber crop is cotton. About half of the nation's output comes from the North China plain and the loesslands, the other half from the Yangtze Valley. Long staple cotton is produced under irrigated conditions in the Wei Ho valley of Shensi and in other parts of China. Elsewhere native Chinese cotton, with a shorter staple up to one inch in length, is grown. About 10 per cent of the total cotton area is irrigated.

TABLE 28

COTTON LINT PRODUCTION

	Output (in million tons)	*Area (in million hectares)*
Pre-1949 Peak (1936)	0.84	
1949	0.44	2.5
1950	0.71	3.6
1951	1.04	5.45
1952	1.304	5.52
1953	1.187	5.1
1954	1.065	5.3
1955 Estimate	1.503	
1957 Plan	1.635	6.27

Note: Non-Communist sources give the pre-1949 peak output in 1936 as 1,110,000 tons.

Among China's lesser vegetable fibers are jute and the related ambary hemp or kenaf, also ramie, hemp and flax. Jute and ambary hemp, grown in Chekiang, Kwangtung and Kiangsi are used for making burlap bags. The five-year plan calls for an increase of production of these fibers from 305,000 tons in 1952 to 365,000 in 1957, making China the third largest producer, after Pakistan and India. Ramie, a strong bast fiber, is cultivated in the middle Yangtze Valley and Hunan and is used for lightweight industrial fabrics. Hemp and flax are found in the cooler climates of Manchuria and Inner Mongolia.

Silk production has greatly declined in China since before the Second World War. In 1949, the cocoon crop was about one-sixth of the pre-war level. More that 80 per cent of the cocoons are bred in Kiangsu and Chekiang, Kwangtung and Szechwan. In addition to the mulberry-fed worms, silk is also produced from wild silkworms that feed on oak and ash leaves. Wilk silk is obtained in Shantung and the Liaotung peninsula of southern Manchuria. According to the five-year plan, the production of wild silk cocoons is to remain fairly stable, rising from 61,100 tons in 1952 to 61,750 in 1957. The wild silk is spun and woven into the so-called tussah cloth, a strong, coarse fabric.

TABLE 29

DOMESTIC SILK COCOON PRODUCTION

(in thousand metric tons)

1949	35
1950	43
1951	52
1952	62.2
1953	(no data)
1954	75
1957 Plan	93.4

Tobacco is grown on about 200,000 hectares in China, with the chief producing areas in Honan and Shantung. According to the five-year plan, the output of cured tobacco is due to increase by 76.6 per cent from 1952 to 1957.

TABLE 30

CURED TOBACCO PRODUCTION

(in thousand metric tons)

1949	(no data)
1950	(no data)
1951	251
1952	221
1953	221
1954	241
1957 Plan	390

Another of China's distinctive crops—tea—also lags behind former output levels. The nation produces three major types of tea: black tea, which is fermented; oolong tea, which is partly fermented, and green tea, which is not fermented before firing. The most important districts for green tea are Pingshui and Lungtsing in northern Chekiang and Liuan and Tunki in Anhwei. Black tea is made in Kimen (Keemun) in southern Anhwei and Wenchow in southern Chekiang and oolong tea chiefly in Fukien. Other tea-producing provinces are Hupei and Hunan. In recent years, green-tea districts have been shifting increasingly to black tea, a variety preferred for export to the Soviet Union and the Eastern European countries. In its heyday in the 19th century, China produced about 250,000 tons of tea a year. She has since been replaced by India and Ceylon as the world's leading suppliers.

TABLE 31

TEA PRODUCTION

(in thousand metric tons)

1949	(no data)
1950	67
1951	74
1952	82.4
1953	88
1954	(no data)
1957 Plan	111.85

China obtains her sugar supply from both sugar cane and beets. Sugar cane is grown in Fukien, Kwangtung and Kwangsi as well as in Szechwan. Sugar beets can be cultivated in northern Manchuria and Inner Mongolia, partly under irrigation. The five-year plan aims at a major increase in beet production. Formerly China obtained virtually her entire sugar from cane.

TABLE 32

SUGAR CANE AND BEET PRODUCTION

	Sugar Cane		*Sugar Beet*	
	Output	*Area*	*Output*	*Area*
1951	4.64		0.31	
1952	7.115	.181	0.48	.035
1953	7.32		0.48	
1954	8.72		0.95	
1957 Plan	13.175	.268	2.135	.141

(Output in million tons; area in million hectares)

A major role in China's agriculture is played by the cultivation of oilseeds for the production of vegetable oils as well as industrial oils. In addition to soybeans and peanuts, which are discussed under food crops, the oilseeds include cotton seed (about two-thirds of the total unginned cotton weight is seed), rapeseed, sesame, perilla, linseed, and hempseed. According to the five-year plan the total area sown in oil seeds is scheduled to rise from 5.7 million hectares in 1952 to 7.86 million in 1957. Sesame is grown in the North China plain and rapeseed in the Yangtze Valley as a winter crop rotating with rice. Perilla, linseed and hempseed are north Manchurian crops. A major source of industrial oil, used for high-grade varnishes and enamels, is tung oil, produced by the tung tree. The nation's leading tung oil producers are the provinces of Szechwan, Hunan, Kwangsi and Hupei.

In a country so densely crowded as China, little land can be spared for pasture. More food can be obtained through direct consumption of crops than through feeding them to livestock. Because of this, the per capita livestock population of China is one of the smallest in the world. In 1949, the livestock herds numbered 134 million head and in 1953 231 millions. The most numerous domestic animals were hogs, which can live on farm refuse. Chinese hog population rose from 53 million in 1949 to 95 million in 1953 and slightly over 100 million in 1954. About one-fifth of all hogs were in Szechwan province. There were 8 to 9 million hogs in Kwangtung and 6 to 7 million in Hunan. Pork is the most important meat consumed in the south of China and hog bristles, shipped especially from Szechwan, are an important export item. There are virtually no hogs in the loesslands and the Northwest inhabited by Moslems. These areas have a large sheep and goat population, which for China as a whole rose from about 40 million in 1949 to 70 million in 1953.

TABLE 33

LIVESTOCK POPULATION

(in millions)

	1949	*1951*	*1952*	*1953*	*1954*	*1957 Plan*
Horses	5	5.7	6.13	6.6	7.0	8.34
Cattle	43	52	56.60	62	65	73.61
Mules			1.64			1.97
Donkeys			11.81			13.95
Sheep	25	31	36.88	41	46	68.72
Goats			24.90			44.32
Hogs	53	78	89.77	95	101	138.34
Total			227.73			349.25

Fish supplement the diet near the seashore and in canal areas. Fish and other water products amounted to 480,000 tons in 1949 and 1.9 million tons in 1953. About two-thirds of the total catch came from the sea. Major fishing areas extend along the coast provinces of South China, notably Chekiang, Fukien and Kwangtung.

One of the major problems faced by the Chinese is the expansion of their sown area to increase agricultural production. They must increase their food output to feed the growing urban population and provide a surplus for export and the financing of industrial construction. Among the measures that will be undertaken in this connection is the reclamation of idle land. The Chinese say about 100 million hectares, or again as much as the present area under cultivation, are reclaimable.

TABLE 34

OUTPUT OF FISH AND OTHER AQUATIC PRODUCTS

(in metric tons)

	Total	*Private*	*State-owned*
Pre-1949 Peak	1.6	1.6	—
1949	0.48	0.48	—
1952	1.7	1.6	0.087
1953	1.89	1.78	0.113
1954	2.29	2.14	.148
1955 Estimate	2.4		
1956 Plan	2.58		
1957 Plan	2.807	2.525	0.284

The five-year plan calls for an expansion of cultivated land by more than 2,578,000 hectares, raising the sown area to 110.5 million hectares. This is to be achieved by three means: (1) reclamation by state farms and the establishment of new state farms in large areas of idle land, such as in northern Manchuria; (2) reclamation through resettlement of peasants from densely populated areas, such as Shantung, in northern Manchuria and Inner Mongolia; (3) reclamation by peasants on a local basis. Using all these measures, the Chinese propose to investigate the potential reclamation of 6.6 million hectares by 1957, of which 2,578,000 to 3,300,000 hectares would actually be opened up. This is viewed as only the first stage of a larger land reclamation program to be carried out in the second five-year plan.

Another program designed to conserve and expand the cultivated acreage involves flood control and irrigation projects. Floods have been the historic curse of Chinese agriculture. Alone since 1949, the annual flooded area has ranged from 3.7 million hectares in 1951 to 10 million hectares in the great Yangtze flood of 1954.

TABLE 35

ANNUAL FLOODED AREA

(in million hectares)

1949	8
1950	3
1951	3.7
1952	4.4
1953	6.2
1954	10

The Communists have achieved conspicuous successes in flood control. The most important projects are the control of the Hwai Ho, the construction of the Kingkiang flood-detention basin on the Yangtze, the Kwanting reservoir northwest of Peking and the new Tatsing-Tzeya outlet south of Tientsin. During the first five-year plan the first steps will be taken to control the Yellow River with construction of the dam in the Sanmen gorge.

The area under irrigation is being expanded not only through the construction of large-scale multi-purpose projects. Ponds, culverts, ditches and other irrigation works are being built and repaired on a local basis. The five-year plan calls for an increase in the irrigated area by 4.8 million hectares.

TABLE 36
CROP UNDER IRRIGATION*
(in million hectares)

1949	26
1952	28.7
1953	29.4
1954	30.2
1955 Estimate	31
1956 Plan	33
1957 Plan	33.5

* Includes 6 million to 7 million hectares of double-cropped land.

Attention is also being given to the planting of shelter belts and general afforestation designed to reduce soil erosion. The five-year plan calls for the afforestation of 1.56 million hectares by 1957. Shelter belts were planted on more than 280,000 hectares in 1952, and 400,000 hectares in 1953 and 330,000 in 1954. The most ambitious program is under way in Manchuria along the border of Inner Mongolia. By 1967, a shelter belt 1,100 kilometers long and 300 kilometers wide is expected to take shape there. Smaller projects include a shelter belt along the lower reaches of the Yungting River in northern Hopei and sandbreaks in western Hopei and eastern Honan.

In spite of the already intensive utilization of the land, the Chinese Communists maintain that cooperatives are able to increase agricultural yield above the level achieved by mutual-aid teams and individual peasants. Mao Tse-tung reported in October, 1955, that out of the 650,000 producer cooperatives organized by June, 1955, more than four-fifths had been able to increase yields over previous levels. This is being done through a more rational distribution of labor within the collective and better land utilization. According to the Communists, the agricultural cooperatives are able to use farm implements, flood control measures and cultivation techniques that are beyond the capacity of individual peasants.

Transportation

One of the problems faced by the Chinese Communists is the construction of a transportation network adequate for its program of industrialization. Like the Soviet Union, China is essentially a railroad nation, with waterways and highways playing a secondary transportation role. Railroads handled 90 per cent of all freight in 1954. Like Soviet economic planners, the Chinese press for greater utilization of existing waterways to take some of the transportation burden off the railroads. At the same time railroad construction is being pushed, particularly in the Northwest, to open up underdeveloped parts of the nation.

The Chinese Communists inherited a total length of 25,900 kilometers (16,200 miles) of railroads, of which about one-half was in Manchuria. A large part of this network had been put out of operation in the course of the Second World War and the Civil War ending in 1949. In a remarkably rapid rehabilitation drive, the Chinese Communists succeeded in restoring more than 80 per cent of the lines by the end of 1949, including all the trunk railroads. In the following years, the restoration of old lines and the construction of new ones proceeded on a parallel basis.

TABLE 37
LENGTH OF OPERATING RAILROAD LINES

End of Year	*Kilometers*
1949	21,715
1950	22,238
1951	23,063
1952	24,232
1953	24,690
1954	25,500
1957 Plan	28,300

The rehabilitation of old lines was scheduled to continue through the five-year plan. As late as 1955, several major sections of former operating lines had not been put back in operation. They included, in particular, the Soochow-Kashing cutoff in the Shanghai area, the Peking-Chengteh railroad, and several lines in northern Manchuria.

On the other hand, the railroad network was expanded through the construction of new lines, particularly in the western part of the nation. From 1949 to the end of 1952, 1,473 kilometers of new lines were laid. The five-year plan calls for the construction of 4,084 kilometers of new railroads, of which 1,420 kilometers were completed by the end of 1954. During the first five years of control, the Chinese Communists thus added nearly 2,900 kilometers of new railroads to the network, not counting restoration of previously operating trackage.

One of the earliest construction projects completed by the Chinese Communists was the Laipin-Chennankwan railroad in Kwangsi Province. This line, 420 kilometers long, linked the Chinese railroad system with the network of North Vietnam. The Laipin-Chennankwan line, completed in November, 1951, undoubtedly played a major role in supplying the Vietnamese Communists with arms during the Indochina war and assuring their victory in North Vietnam. After the Indochina armistice, Vietnamese and Chinese restored the railroad leading from Hanoi to the Chinese border at Chennankwan (which was renamed Munankwan). In 1955, through traffic was inaugurated between North Vietnam and China. Reconstruction was also begun on another major link between the two countries. That is the Hanoi-Laokay-Pisechai railroad, connecting with the Kunming rail system. While the Hanoi-Laipin railroad is perhaps more important to the Vietnamese by providing a supply route for Chinese aid, the Hanoi-Pisechai line is a far more significant line for the Chinese. It provides an outlet for the products of the isolated Kunming region, notably the tin of Kokiu, via the Vietnamese port of Haiphong. This relatively short outlet to the sea is likely to play a major role even after the planned inland link between Kunming and the Chinese rail system has been completed.

Related to the Kwangsi rail system is the construction of the Litang-Tsamkong railroad, completed in 1955. This 318-kilometer line links the Hunan-Kwangsi trunk railroad with Tsamkong (known as Chankiang in Mandarin), a developing South China port. The new connection opens up a hinterland for Tsamkong and at the same time supplies the first seaward outlet for landlocked Kwangsi Province.

In July, 1952, the Chinese Communists completed the key railroad from Chungking to Chengtu in Szechwan Province. This line, 505 kilometers long, is to be the basic link of a new rail system in West China. Planned and partly completed by the Nationalists, the Chungking-Chengtu railroad connects the two largest cities of Szechwan via the sugar center and future rail hub of Neikiang. From Neikiang, the Chinese propose to build a railroad through the rugged Upper Yangtze basin to the Kunming region of Yünnan. The Neikiang-Kunming line will

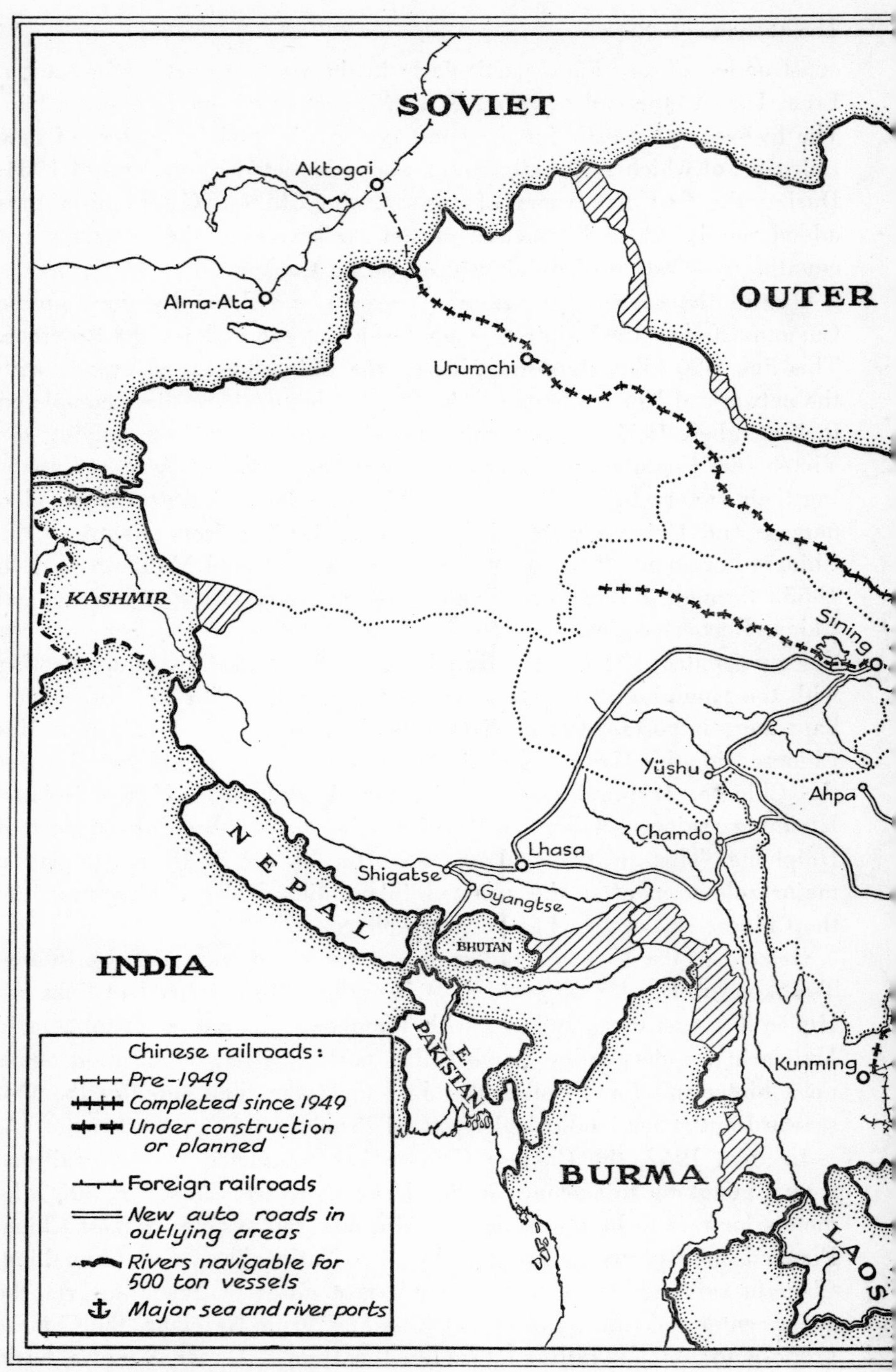

Transportation Lines of China

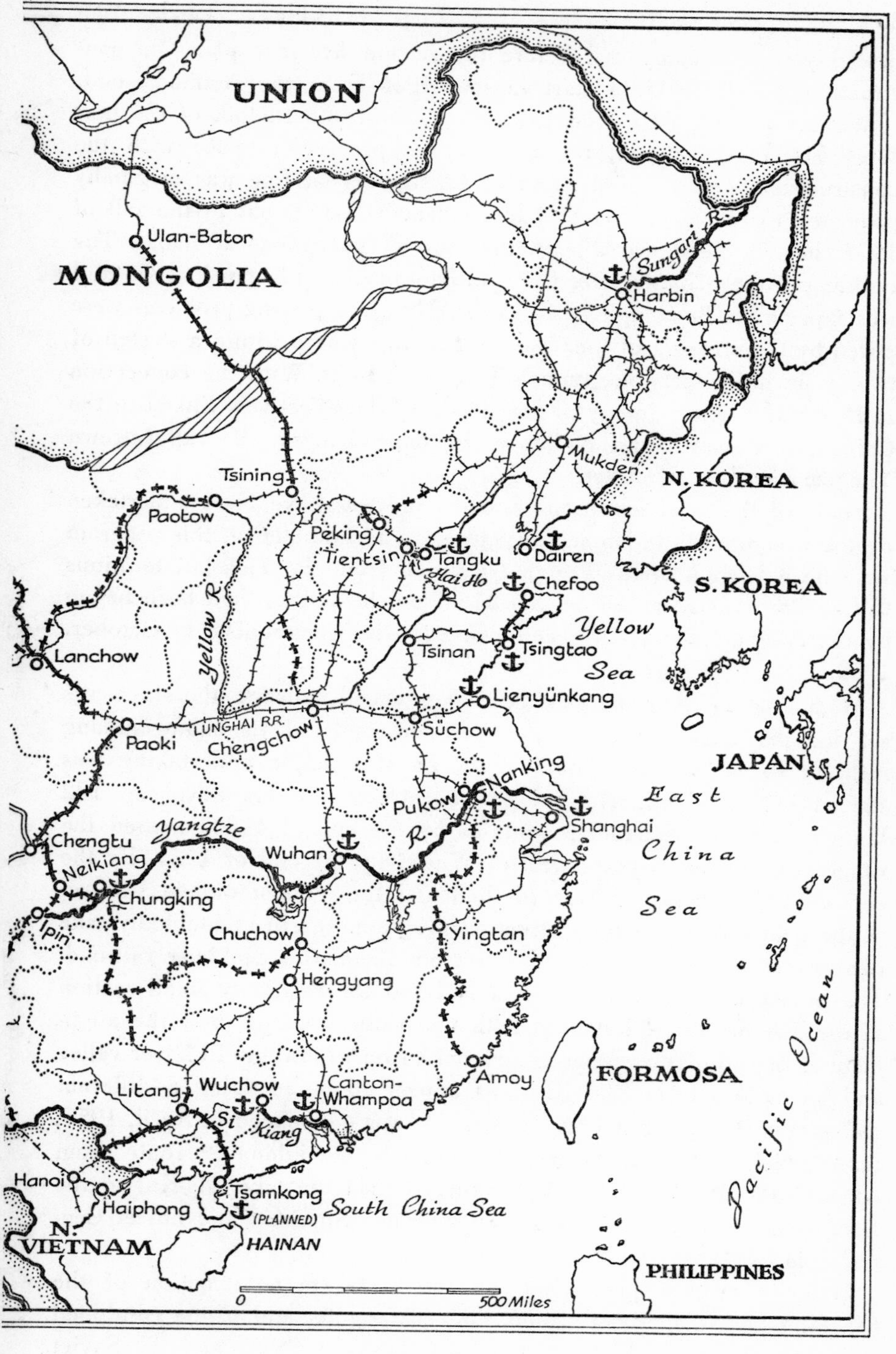

UNION
Ulan-Bator
MONGOLIA
Sungari R.
Harbin
Mukden
N. KOREA
Tsining
Paotow
Peking
Tientsin
Tangku
Dairen
Hai Ho
Chefoo
S. KOREA
Yellow R.
Lanchow
Tsinan
Tsingtao
Yellow
Sea
Lienyünkang
Paoki
LUNGHAI RR.
Chengchow
Süchow
JAPAN
Nanking
Pukow
East
China
Sea
Shanghai
Yangtze
R.
Chengtu
Neikiang
Wuhan
Chungking
Ipin
Chuchow
Yingtan
Hengyang
Amoy
FORMOSA
Pacific Ocean
Litang
Wuchow
Canton-
Whampoa
Si
Kiang
Hanoi
Haiphong
Tsamkong
(PLANNED)
South China Sea
N.
VIETNAM
HAINAN
PHILIPPINES
0
500 Miles

probably not be completed before the second five-year plan. Its construction is scheduled to start in late 1956 from the Neikiang end.

While they delayed the construction of the southern link of the new West China rail system, the Communists proceeded apace with the construction of the section north of Chengtu. That line was originally projected to reach the Lunghai railroad at Tienshui, but in the fall of 1953 the alignment was altered in favor of a terminus at Paoki. The building of the 678-kilometer Chengtu-Paoki railroad began in 1953 and was expected to be completed in 1956. Major engineering problems were posed by the crossing of the Tsin Ling divide, where within a stretch of twenty-six miles forty-one tunnels had to be built. With the connection at Paoki, the rich economy of Szechwan will be effectively linked to the Chinese rail system and no longer be dependent on the rapid-strewn Yangtze River as an outlet.

Some of the most ambitious railroad projects have been undertaken by the Communists in China's Northwest. The first step in this program was the extension of the Lunghai railroad from the Tienshui terminus to Lanchow. Construction on this 346-kilometer section had been begun by the Nationalists and was completed by the Communists in October, 1952.

With Lanchow incorporated into the railroad network, the stage was set for the construction of the long-contemplated Lanchow-Sinkiang railroad to the Soviet Union. Work on this major undertaking was started in late 1952. The railroad construction crews advanced 182 kilometers to the Wukiao Mountains by the end of 1953, crossed the range and reached a point west of Wuwei by the end of 1954. By the end of 1955, Changyeh was reached and the Yümen oilfield was set as the goal for the 1956 construction program. It will undoubtedly take two or three five-year plans to complete the entire Sinkiang railroad. The Soviet Union has undertaken to build the relatively small section of the line on Soviet territory. Although Chinese maps show the alignment of the railroad as proceeding from Urumchi into the Ili River valley and on to Alma-Ata, the Russians appear to be planning a different connection with the Soviet rail system. It was announced in April, 1955, that Soviet survey teams were studying a 306-kilometer route from Aktogai (station of the Turksib railroad) via the lake Ala-Kul to the Dzungarian Gates, historic routeway between Sinkiang and Soviet Central Asia.

While work was proceeding on the long-term construction of the Sinkiang line, the Soviet Union, Outer Mongolia and China combined their efforts to complete a shorter link between China and the Soviet

Union. This route connects Tsining (on the Peking-Paotow railroad) with Ulan-Bator, Outer Mongolia's capital, via Erhlien (China) and Dzamyn-Ude (Outer Mongolia). At Ulan-Bator, the new trans-Mongolian line joins a railroad from the Trans-Siberian, completed in 1947. Work on the Tsining-Ulan-Bator railroad was agreed on in September, 1952, begun in early 1953 and completed in 1955. On January 1, 1956, through traffic between China and the Soviet Union was inaugurated over the line, which shortens the distance between Peking and Moscow by 721 miles compared with the original roundabout Manchurian route.

The impending shift of most of Soviet-Chinese rail traffic from Manchuria to the new Mongolian route required improvements on certain connecting lines. In particular, the Chinese Communists built the Fengtai-Shacheng cutoff to eliminate excessive grades and the light rail construction of the original Nankow Pass section of the Peking-Paotow line. The new cutoff, using heavier rails and lesser grades, proceeds along the valley of the Yungting River and avoids the initial mountain route. The 106-kilometer cutoff was built from September, 1952, until June, 1955. In addition to the new line, about 100 kilometers of the Peking-Paotow railroad were to be double-tracked in 1955 to handle the added trans-Mongolian traffic starting in 1956.

Plans call for a connection between the trans-Mongolian and Sinkiang railroads. The link, parallel to the upper Yellow River, is between Paotow and Lanchow over a distance of 1,100 kilometers. A survey of the route was begun in April, 1953 and construction from the Paotow end was started in 1955. The Paotow-Lanchow railroad will probably be completed during the second five-year plan in time to serve as a western outlet for the projected steel mill of Paotow.

Other railroads constructed in China since 1949 include several hundred kilometers of light forest railways in the lumbering areas of the Great Khingan Mountains and in the Little Khingan north of Ichun. Finally, construction is under way since 1955 on the Yingtan-Amoy railroad, linking that Southeast China port with Yingtan, station on the Chekiang-Kiangsi line. When completed, the Amoy railroad will not only provide the first rail transportation for Fukien Province, but will be a strategic supply route for the Communist forces on the Formosa Strait.

Only about 7 per cent of China's railroads are double-tracked, with double trackage due to increase from 1,457 kilometers in 1952 to 2,971 in 1957. The main twin-track lines are Peking-Mukden, perhaps the most heavily traveled of all China's railroads; Harbin-Dairen, the north-south Manchurian trunkline, and Mukden-Antung, leading to North Korea.

TABLE 38
RAILROAD ROLLING STOCK

	In Service		
	1952	*1955*	*1957 Plan*
Locomotives	3,310	3,600	3,860
Freight cars	65,330	84,130	99,050
Passenger cars	2,448	3,838	3,885
	Annual Construction		
	1952		*1957 Plan*
Locomotives	20		200
Freight cars	5,792		8,500
Passenger cars	6		300

Like the Russians, the Chinese are making a concerted effort to make the fullest use of the existing operating lines and rolling stock by reducing turnaround time and increasing the average daily runs of freight cars and locomotives.

TABLE 39
AVERAGE LOCOMOTIVE PERFORMANCE

	Average Daily Run (in kilometers)	*Average Load Hauled (in metric tons)*
Pre-1949 Peak	254	743
1950	337	1016
1952	417	1214
1954	426	1245

As a result of improved locomotive performance, the Chinese Communists have been able to expand considerably the volume of freight carried by the railroads. A major part of this increase has been due to the industrial construction program. Materials destined for construction projects and related activities make up about three-fourths of China's total rail freight.

Water-borne transportation handled about 10 per cent of all freight traffic in 1954. In an effort to ease the load of the railroad system, the Chinese planners are seeking to increase the share of water-borne freight traffic from 8.5 per cent in 1952 to 14.5 per cent in 1957. The total length of navigable rivers and canals in China is put at 69,000 miles. Actually only three major rivers with a total navigable length of 2,000 miles are suitable for large-scale movements of goods. They are the

Yangtze River, the Si Kiang (West River) and the Sungari River in Manchuria. Other streams and canals are accessible only to shallow-bottom barges and junks. The Yangtze is by far China's most important waterway, penetrating deeply into the hinterland as far as Szechwan. Major Yangtze ports are Chungking, Hankow, Nanking and Shanghai. The Si Kiang, in South China, handles much of the trade of eastern Kwangsi and western Kwangtung. Its ports are Wuchow and Canton. The Sungari, which serves northern Manchuria, has most of its traffic between Harbin and its confluence with the Amur River.

TABLE 40

RAIL FREIGHT TRAFFIC

	Ton-kilometers (billions)	*Tons Originated (millions)*	*Average Length of Haul (kilometers)*
1950	39	100	394
1951	51	111	484
1952	60.15	132.06	455
1953	78	158	492
1954	93	190	490
1957 Plan	120.9	245.5	492

Coastal shipping, which accounts for 25 to 30 per cent of all water-borne traffic, makes use of China's 7,000 miles of coastline on the Yellow Sea, the East China Sea and the South China Sea. Major ports are Dairen, Tientsin with its new outer port of Tangku, and Tsingtao on the Yellow Sea, Shanghai on the East China Sea, and Canton with its outer port of Whampoa on the South China Sea. The Chinese Communists propose to develop a new port at Tsamkong (Chankiang), new railhead at the base of the Luichow Peninsula on the South China Sea. The military situation in the Formosa Strait has largely brought to a standstill the coastal trade of such important ports as Swatow, Amoy and Foochow.

Highway transportation plays a major role in outlying western regions still without railroads. The Chinese Communists put the total length of highways at 88,000 miles (142,000 kilometers) as of the end of 1954. About 6,000 miles of new truck roads are said to have been added since 1949. The most important new highways are the Sikang-Tibet road (1,400 miles) and the Tsinghai-Tibet road (1,300 miles), which for the first time provided modern transportation links between Tibet and the rest of China.

TABLE 41
WATER-BORNE FREIGHT TRAFFIC

	*Inland Waterways**		*Coastal Shipping*	
	Million tons	*Billion t/km*	*Million tons*	*Billion t/km†*
1952	9.34	3.63	3.88	1.98
1953	14.6	5.6	4.5	2.0
1954	19.2	7.8	7.4	3.5
1957 Plan	36.864	15.292	11.461	5.751

* Inland waterways data exclude local junk traffic and include essentially Yangtze and Sungari river traffic.

† Coastal traffic is expressed in billion ton-nautical miles.

TABLE 42
TRUCK FREIGHT TRAFFIC

	Million tons	*Billion t/km*
1952	20.72	.68
1953	32.3	1.3
1954	46.2	2.1
1957 Plan	67.493	3.211

Airlines link Peking with most of the large cities of China. Three international services link China and the Soviet Union. They are Moscow-Peking, Chita-Peking and Alma-Ata–Urumchi (Sinkiang). These airlines, administered by a Chinese-Soviet joint stock company after 1950, were placed under Chinese management as of January, 1955. By the end of 1953, the Chinese airlines operated over nearly 10,000 miles of routes. An additional 10,000 miles are to be opened in the course of the five-year plan. At the same time, air freight is scheduled to increase from 2.43 million ton-kilometers in 1952 to 8.05 million in 1957.

Foreign Trade

China's foreign trade structure has undergone major changes since the advent of the Communist regime in 1949. Under the Nationalist regime, trade had been largely with the non-Communist nations, in particular the United States, Japan and Britain. Imports generally exceeded exports and were made up to a great extent by consumer goods. Under the Peking regime, and particularly after the start of the Korean war in 1950, the bulk of China's trade shifted abruptly from the non-Communist nations to the Soviet bloc. In addition, the structure of

China's imports changed from a preponderance of consumer goods to industrial equipment, industrial raw materials and other goods required for China's economic development program. In 1954, for example, capital goods made up 89 per cent of China's imports. For the five-year plan as a whole consumer goods are not expected to exceed 15 per cent of imports.

TABLE 43
FOREIGN TRADE

	Total Volume (in billion yüan)	*Soviet Bloc Share (in per cent)*
1950	4.1	35
1951	5.7	61
1952	5.97	72
1953	8.12	75
1954	8.49	80
1957 Plan	10.0	

In 1954, China's foreign trade amounted to more than 9 million tons by weight and 8.49 billion yüan by value. Imports and exports were essentially balanced. Imports consisted of capital goods, exports of agricultural products and ores. The Soviet Union, for example, shipped to China all types of industrial equipment for steel, machine-building and chemical plants, oil and oil products, chemicals, agricultural machines, drugs, pedigreed stock and selected seeds. China, in return, shipped to the Soviet Union tungsten, tin and molybdenum; fibers, such as wool, silk and jute, and soybeans, rice, peanuts, tea, meat, fruit, cork, bark, tung oil and other vegetable oils, tobacco, silk cloth and hides.

PART II

Chapter 4

THE NORTH CHINA PLAIN

The North China plain includes the provinces of Hopei (with the independent cities of Peking and Tientsin), Honan and Shantung. The region covers an area of 200,000 square miles, or 5 per cent of the area of China. Its 1953 population was 140,000,000, or 24 per cent of the nation's total. This represents an average population density of 700 per square mile.

The region owes its unity to the depositional work of the Yellow River, for which it is sometimes named the Yellow River plain. It is one of the best-defined geographic regions of China, bounded by the Yellow Sea and its great embayment, the Po Hai, in the east; by abrupt mountain scarps in the north and west, and by lower hills in the southwest. Only in the southeast does the region pass gradually into the Lower Yangtze plain.

The northern mountain border, where the Yen Shan is the most prominent range of hills, is crowned by the Great Wall. Several important pass-gates in the northern border have served as historic invasion routes in the past and now accommodate major transportation routes between the plain and the neighboring regions.

Perhaps the best-known routeway is Shanhaikwan (mountain-sea-pass), where the Great Wall meets the sea. This is the principal gateway to Manchuria, used in the 17th century by the invading Manchu tribes. Today the Peking-Mukden double-tracked main line passes here, joining southern Manchuria, China's industrial heart, to the rest of the nation.

Westward from Shanhaikwan, the northern border follows the Great Wall. Where the wall is pierced by two streams, the Lwan Ho and the Chao Ho, are two minor passes linking Hopei with the former province of Jehol. They are Sifengkow, in the Lwan valley, and Kupehkow, in the Chao valley. The Japanese used the Kupehkow route in the construction of the railroad from Peking to Chengteh in 1939. Reconstruction of the line was under way in 1956 by a different pass-route.

Northwest of Peking, the wall-crowned Yen Shan is crossed by Chü-yungkwan pass near Nankow, a town for which the pass is often named in the Western literature. This gateway is to Mongolia what Shanhaikwan is to Manchuria. It is crossed by the old Peking-Kalgan railroad, a former key transportation link between North China and Inner Mongolia. The main traffic now uses the Fengtai-Shacheng cut-off through the Yungting valley.

The Taihang Mountains, which border the North China plain on the west, are an escarpment of the loess upland province of Shansi. These mountains, rising suddenly from the plain to more than 3,000 feet, present a solid front inhibiting transportation. Only one of several passes constitutes a major routeway. That is the Niangtzekwan, used by the railroad from Shihkiachwang to Taiyüan.

In western Honan, where the North China plain is encroached upon by the Funiu Mountains and its outliers, the Lunghai railroad is restricted to a number of passes between the mountains and the Yellow River. These passes are, from east to west, the Hulaokwan, the Hankukwan and, in the extreme west on the Shensi border, the major gateway of Tungkwan at the right angle bend of the Yellow River.

Finally, along the southern margins of the plain, the Hwaiyang Mountains are crossed by a low pass known as the Wushengkwan. This gateway also has been put to good use by China's railroad builders in laying the track for the Peking-Hankow trunk line.

Thus surrounded by mountains, the North China plain is in itself a region of very low relief. The product of alluvial deposition of the Yellow River and other streams descending from the loessial uplands in the west, the plain stands in sharp contrast to the bordering mountains that rise to more than 3,000 feet above the nearly level lowland.

The Yellow River enters the plain along the Honan-Shansi border and then proceeds on its aggraded, dike-enclosed course 450 miles east and northeast to its mouth on the Po Hai. This course has been used by the river since 1855, except for the relatively brief diversion from 1938 to 1947 when the stream flowed southeast into the Hwai Ho system. The North China plain can be compared to a gigantic alluvial fan over which the course of the Yellow River has swept back and forth like the tail of a gigantic dog. Because the Yellow River flows at an elevation of ten to twenty feet above the surrounding countryside, it receives no tributaries throughout its entire lower course in the North China plain. Only two streams join it immediately after its exit from the mountains; they are the Tsin Ho, which descends from the Shansi plateau, and the Lo Ho, which flows to the Yellow River from the Funiu Mountains.

North of the Yellow River, in Hopei, the North China plain is drained by the complex river system of the Hai Ho. The Hai Ho itself is only a short stream flowing thirty miles from Tientsin to the sea. But it is the outlet of five major streams converging fanlike at Tientsin. These are the Northern Canal, a section of the Grand Canal formed at Tungchow east of Peking; the Yungting River, rising in northern Shansi as the Sangkan River; the Tatsing River, formed in central Hopei; the Tzeya River, formed in south central Hopei by the junction of the Huto and Fuyang rivers; and the Southern Canal, a section of the Grand Canal that receives the Wei Ho from northern Honan.

South of the Yellow River, the North China plain is drained by the Hwai Ho, whose principal tributaries rise in southern Honan. The longest affluents, including the Ying Ho and the Hung Ho, rise in the Funiu Mountains.

East of the Grand Canal, which connects the Hwai Ho and Hai Ho river systems, are the Shantung uplands, a region of ancient metamorphic and igneous rocks that have resisted weathering. These uplands once were an island, later transformed into a peninsula as the shifting Yellow River gradually filled in the sea on the northern and southern sides of the uplands. The highest part of the uplands, the Tai Shan (5,000 feet), is a mass of basic extrusive rocks standing out sharply in fault scarps above the surrounding plain. On its eastern side, the Tai Shan is separated by the Kiaolai corridor from the hills that form the actual Shantung promontory, rising to 3,700 feet in the Lao Shan northeast of Tsingtao. The Kiaolai corridor is a broad water-level valley extending across the Shantung peninsula from Laichow Bay in the north to Kiaochow Bay in the south. Under the Ming dynasty (1368-1644) a canal was built through this corridor, connecting the Po Hai and the Yellow Sea. The waterway has fallen into disuse.

In accordance with the relief, the North China plain presents two contrasting types of coast lines. The shore north of the Yellow River mouth is low-lying and simple, with virtually no natural harbors. Although the shoreline is one of submergence, the absence of relief in the initial topography has resulted in a simple coast. The only natural port along this coast is Chinwangtao.

The coast of Shantung, by contrast, is rocky and much indented. It abounds in natural harbors, of which the most important are Lungkow, Chefoo, Weihai, and the port of Tsingtao on Kiaochow Bay.

The climate of the North China plain is the monsoon-controlled variety of the humid middle-latitude continental climate. It is distinquished by hot, rainy summers when the region is dominated by Tropical Maritime air masses and by cold dry winters under the influence of Polar Continental air. The typical annual temperature range is from 25°

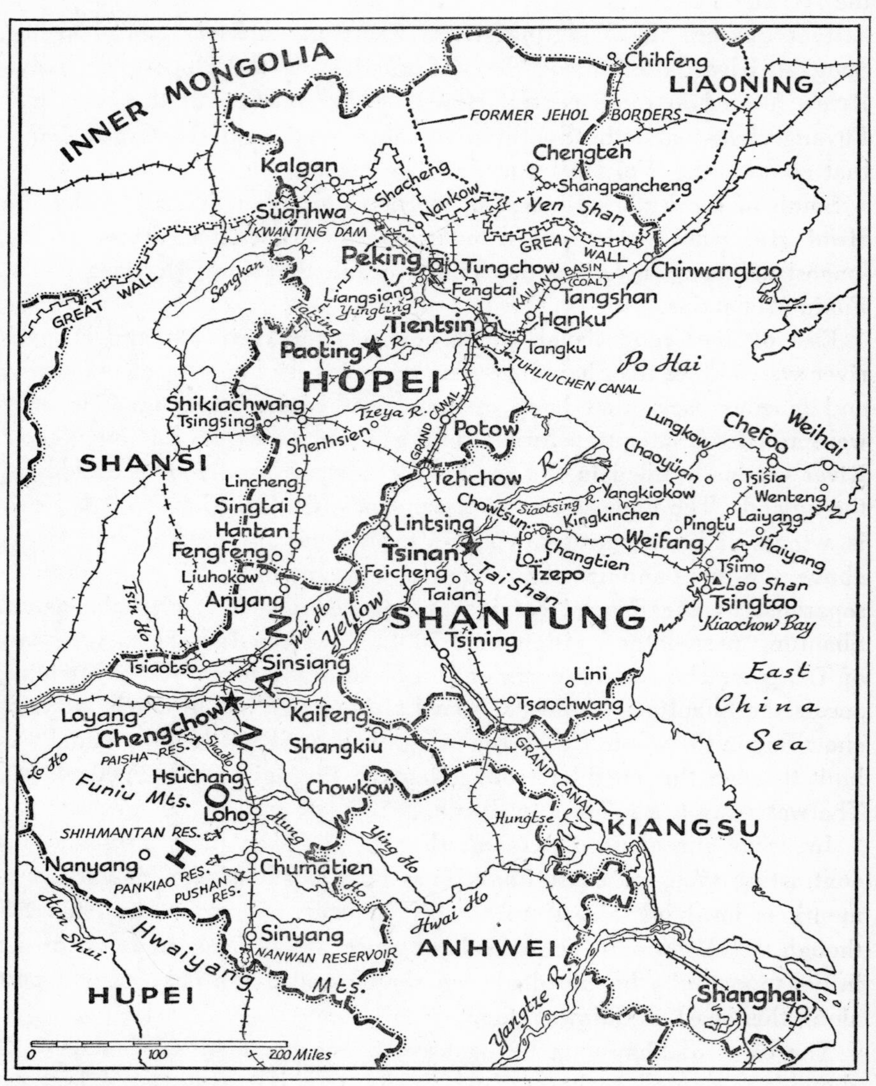

North China Plain

F (—4° C) in January to 80° F (27° C) in July. The annual range is greater inland, while somewhat warmer winters and cooler summers prevail along the Shantung coast.

Rainfall reaches a maximum in July, with virtually all the precipitation occurring from May through September. The average annual total is 25 inches, with generally higher amounts along the coast and toward the south. Strong winds associated with the northeast monsoon blow loess from the western uplands, spreading it throughout the level plain.

The wind-blown loess and the river-laid alluvium provide the parent material for the calcareous and saline young alluvial soils typical of the flood plains of North China. In poorly drained areas with a high water table, both in inland lake depressions and near the coast, salinity increases and tends to depress fertility. In the mountain margins of the North China plain and the Shantung uplands, brown podzolic soils support a mixed deciduous and coniferous forest where natural vegetation remains. The peculiar shakiang soil, characterized by poor drainage and a horizon of lime concretions, occurs in central Honan and in Shantung at the west foot of the Tai Shan. Noncalcareous recent alluvial soils are found in southern Honan.

The predominantly calcareous alluvium of the North China plain and the summer rainfall have made the region one of the most important agricultural areas of China. This is the so-called winter wheat-kaoliang region. Irrigation is uncommon. Wheat and barley are the two winter grains, while kaoliang, millet and corn are planted in the summer. The North China plain produces about one-half of China's total output of each of these grains. Rice cultivation is quite insignificant and is pursued in southernmost Honan. Soybeans are widely grown throughout the region, which produces about one-third of China's total output.

The Shantung peninsula is China's leading peanut-growing area and the North China plain as a whole produces about 75 per cent of China's peanuts. The alluvial soils also favor the growing of cotton, of which the entire region produces about two-thirds of China's total. Like peanuts, tobacco is favored by the sandy soils of Shantung and Honan, while fruit is also associated with the podzolic brown upland soils.

Fisheries are widely developed off the North China coast, particularly around the rocky Shantung peninsula. There the indented coastline and the abundance of offshore islands favor the growth of plankton and other fish food.

Livestock raising is an auxiliary activity of the farm population. Oxen, donkeys and mules are particularly common, as they serve as important draft animals. Hogs are fed on the by-products of agriculture and sheep are raised chiefly for meat.

Industrially, the North China plain is important as a coal producer, with the main mines found along the foot of the northern and western mountain margins and in the Shantung uplands. Iron ore is found chiefly in the Lungyen deposit outside the North China plain itself, but also in small amounts in Shantung. Important salterns are exploited along the coast. Manufacturing industry is concentrated in the Peking-Tientsin belt and along the Tsinan-Tsingtao railroad.

Railroads are the main form of transportation in the North China plain, which has the densest rail net south of the Great Wall. Waterways play a minor role because of their shallowness and irregular flow. Roads are only of local importance.

The relatively dense railroad development results from a combination of factors. Railroads focused from the very start on Peking, the nation's capital; the predominant lowland relief facilitated railroad construction; the importance of railroads was greatly enhanced through the virtual absence of good navigable waterways; and, finally, construction of lines was sponsored in part by foreign interests active in North China. The Peking-Hankow and Tientsin-Pukow railroads are the main north-south trunk lines, while the Lunghai, Tsingtao-Tsinan-Tehchow-Shihkiachwang and Tientsin-Peking connections provide east-west links.

Except for the Hai Ho below Tientsin, which is accessible to small coastwise vessels of less than 3,000 tons, North China's waterways are suitable only for junk traffic. The main junk arteries are the combined Wei Ho and Southern Canal route and the Siaotsing River, a delta arm of the Yellow River. Ocean-going trade proceeds through the ports of Chinwangtao, Tientsin-Tangku, Chefoo, Weihai, and Tsingtao.

The densely-settled North China plain has a homogeneous Chinese population speaking the northern Mandarin dialect. While population density is about 750 or more per square mile in the plain proper, it drops to from 150 to 400 in the hilly parts of Shantung where arable land is more limited.

HOPEI PROVINCE

Capital: Paoting; area: 75,000; population: 39,000,000

Prior to 1949, Hopei had an area of 54,000 square miles and a population estimated at 29,000,000. In 1949, Hopei ceded about 4,000 square miles of territory along its south and southeast borders to the newly-formed province of Pingyüan and to Shantung. From 1949 to 1952, the provincial area was 50,000 square miles and the population estimated at 31,000,000. In November, 1952, Hopei regained virtually all the territory ceded in 1949 and furthermore acquired about 15,000 square miles of the abolished province of Chahar. Until the June, 1953, census established the present figure, the population of the enlarged province of Hopei was estimated at 32,000,000. Finally, in early 1956, Hopei annexed the southern part of partitioned Jehol Province.

Until the annexation of parts of Chahar and Jehol, Hopei had been entirely within the North China plain. The northern territorial gains projected part of Hopei onto the Inner Mongolian plateau and the Jehol uplands, where natural conditions differ considerably from those of the North China plain. Both January and July average temperatures are about five degrees Fahrenheit lower than those prevailing in the North China plain, but, more important, average annual precipitation drops to 15 inches from the average of 25 inches in the plain. These climatic differences can be explained by the location of the former Chahar and Jehol areas with respect to the climatic source regions. These areas are more exposed to the cold, dry Polar Continental air dominating the region during the winter, which accounts for the lower January temperature. On the other hand, they are situated in the lee of the Yen Shan, which offers a considerable obstacle to the hot and rainy Tropical Maritime air originating in the seas off China. The climatic barrier of the Yen Shan operates to depress the July temperature and the annual precipitation.

The chernozems and the dark chestnut soils developed in the former Chahar area are among the most fertile soils of China, but limited rainfall greatly restricts their usefulness. In contrast to the North China plain, all crops are summer-grown, with spring wheat, millet, potatoes the chief products. On the drier margins, extensive livestock raising is the principal activity.

In the greater part of Hopei, conditions typical of the North China plain prevail. The province is one of China's leading winter wheat and cotton areas. Wheat is grown throughout the plain and soybeans chiefly in the seaward areas. Cotton is concentrated in the river basins of the Wei Ho, Tatsing River, Tzeya River and the Northern Canal.

During the five-year plan, the output of food crops is scheduled to rise only slightly on a total sown area of 8.2 million hectares. Planned output for 1957 is 9.083 million tons of grain, an increase of 1.7 per cent over 1952. About 40 per cent of the total grain acreage is in wheat. However, in 1954, a poor year, the grain crop was only 7.5 million tons. In normal years, Hopei produces one-quarter of China's cotton crop, but production has fluctuated in recent times. On an average sown area of 1.1 million hectares, Hopei produced 292,500 tons of cotton lint in 1952 and 263,000 tons in 1954. The 1957 goal is 371,800 tons, out of a total of 1,635,000 tons for all China. Oil crops take up an average of 470,000 hectares in Hopei Province, about 65 per cent of the acreage being in peanuts.

Conditions in the province are favorable for fruit growing, especially along the foot of the bordering mountain ranges. Tientsin is known for its pear orchards, Liangsiang for chestnut trees and Shenhsien for its peaches.

As part of the flood-prevention program, two major projects have been completed in Hopei Province since 1949; the Kwanting reservoir on the Yungting River northwest of Peking and the Tatsing-Tzeya river outlet south of Tientsin.

The Kwanting reservoir was started in October, 1951, and completed in May, 1954. Situated 45 miles northwest of Peking, just beyond the Great Wall, the reservoir was formed by the construction of an earth dam, 150 feet high and 1,000 feet along, across the gorge of the Yungting River. When filled to capacity, the reservoir covers an area of 85 square miles and accommodates 1,800,000 acre-feet of water. Kwanting is a multi-purpose project, serving not only as a flood-detention reservoir but providing irrigation water for the lower reaches of the Yungting River. It also generates hydroelectric power for the Peking-Tientsin industrial district.

The Tatsing-Tzeya project is designed to ease the load the Hai Ho is required to carry during the summer high-water stage. The Tatsing and Tzeya rivers are two of the five major waterways converging on the Hai Ho at Tientsin. Through the construction of an alternate 25-mile channel south of Tientsin, the Tatsing and Tzeya rivers discharge part of their flood waters directly to the sea and reduce the danger of flooding along the Hai Ho. Construction on the alternate Tatsing-Tzeya outlet was started in March, 1951, and completed in the summer of 1953. The new channel is called the Tuhliuchen Canal, for a village near the Tatsing-Tzeya confluence where the canal takes off toward the sea, by-passing Tientsin.

Coal is Hopei's leading mineral resource, with deposits found chiefly along the south foot of the Yen Shan and the east foot of the Taihang Mountains.

The best known and one of China's most important coalfields is the Kailan basin, named for the towns of Kaiping and Lwanhsien (sometimes Lanhsien). Exploited since 1879, the Kailan basin owed its development primarily to a favorable seaboard location that assured it a bunker market at its ice-free port of Chinwangtao. It produces good steam-raising coal and has in the past yielded coal suitable for coking. It is China's leading coal producer and is due to retain its pre-eminent position through the first five-year plan. The principal mines of the Kailan basin are Sükochwang near Tangshan, Makiakow near Kaiping, Chaokochwang, Tangkiachwang and Linsi near Kuyeh, all along the Peking-Mukden railroad. Kailan's 1957 coal output is planned to be 9,680,000 tons.

The Kailan field is situated 60 miles west of its shipping port of Chinwangtao. Just north of the port, in the foothills of the Yen Shan, are the smaller coal mines of Shihmenchai near Liukiang.

West and southwest of Peking, within the capital's municipal limits, are a number of small coal mines in a tectonically much disturbed zone. These mines are Mentowkow, Changkowyü, Chaitang, and Chowkowtien. They are situated on spurs of the Peking-Hankow railroad. The Mentowkow anthracite mine, the largest of this group with an annual output of more than 1,000,000 tons, is linked directly by rail with Peking.

Farther south, along the east foot of the Taihang Mountains, are the coal mines of Tsingsing, west of Shihkiachwang near the Shansi line, and Lincheng and Fengfeng, both on spur lines of the Peking-Hankow railroad. Fengfeng, situated in southernmost Hopei near the Honan border, is being developed as a major coking coal supplier for North China and Manchuria. It was set up as a special mining ch'ü in 1950 and became a city in 1954. By 1953 its output had reached about 5,000,000 tons. Fengfeng supplies the coke needs of the Shihkingshan, Anshan and Penki steel plants.

One of China's main iron ore sources was acquired by Hopei with the annexation of part of Chahar in 1952. That is the iron ore district known variously as Lungyen (for the Lungkwan and the Yentungshan deposits) or Süanlung (for the towns of Süanhwa and Lungkwan). The ore is sedimentary hematite, of relatively high grade (50 per cent iron), and siliceous. Its phosphorus content is too high for Bessemer treatment, but it is suitable for basic open-hearth furnaces. The reserves have been put at 92,000,000 tons. Mining began in 1919 at the Yentungshan deposit, just northeast of Süanhwa, from where the ore was shipped by rail to the Hanyang works. But operations ceased soon thereafter and were not renewed in earnest until the Japanese occupation during the Second World War. The Japanese built a 30-mile rail spur to the Pangkiapu deposit, east of Süanhwa, and built several small blast furnaces to smelt the ore on the spot. By 1942, annual output reached 900,000 tons of ore. After having been shut down for nine years, three blast furnaces were rebuilt in 1953 at Süanhwa and the district now supplies both iron ore and pig iron to the steel plants at Shihkingshan, Tientsin and Tangshan.

The only other iron ore in Hopei is a small group of deposits near Lwanhsien, just east of the Kailan coalfield. This is very lean iron ore with an excessive silica content and would require concentration before blast furnace use.

Aside from the basic minerals of coal and iron, Hopei also produces gold and salt. Gold is mined in the Yen Shan, notably in the Malanyü mine near Tsunhwa, which has been in operation since 1932. Relatively more important are the Changlu salines extending along the coast of the Po Hai north and south of Tangku. The salt district, which produces its salt through evaporation from sea water and accounts for about one-fourth of China's total salt production, has its center at Hanku on the Peking-Mukden railroad. Hanku has a chemical plant.

Hopei's industry is concentrated in the belt extending from Peking along the railroad through Tientsin and the Kailan coal basin. Metallurgical plants are found at Shihkingshan, west of Peking, Tientsin and Tangshan. Of these, only the Shihkingshan plant is an integrated iron and steel producer. Situated twelve miles from Peking's western gates but still within the capital's municipal borders, Shihkingshan lies on the Yungting River and on the rail spur to the Mentowkow anthracite mine. Shihkingshan was first built shortly after the First World War and was expanded in the second war under Japanese occupation. The plant's blast furnace department includes one 250-ton furnace originally built in 1924 and three smaller furnaces. Pig iron output at peak capacity is expected to be 400,000 tons, five times the production attained under the Japanese. The plant uses iron ore from the Lungyen district and coking coal from mines along the foot of the Taihang Mountains—Liuhokow, Tsingsing and now increasingly from Fengfeng.

Like the Lungyen district, Shihkingshan supplies pig iron to Tientsin and Tangshan, which have only steel furnaces. Facilities available at Tangshan include an electric furnace.

Other industries developed in Hopei include the cement, with mills at Tangshan and Liuliho, southwest of Peking. As China's major cotton growing area, Hopei has also played an important role in the cotton textile industry. Older plants situated at Tientsin and Shihkiachwang have been supplemented since 1949 by new large mills in the heart of the cotton belt. The new plants are at Hantan (completed in 1953) and at Shihkiachwang (completed in 1954). Three cotton mills have been or are being built in Peking with a total capacity of 230,000 spindles and 7,000 looms. In addition to cotton, Peking and Tientsin also produce woolen goods from raw wool shipped out of China's northwest.

Hopei has two metropolitan centers—Peking and Tientsin—with populations exceeding 1,000,000 and a third city—Tangshan—with a population in excess of 500,000. Peking and Tientsin are not administratively part of the province, but are directly under the jurisdiction of the central government. In addition, there are five cities with a population of more than 100,000: Kalgan, Chinwangtao, Paoting, Shihkiachwang and Hantan; and seven cities with a population of more than 50,000: Süanhwa, Hanku, Potow, Singtai, Tungchow, Fengfeng and Chengteh.

Peking, China's ancient capital, has once again reverted to its political pre-eminence. As Yenking, it was the capital of the Liao dynasty set up in the tenth century by the Kitan Tatars who had invaded North China from the north. The city's name changed frequently under subsequent dynasties. It was Chungtu under the Chin dynasty set up in the twelfth century by the Golden Horde. The city's greatest period came in the late thirteenth century, when Kublai Khan moved his capital here from Karakorum. During this period the city was called Tatu by the Chinese and Khanbalyk by the Mongols. The latter name was rendered Cambaluc by Marco Polo who visited here about 1275. The city continued as capital under the Mongols' Yüan dynasty until 1368. Under the early Mings, it was briefly replaced by Nanking, but resumed its political leadership in 1421 under the name of Peking ("northern capital"). It retained the name and the leadership through the Manchu dynasty (1644-1911) and into the early years of the republic. In 1928, the Nationalists transferred the seat of government to Nanking and Peking was renamed Peiping ("northern peace"), a name it had briefly held under the early Mings. In 1949, the city once again became China's capital under its historic name.

The present city pattern dates from the days of Kublai Khan. Peking proper consists of two contiguous walled cities: the Inner City (a rectangle measuring four miles by three miles) adjoined on the south by the Outer City (five miles by one and a half miles). The innermost part of the Inner City is the old imperial palace of the Mings and Manchus, historically known as the Forbidden City and now converted into a museum. It is surrounded by the former Imperial City, whose walls were razed after 1949. This central part of the Inner City is the most beautiful of the capital, set among lakes and parks. It is the seat of the government, which has its offices around the elongated lake called

Chungnanhai. Southeast of the Imperial City is the Legation Quarter, where foreign powers were permitted to establish offices after the Boxer Rebellion of 1900. Along the south edge of the Imperial City, Chang An Chieh, one of the capital's main thoroughfares, leads past Tien An Men ("gate of heavenly peace"), Peking's Red Square and scene of political meetings and demonstrations.

The Outer City, which contains the famous Temple of Heaven and the Temple of Agriculture, is the commercial quarter and has only about one-fourth the population of the Inner City. At the wall separating the two cities is Chien Men, Peking's main railroad station.

The capital's higher educational institution are situated largely in the western suburbs along the road leading to the old summer palace and the Western Hills, a resort area. Future city planning calls for further residential and educational development west and northwest of the city proper, with industries concentrated east of the city. Already established there are the cotton mills, a machine tool plant, and an agricultural implements factory. Other industries within the municipal district include the iron and steel plant of Shihkingshan, the anthracite mine of Mentowkow, and railroad repair shops at Changsintien.

Peking's municipal district, in keeping with its new political role, has been expanded on two occasions since 1949. Shortly after 1949, its area increased from 270 to 500 square miles, and in 1953 further annexation of territory placed Peking's western municipal limits along the Great Wall, giving the district an area of about 1,500 square miles. The population of the municipal area in June, 1953, was 2,768,149, making Peking China's second largest city. The capital's population has risen steadily since it reassumed its role as seat of the government. The figure increased from 1,721,546 in 1948 to 2,030,986 in 1949 and to 2,240,000 in 1951. Of the 1953 total, however, the twin walled city accounted for only 1,050,000—830,000 in the Inner City and 220,000 in the Outer City—while 1,700,000 were distributed through the municipal area outside the city proper.

Historically, Peking has occupied a strategic position in the North China plain near the gateways to Mongolia and Manchuria and was usually the first Chinese city to fall to the invaders. In the past, Peking, or rather its river port of Tungchow, ten miles east, was the northern terminus of the Grand Canal, which linked the northern capital with the southern parts of the country. In the railroad age, Peking has maintained its importance as a transportation focus. Lines radiate from here to Hankow and Canton, Kalgan and Paotow, Tientsin and Mukden, Tungchow and Chengteh. Since 1955, China's capital is linked to the

Soviet Union both via Manchuria and by the shorter route through Outer Mongolia.

In the past, Peking has been of negligible industrial importance. It was noted for handicraft trades, such as rugs, enamel and lacquerware, and had the light consumer industries to be expected in a city of that size. In connection with the industrialization drive, the Chinese regime has been expanding industry even in Peking and the capital is beginning to play a significant role in the production of iron and steel, cotton textiles and machinery.

Seventy miles southeast of the capital stands Tientsin, China's third largest city. Like Peking an independent municipal district directly under the central government and nearly equal in population to the capital, Tientsin has nevertheless a quite different personality. While Peking still retains the charm of classical Chinese culture and the dignity of an ancient imperial capital, Tientsin is the product of the machine age, a bustling industrial center of the Western type. Of little significance until the mid-19th century, Tientsin was occupied by the British and French in 1858 and 1860 and thereafter opened to foreign trade. Concessions were granted to Britain, France, Japan, Germany, Italy, Austria-Hungary, Belgium and Russia and after the city's destruction in the Boxer Rebellion (1900) the city walls were razed and reconstruction proceeded along Western lines.

Tientsin has developed as a natural outlet for the products of North China and Inner Mongolia. It is situated on the Hai Ho, twenty-five miles from the sea, at the point where five major streams converge to form the short outlet to the Po Hai. The large amounts of sediments brought from the entire Hai Ho system choke the river and form offshore sand bars. Only continuous dredging was able to keep the waterway open for small vessels. At high tide and under the best conditions, ships of 3,000 tons and a 15-foot draft were able to make their way to Tientsin along the tortuous course of the Hai Ho. Medium-sized ocean vessels were forced to anchor twenty-five to thirty miles out at sea off the Taku Bar. With the aim of improving accessibility the Japanese initiated port improvement work during the Second World War. Construction of an artificial outer harbor at Tangku, opposite Taku on the north bank of the Hai Ho estuary, was continued after the war. The New Port (Chinese *Sinkang*) of Tangku was formally opened in October, 1952. A deep-water area of about seven square miles is now protected by two moles against further deposition of river-borne sediments. The new harbor can accommodate four 10,000-ton and five 3,000-ton ships. A lock gives access to the Hai Ho itself and permits smaller ships to go up the river to Tientsin. The port freezes about two months in winter but is usually kept open by icebreakers. In severe winters, Tientsin's traffic can be detoured through the port of Chinwangtao.

Tientsin's importance for the maritime trade is matched by its landward communications. It is situated on the Peking-Mukden railroad and on the trunk line to Pukow, on the Yangtze River opposite Nanking. Through Peking, Tientsin has access to Inner Mongolia. Junks can make use of the five waterways converging at Tientsin, particularly the Grand Canal-Wei Ho route leading to Sinsiang in northern Honan.

As one of China's leading ports, Tientsin has also developed into a key industrial center, noted particularly for its cotton and woolen mills and food-processing industries. Since 1949, greater attention has been devoted to the city's metallurgical and metal-fabricating industries, which include a steel foundry, an auto-assembly plant and a bicycle factory. Paper, matches and tobacco products are also manufactured here. An important chemical industry has developed on the basis of the near-by Changlu salines. Chemical plants at Tangku produce soda ash and caustic soda. Tientsin is the projected site for China's second tractor plant, which is being set up on the basis of the auto-assembly plant and another machinery enterprise.

Tientsin's population in June, 1953, was 2,693,831. Like Peking, Tientsin rapidly expanded after 1949. Its population was 1,772,840 in 1948. Part of the increase resulted from expansions of the municipal area in 1949 and 1953. At first, the Tangku-Taku port area was incorporated into Tientsin, raising the municipal area from 21 to 100 square miles. The next step was to join the two separate sections into an enlarged municipal district of 800 square miles, which includes a considerable area on the south bank of the Hai Ho.

Hopei's third largest city is Tangshan, the industrial metropolis of the Kailan coal basin. With a 1953 population of about 700,000, it includes a considerable part of the Kailan basin within its municipal boundaries. It has steel and cement industries and a large power plant based on the local coal resources. Tangshan is on the Peking-Mukden railroad, about halfway between Tientsin and Chinwangtao, its two ports. Chinwangtao is Hopei's only ice-free port and handles chiefly the shipments of Kailan coal. Southwest of Chinwangtao is Pehtaiho, one of China's most popular beach resorts.

Other key centers of the North China plain section of Hopei are located along the Peking-Hankow railroad. Paoting is the provincial capital and an agricultural center. Its 1953 population is 170,000. It is situated on an arm of the Tatsing River and is a navigation head for junk traffic. Shihkiachwang is a rail hub and cotton-milling center at the junction of the Peking-Hankow and Tehchow-Taiyüan lines. Shihkiachwang was only a small village 30 years ago. It developed rapidly as a railroad center, especially after the narrow-gauge line to Taiyüan was converted to standard gauge and the connecting railroad from Tehchow was built by the Japanese. Today it has a population of about 200,000. Among its industries is a plant producing steam-driven locomobiles. Cities along the railroad to Hankow are Singtai, an agricultural center, and Hantan, site of a new cotton mill. Hantan's population rose from 30,000 in 1949 to 100,000 in 1953 in connection with industrial construction. Near by is the new coal city of Fengfeng.

In former Chahar, the plateau section of Hopei, Kalgan and Süanhwa are the principal urban centers. Kalgan, whose Chinese name is Changkiakow, is a historic transportation and commercial center on the southern margin of Inner Mongolia. Here converge rail lines from Peking and Paotow and highways from Ulan Bator and the Chahar and Silingol leagues of Inner Mongolia. Although Kalgan is situated outside the political frontiers of the Inner Mongolian Autonomous Ch'ü, the city continues to play a major role in the life of the adjoining Inner Mongolian leagues. Kalgan is situated on a branch of the Yang Ho, a headstream of the Yungting River. It consists of a Chinese section on the western (right) bank and a Mongol section and railroad settlement on the eastern bank. It receives hides and wool from the northern steppe and ships tea, cotton goods, sugar and tobacco to the herders. Developed as a trade center under the Manchu dynasty, Kalgan long handled the tea traffic on the overland route from China to Russia. The city expanded after it was reached by the railroad from Peking in 1909. Further expansion can be expected in connection with the operation of the new Mongolian railroad to the Soviet Union.

Southeast of Kalgan along the railroad lies Süanhwa, previously mentioned as the center of the Lungyen iron mining and smelting district.

Chengteh, the former capital of Jehol Province, passed to Hopei in 1956. Situated on a tributary of the Lwan Ho, the city is the economic center of the southern Jehol uplands. It is linked by rail with Peking and with Manchuria.

HONAN PROVINCE

Capital: Chengchow; area: 65,000; population: 44,214,594

Prior to 1949, Honan had an area of 64,000 square miles and a population estimated at 30,000,000. From 1949 to 1952, Honan ceded the section north of the Yellow River to the short-lived province of Pingyüan. During this period, Honan was reduced to an area of 60,000 square miles and a population estimated at 35,400,000. After the abrogation of Pingyüan, Honan was restored to about its pre-1949 area with a population estimated at 40,200,000 prior to the census of June, 1953.

The eastern half of Honan Province, both north and south of the Yellow River, is an integral part of the North China plain with the typical winter wheat and kaoliang crop association. In 1954, a poor crop year, Honan produced 12,000,000 tons of grain (7 per cent of China's total), of which 3,300,000 tons was winter wheat. A major summer crop is cotton, of which the province produced 140,000 tons in 1954, about 12 per cent of China's total production. Soybeans, peanuts and tobacco are major crops. In normal years, Honan is first among China's provinces in wheat and tobacco and third in cotton production.

In the western part of Honan, the easternmost outliers of the Tsin Ling mountain system reach elevations up to 6,000 feet in the Funiu Mountains. This hilly region, where the sown area is greatly reduced and settlement is sparse, stands in sharp contrast to the intensively cultivated plains of the province. However, the mountains perform a useful function in sheltering part of Honan from the cold northwesterly winter monsoon. This sheltered area, centered on Nanyang in the southwestern part of Honan, has an agriculture similar to the rice-wheat association of the Middle Yangtze plain. In this southward-oriented area, rice, wild silk and the cultivation of sesame play an increasing role in the rural economy. Although Nanyang is linked by roads with the rest of Honan, its natural outlet is to the Han Shui, major tributary of the Yangtze in the south.

River reclamation work in Honan has been concerned with regulation of the Yellow River and the Hwai Ho system. Work along the Yellow River has included the strengthening of dikes that contain the stream at a level above the surrounding countryside, and the construction of the People's Victory Canal. This thirty-mile-long canal links the Yellow River north of Chengchow with the Wei Ho at Sinsiang. The canal, which runs parallel to the Peking-Hankow railroad, was completed in 1953. A combined navigation and irrigation project, the new waterway diverts Yellow River water to the shallow Wei Ho and supplies a system of irrigation ditches between Sinsiang and the Yellow River. The raised water level has made the Wei Ho navigable for 100-ton junks from Sinsiang to Tientsin.

The first phase (1952-67) of the Yellow River project calls for construction of the Sanmen hydroelectric dam on the Honan-Shansi border.

The Sanmen dam, to be built between 1957 and 1961, is expected to have an electric generating capacity of 1,000,000 kilowatts. The dam is planned to reduce maximum downstream flow from 37,000 cubic meters to 8,000 cubic meters a second. Another Honan project is the Taohwayü diversion dam near Chengchow. It will expand the irrigated area and render the Yellow River navigable for 500-ton junks in its lower course.

In the Hwai Ho system, work has continued for several years on the construction of detention reservoirs in the headwaters of the Hwai Ho and its tributaries. These reservoirs have been built roughly along a north-south line west of the Peking-Hankow railroad. Five projects have been completed thus far in this zone. They are, from north to south, the reservoirs of Paisha (completed 1952), Shihmantan (1951), Pankiao (1952), Pushan (1954), and Nanwan (1955).

Honan is not a mineral-rich province. Its coal deposits along the south and east foot of the Taihang Mountains are a continuation of the deposits in Hopei. Like their northern neighbors, the Honan deposits are linked by spurs to the Peking-Hankow railroad. They are Liuhokow and Hohpitsi in the Anyang area near the Hopei border and the Tsiaotso, on a spur from Sinsiang. The coal from Liuhokow is bituminous and of coking quality, while Tsiaotso is a major anthracite producer. Iron ore deposits in the vicinity of Tsiaotso plus the presence of anthracite have caused the area to be set up as a special industrial and mining ch'ü. Planned 1957 output at Tsiaotso is 2,300,000 tons of anthracite. Work began in 1956 on extending the Tsiaotso rail spur into Shansi to Changchih and Taiyüan.

The province's industry is largely devoted to the processing of food and industrial crops. This includes cotton mills, notably at Chengchow, flour and oilseed mills. The processing centers, nearly all of which are also the province's largest cities, are situated along the two main rail lines intersecting at Chengchow: the east-west Lunghai railroad and the Peking-Hankow line. One or two urban centers have developed at navigation heads for junk traffic.

By far the dominant urban center is Chengchow, capital of the province since October, 1954. This rail center owes its existence largely to its location at the intersection of two of China's main trunk railroads. It developed rapidly as a marketing city for the agricultural output of central Honan. Further impetus was given to its growth after 1949. The city has a textile machinery plant, three cotton mills with a fourth under construction in 1955, a flour mill and a large oil and fats processing plant. Many of the new industries are concentrated in a new industrial district developed in the city's western outskirts. As a result of this economic development, the population of Chengchow rose from 130,000 in 1949 to nearly 500,000. North of the city the Peking-Hankow railroad crosses the Yellow River.

Other urban centers along the Lunghai railroad are Kaifeng, Lovang and Shangkiu. Kaifeng, Honan's former capital, is one of China's oldest cities. It was China's capital for more than 200 years under the so-called Five Dynasties (907-960) and the Northern Sung dynasty (960-1127). It owed its political importance to its central position in the North China plain and to good water communications with the southeast. The city gradually lost its economic importance as the waterways silted up and the Yellow River presented an increasing flood threat. With the rise of Chengchow in the twentieth century, economic activities slowly shifted to the new rail hub and this movement has been culminated by the transfer of the provincial government.

While Kaifeng has been eclipsed by its industrial rival, another of China's ancient capitals is passing through a renaissance. This is Loyang, center of a small agricultural area irrigated by the Lo Ho, a right tributary of the Yellow River. Loyang was China's capital even before Kaifeng, under the Chou dynasty (770-255 B.C.) and the Eastern Han dynasty (25-221 A.D.). Loyang was eclipsed as a political center in the thirteenth century by Kaifeng. For centuries it remained a sleepy agricultural town, frequented occasionally by tourists who came to see near-by tombs and ruins that bore witness to the city's former greatness. In 1955, Loyang was rudely awakened when it was chosen as the site of China's first modern tractor factory. The plant stands on the western outskirts of the city, an anachronistic monument of the machine age amid ancient burial grounds. With a projected capacity of 15,000 tractors, the plant is to be commissioned in 1959.

Elsewhere in Honan, major urban centers are aligned along the Peking-Hankow railroad. North of the Yellow River are Anyang and Sinsiang, farther south, is a transportation hub at the crossing of the known for excavations of artifacts dating from the Shang (Yin) dynasty (1766-1122 B.C.). Near by are the coal mines of Liuhokow and Hohpitsi. Sinsiang farther south, is a transportation hub at the crossing of the Peking-Hankow line and the navigable Wei Ho. From here a spur line leads west to the Tsiaotso mining and industrial ch'ü and 100-ton junks can reach Tientsin along the Wei Ho-Grand Canal route. Sinsiang was the capital of the short-lived province of Pingyüan (1949-1952).

South of the Yellow River, along the railroad beyond Chengchow, are four cities that serve as collecting centers for the surrounding farm areas. They are, from north to south, Hsüchang, Loho, Chumatien and Sinyang. Hsüchang is the center of Honan's most important tobacco-growing district. Loho, which is situated on the railroad, has apparently replaced the hsien town of Yencheng, just northwest on the Sha Ho, a headstream of the Ying Ho. Chumatien, long a regional center, has been made a city in keeping with it economic importance. Finally, Sinyang is the regional center for southernmost Honan, near the Hupei border. From here roads lead southward across the low passes of the Hwaiyang Mountains to the Middle Yangtze plain.

Only two Honan regional centers have maintained their position in spite of remoteness from rail lines. They are Nanyang and Chowkow. Nanyang is the regional center of the southwestern, sheltered part of Honan, looking toward the Middle Yangtze plain, Chowkow, known as Chowkiakow until 1950, is head of navigation for junks on the Ying Ho, major tributary of the Hwai Ho.

SHANTUNG PROVINCE

Capital: Tsinan; area: 54,000; population: 48,876,548.

Prior to 1949, Shantung was credited with an area of 57,000 square miles and a population of 38,900,000. In 1949, the westernmost part of Shantung was ceded to the temporary province of Pingyüan, but the loss of territory was partly made up by gains from Hopei and Kiangsu provinces. The area from 1949 to 1952 was given as 53,000 square miles and the population estimated at 41,000,000. Although the pre-1949 frontiers were restored in 1952, the new area was given at 54,000 square miles, instead of 57,000 listed before 1949. Prior to the 1953 census, the population of the present area was estimated at 45,000,000.

Shantung Province is about evenly divided between mountains and plains. Lowlands are found along the western border, which is an integral part of the North China plain, and along the Kiaolai corridor, which bisects the peninsula between the two upland masses. The higher western upland, dominated by the Tai Shan, is well inland, while the lower eastern upland forms the Shantung promontory proper.

Shantung has the winter wheat-kaoliang crop association typical of the North China plain. In 1954, total grain production was 13,200,000 tons (7.5 per cent of China's total), including about 4,000,000 tons of winter wheat. Together with grains, soybeans are grown through most of the province. The area under soybeans is about 2,000,000 hectares and the average yearly output about 2,500,000 tons (25 per cent of China's total production). Another Shantung specialty is peanuts, which cover 660,000 hectares, chiefly in light sandy soils around Tsinan, Tsingtao, Weifang and Tehchow. With an annual output of 1,140,000 million tons of peanuts (in 1954), Shantung accounts for about one-half of China's total production. Unlike peanuts, cotton grows best in the calcareous alluvial soils of the Yellow River plain. About 740,000 hectares are in cotton in the western Shantung lowlands, 15 per cent of China's total cotton area.

The Shantung peninsula is known for the cultivation of the wild silk-worm, which feeds on oak leaves. The wild silk is spun and woven into a thin soft fabric of yellow-brown silk known as pongee. The best known wild silk centers are Laiyang, Tsisia, Wenteng and Haiyang, all in the eastern uplands of the Shantung promontory. Chefoo has long been noted as the shipping port for wild silk. Tobacco also favors sandy soils, such as are found near Weifang, and Shantung produces about 20 per cent of China's tobacco. Finally, fruits are a Shantung specialty. Best known are the peaches of Feicheng, pears of Laiyang, persimmons of Taian, and grapes of Tsimo. Fruits are generally exported via Chefoo and Tsingtao.

While richly endowed with agricultural production, Shantung is also a major mineral province. It has been China's third most important coal producer, after Liaoning and Hopei. The coal centers are situated along the northern and southwestern edges of the Tai Shan uplands. The northern fields are served by the Tsinan-Tsingtao railroad. Most important is the new city of Tzepo set up in 1954 on a southern spur of the main line. It is named Tzepo for its two main component cities—Tzechwan (mine at Hungshan) and Poshan—situated on the coal-mining spur. The city of Poshan itself has become the administrative seat of the new city. The rank of the Tzepo coals varies from semi-bituminous in the south to semi-anthracite in the north. The coals are low in ash and have excellent steam-raising qualities. The southern coals, moreover, are suitable for coking. West of the Tzepo field is the lower-grade Changkiu field, which yields coal with a higher ash content and has not experienced the same rapid development as its eastern neighbor. The main coal mine of the Changkiu field is at Wentsu, on a southern spur from Mingshui. Eastward along the main line toward Tsingtao is the Weifang coalfield. Weifang is the new municipal name given to the twin cities of Weihsien and Fangtze. Fangtze is the actual coal-mining center south of Weihsien. The coal here is bituminous of noncoking grade and is a good steam-raiser.

On the southwestern edge of the Tai Shan uplands is the coal-mining center of Tsaochwang, on a spur of the Tientsin-Pukow railroad, Tsaochwang was put out of commission during the civil war and resumed operations only in March, 1953, after a six-year halt. Its planned 1957 output is 1,750,000 tons.

Other than coal, Shantung has deposits of iron ore, gold, alunite, kaolin. The iron mine is situated at Tiehshan ("iron mountain") on a short northern spur leaving the Tsinan-Tsingtao railroad at Kinlingchen. This deposit is a contact metamorphic ore body of magnetite-hematite. It has been mined intermittently since 1919. The iron content is 55 per cent and the ore is nonphosphoric and self-fluxing. The deposit was one of China's ancient iron-smelting centers and a modern metallurgical plant based on this deposit and the Tzepo coking coal has long been envisaged. Gold is found in small scattered deposits in the eastern uplands, notably at Chaoyüan and Pingtu. Finally, alunite and kaolin are associated with the coal measures of the Tzepo field. They are used in the mnufacture of ceramic and refractory products at Tzepo.

Except for the ports along the Shantung peninsula, the province's main urban centers have gravitated to the two main rail lines: the Tientsin-Pukow line, crossing the western part of Shantung from north to south, and the Tsinan-Tsingtao line, which links the two largest cities.

Inland rail communications are supplemented by coastwise shipping around the peninsula, but inland waterways, like in the rest of the North China plain, are quite inadequate. The only waterway accessible for large junks is the Siaotsing River, an arm of the Yellow River delta, which is navigable from Lokow, river port of Tsinan, to Yangkiokow, a small coastal trade port on Laichow Bay of the Po Hai. The Grand Canal, which crosses the western part of the province from north to south, appears to have been silted up and is used only north of Lintsing, where it joins the Wei Ho, and south of Tsining, where the water level of the canal is maintained by a series of lakes called Nanyang, Tushan, Chaoyang and Weishan.

Tsingtao, the province's largest city, is the product of Western colonization in China. Ceded to Germany in 1898 as part of the Kiaochow lease, it developed first under German rule and after 1914 under the Japanese before it was surrendered to China in 1924. It is one of China's best ports with a sheltered deep-water harbor at the entrance of Kiaochow Bay. The larger of two ship basins is enclosed by a 2.5-mile-long circular mole and accommodates ships of thirty-feet draft. The smaller basin is suitable for coastwise junks. Tsingtao's industries include textiles, flour, vegetable oils and paper. Heavy industry is concentrated in the northern industrial suburbs of Szefang (locomotive works) and Tsangkow (cement). The population of Tsingtao was 917,000 in 1953. The municipal area goes far beyond the city proper and includes the entire peninsula east of Kiaochow Bay, an area of 300 square miles. In the municipal area rises Lao Shan, highest point of the eastern Shantung uplands, known both as a beach and a hill resort. Having good rail connections with the Shantung hinterland, Tsingtao is the principal maritime outlet for the province's peanuts and soybeans, or their by-products, as well as coal.

At the other end of Shantung's east-west railroad lies Tsinan, the second largest provincial city. Unlike Tsingtao, Tsinan is an ancient Chinese city that flourished for centuries but one whose importance was greatly enhanced by railroad development. The provincial capital, it is situated on the lower Yellow River, an economic factor of dubious importance, and at the intersection of the Tientsin-Pukow and Tsinan-Tsingtao railroads.Tsinan is the agricultural processing center for western Shantung. Its economy is similar to that of Tsingtao—textiles, flour, vegetable oils. The city consists of the old walled town with scenic Taming Lake and the eastern commercial city. Lokow, the city's river port, is upstream head of navigation on the Siaotsing River (fed by Taming Lake) and downstream terminus of the erratic junk traffic on the Yellow River. Tsinan's population was 680,000 in 1953.

Between the two termini of the Tsinan-Tsingtao line are the industrial centers of Changtien and Chowtsun (until 1954 merged under the name of Changchow) and Weifang (merged from Weihsien and Fangtze). Changchow is now part of the coal city of Tzepo. Weifang is center of an agricultural district, producing tobacco and peanuts, in addition to its coal mines.

Other centers in western Shantung are Tehchow, a transportation center on the Grand Canal-Wei Ho route and junction of the Tientsin-Pukow and Tehchow-Shihkiachwang railroads; Lintsing, river port on the same water route; and Tsining, navigation head for the southernmost section of the Grand Canal.

Shantung's ports, in addition to Tsingtao, are Chefoo, Weihai, and Lungkow. Chefoo, whose modern Chinese name is Yentai, was opened to foreign trade in 1858 but was never more than a port of local importance for lack of good hinterland communications. It had a population of 116,000 in 1953. Late in 1955, Chefoo was linked by a rail branch with the Tsingtao main line. Weihai, formerly called Weihaiwei, stands on the site of a Ming dynasty fort that gave the city its name (Weihaiwei means "awe-inspiring sea fort"). It was leased to Britain in 1898 and served as a British naval base until its return to China in 1930. Lungkow is of minor importance.

Chapter 5

THE LOWER YANGTZE PLAIN

The Lower Yangtze plain includes the provinces of Anhwei and Kiangsu (with the independent city of Shanghai). The combined area of these two provinces is 95,000 square miles, or 2.5 per cent of all China. Their total population in 1953 was 78,000,000 or 13 per cent of the entire nation. The average density of 750 persons per square mile exceeds even that of the North China plain.

The region lies on the shore of the Yellow Sea on both sides of the lower Yangtze River and the Hwai Ho. Unlike the North China plain, it is not sharply delimited by natural features; in fact it may in part be regarded as a southeastern extension of the northern lowland. Only in the southwest do hill ranges separate the Lower Yangtze plain from the Middle Yangtze plain. Except for occasional hilly sections, the Lower Yangtze plain is an alluvial lowland laid down by the rivers over long ages. It can be divided roughly into three subregions: the Kiangnan plain, the Yangtze-Hwai Ho lowland, and the Wuhu plain.

Kiangnan means "south of the [Yangtze] river" and refers to the triangular delta plain south of the river's estuary. The river once emptied into the ocean above Chinkiang, but the steady accumulation of sediments, of which the Yangtze carries 600,000,000 tons a year, has pushed the delta plain steadily eastward at the rate of one mile every sixty to seventy years. The plain is now crisscrossed by a maze of canals and dotted by a large number of shallow lakes and ponds, of which Tai Hu is the largest. This is one of China's most densely settled industrial and agricultural areas, with the metropolitan centers of Shanghai, Soochow, Wusih and Chinkiang.

The Yangtze-Hwai Ho lowland north of the Yangtze estuary is the product of deposition of the Yangtze River and the Hwai Ho. The Hwai Ho once had its own outlet to the sea, but in 1194, during one of the periodic course shifts of the Yellow River, this stream usurped the lower course of the Hwai Ho and gradually filled its outlet with sediment. In backing up, the Hwai Ho formed Hungtse Lake, a natural flow-equalizing reservoir, from which it sought outlets via the San Ho and the Grand

Canal to the Yangtze and via constantly shifting channels directly to the sea. In times of flood these waterways were unable to contain the rising volume of water, burst their dikes and flooded the surrounding countryside. This is the area where work has been under way since the Second World War to regulate the Hwai Ho system. The most significant projects thus far have been the North Kiangsu Irrigation Trunk Canal, a new outlet for the Hwai Ho, extending from Hungtse Lake at Kaoliangkien 105 miles northeast to the sea at Pientankang, and the San Ho dam, which regulates the San Ho outlet of Hungtse Lake. The new outlet was completed in 1952 and the San Ho dam in 1953.

In the northernmost part of the Hwai Ho lowland, on the Kiangsu-Shantung border, flood prevention has also been the object of the Yi-Shu project. The Yi Ho and the Shu Ho descend in virtually parallel courses from the Shantung uplands and have often caused floods in northernmost Kiangsu for lack of direct outlets to the sea. Starting soon after 1949, new outlets were built for both rivers directly to the Yellow Sea. The basic work was completed in 1952.

The Wuhu plain is formed by Yangtze sediments in a hill-enclosed basin between the Hwang Shan on the south bank of the Yangtze and the Hwaiyang Mountains on the north bank. The northern hills are the easternmost outliers of the central mountain belt and rarely exceed 500 feet in elevation. In the south, the hills are higher, rising to 5,600 feet in the Hwang Shan. Along the Anhwei-Chekiang border, the Tienmu Mountains are the result of volcanic activity and consist largely of black basalt. Nanking, Wuhu and Anking are the chief cities of the Wuhu plain.

The Lower Yangtze plain is traversed from west to east by the Yangtze River. The river enters the region at Tungliu from its middle plain, flows in a wide meandering course northeast to Nanking and turns east a short distance to Chinkiang where the true delta begins. The Yangtze receives no major tributaries throughout the lower plain, but is connected by a dense network of minor waterways both with the Hwai Ho system in the north and the Tai Hu system in the south. The Hwai Ho traverses the northern part of the region, generally in an eastnortheasterly direction, and receives a number of tributaries, chiefly on the left. The lake Tai Hu is the center of a complex system of lakes and small canals serving the Kiangnan lowland. The chief waterways here are the Kiangnan Canal, the southernmost section of the Grand Canal, Soochow Creek and the Whangpoo River.

Like the North China plain, the Lower Yangtze plain is dominated climatically by the interplay of Tropical Maritime air masses, which dominate in the summer, and Polar Continental air in the winter. However, because of the more southeasterly position of the Yangtze plain, its climate is more distinctly influenced by summer monsoon conditions than by the cold, dry winter monsoon. The average July temperatures are approximately the same as in the North China plain—about 80° F (27° C)—because of the north-south alignment of the summer isotherms. But the more southerly situation of the region accounts for higher January temperatures of about 35° F (2° C). As in the case of the northern plain, continentality increases inland, with hotter summers and somewhat cooler winters.

A variety of factors combine to produce more or less uniform rainfall distribution throughout the year, certainly the most uniform distribution anywhere in eastern China. The average annual precipitation is 45 inches, almost twice as much as in the northern plain. Moreover, although there is a definite summer maximum, only about 40 per cent of the rainfall comes in the three summer months June through August. The relatively regular annual rainfall distribution results from the combination of the monsoon rains in the spring, cyclonic storms in the summer and winter and typhoons in the fall.

Three major soil types may be distinguished in the Lower Yangtze plain. The northernmost parts of Anhwei and Kiangsu, which are actually an extension of the North China plain, have calcareous alluvial soils. The middle Hwai Ho valley in Anhwei and the Yangtze valley proper also have alluvial soils, but these are noncalcareous, partly because of the nonloessial character of the rivers' source regions, partly because of the great leaching of the soil. Finally, the hills north and south of the Yangtze River are characterized by leached forest soils, either podzolic types, as in north central Anhwei, or red lateritic soils, as in the southern Anhwei uplands.

The Lower Yangtze plain is one of China's leading agricultural regions, with about 50 per cent of the total area under cultivation. Nowhere is farmland more intensively utilized. Virtually all the land is in crops, with the exceptions of the uplands in southern and central Anhwei and the large area occupied by lakes. Because of the high rural population density, many hands are available to till the land and farming reaches a high intensity even by Chinese standards.

The region is part of three conventional agricultural divisions. The northernmost section, like the North China plain, belongs to the winter wheat-kaoliang area; the central section is taken up by the Yangtze rice-wheat area, while southernmost, sheltered Anhwei is part of the rice-tea area. Rice and cotton are the common summer crops, wheat,

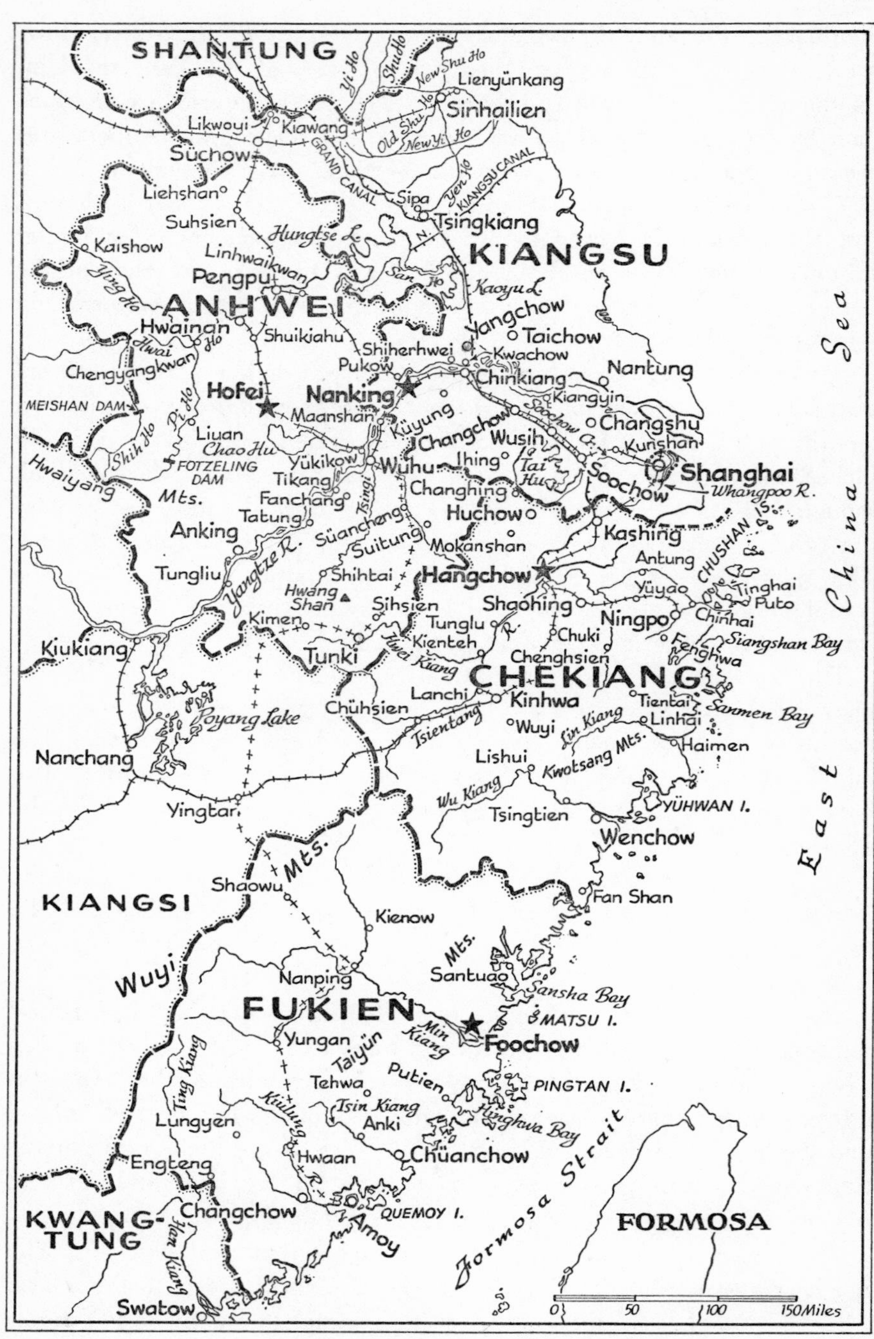

Lower Yangtze Plain and Southeast Coast

barley and oilseeds are grown in the winter, and tea and silk are distinctive specialty crops.

Summer rice and winter wheat are generally double-cropped throughout the Yangtze valley, with the chief production areas in the Wuhu plain of Anhwei and in the Tai Hu basin of southern Kiangsu around Wusih. Lesser food crops, used in part also as animal feed, are barley, soybeans, corn and sweet potatoes.

The high rural population density and the abundance of manpower, as well as favorable climatic and soil conditions, have made the Kiangnan lowland of southern Kiangsu one of China's leading silk-producing areas. About 90 per cent of all farm households engage in the cultivation of mulberry trees and the breeding of silkworms. Two silk-production areas are of outstanding importance: the Tai Hu basin, with mills in Soochow and Wusih, and the Wuhu plain, with mills in Nanking, Chinkiang and Süancheng.

Cotton is grown largely near the coast, where the calcareous alluvium is unsuitable for rice. The coastal alluvium is moreover sandy in texture, whereas rice prefers clay-pan soils that permit the fields to be kept flooded. Such sandy, calcareous alluvium is found in northern Kiangsu, but also in a strip of the Kiangnan lowland west of Shanghai. There, in the Taitsang-Kunshan area, about 60 to 70 per cent of all land is under cotton. Shanghai is, of course, China's leading cotton-milling center. Nantung, on the north bank of the Yangtze, is known for a long-staple fiber of high quality.

Other crops are oilseeds, grown largely along the Shanghai-Soochow railroad between Kunshan and Soochow west of the cotton belt, and peanuts near the Shantung line in northern Kiangsu. Tea is associated specifically with the Tunki area in southern Anhwei.

The Lower Yangtze plain has long been known as a land of rice and fish. Fisheries abound in the multitude of shallow lakes and waterways, particularly in the lakes Tai Hu and Chao Hu and in the Yangtze estuary.

Minerals are of moderate importance in the regional economy. Coal is found chiefly at Hwainan, on the south bank of the Hwai Ho. The coal is bituminous and of coking grade. Iron ore is found along the south bank of the Yangtze at Maanshan and Fanchang, with blast furnaces at Maanshan itself. Maanshan, in turn, supplies pig iron to the Shanghai steel and metal-fabricating industry. The coastal salines of Kiangsu have long been important salt producers. Traditionally, salt has been obtained by evaporation in the saltworks north of the Hwai Ho (the Hwaipei field) and by boiling south of the river (the Hwainan salt field). The northern salt has been marketed at Sipa, a northern river suburb of Tsingkiang, while the southern salt has been shipped in the past to the Yangtze River port of Shiherhwei, just east of Icheng. Southern salt production has been declining in recent years.

The Lower Yangtze basin, and in particular the Kiangnan triangle, is China's leading area of light industry, notably cotton and silk textiles, processed foods, paper and chemicals. These industries developed largely through the stimulus of foreign capital investments in association with a favorable seaboard location, a raw-material base and abundant manpower.

The region's economic development was also favored by the establishment of a dense rail net. The most important lines connect Shanghai, Nanking and Wuhu on the south bank of the Yangtze River. On the north bank are the Tientsin-Pukow railroad, with its Hwainan branch, and the easternmost section of the Lunghai line.

Water transportation centers on the great Yangtze artery, which is accessible to ocean-going vessels of 5,000 to 10,000 tons. A large number of lesser waterways branch off on the north and south banks, but these are accessible only for junks.

The population of the Lower Yangtze plain is homogeneously Chinese, but speaking several varieties of Mandarin. The northern Mandarin is spoken in the northern section adjoining the North China plain. The so-called Lower Yangtze dialect predominates in the central parts of Anhwei and Kiangsu, while the Wu (Shanghai) dialect is spoken in the Kiangnan lowland. A separate linguistic island of the Hweichow dialect is found in the southern uplands of Anhwei province. Population density is highest in the Kiangnan lowland, where it rises to more than 1,000 per square mile. Other densely settled areas are in southwestern Kiangsu around Nanking and Chinkiang and in the Yangtze valley of central Anhwei. The lowest population density—about 150 per square mile—is found in the southern Anhwei uplands.

KIANGSU PROVINCE

Capital: Nanking; area: 40,000; population: 41,252,192

After the Communist take-over in 1949, Kiangsu was administered as two separate units, North Kiangsu and South Kiangsu, separated by the Yangtze River. The province was reunited in November, 1952, at which time it reacquired territory briefly ceded to Shantung and Anhwei. The temporary partition of the province was an outgrowth of the civil war, during which the Communists had held the north bank of the Yangtze for a considerable time before the continued southward advance. The establishment of Communist institutions was therefore further advanced on the north bank than in the south. In view of the difference in existing conditions, the Peking regime found it expedient to administer the two parts of Kiangsu separately until conditions had been equalized.

Kiangsu is almost entirely a lowland, except for low hills near the Anhwei border. It is in effect a southeasterly continuation of the North China plain, with similar topography, climate and soils. Typical Yangtze valley conditions become dominant only in the southern part of the province. Less than one-third of Kiangsu is situated on the south bank of the Yangtze River and the entire province is crisscrossed by waterways and dotted with lakes. Some of China's largest lakes are here: Hungtse and Kaoyu lakes, which are part of the Hwai Ho reclamation projects, and Tai Hu, on the Chekiang border in the south. The coast is low-lying and straight. Sandbanks offshore hinder navigation and only in the Yangtze estuary and in the north at Lienyünkang can the coast be approached.

North of the Hwai Ho, winter wheat and summer kaoliang and millet are the chief grains, with cotton (in the Süchow area), corn, soybeans, sweet potatoes also grown in the summer. South of the Hwai Ho, winter wheat and barley and summer rice are the grains, and cotton, soybeans and silk other key products. During the summer, rice is cultivated on clay pans formed from Yangtze River alluvium, while cotton favors the sandy, noncalcareous and saline soils found near the coast. Winter wheat is sown on an average of 2,200,000 hectares, with the average yield about 1.2 tons per hectare. Kiangsu thus accounts for more than 10 per cent of China's wheat output. In the summer, cotton covers 600,000 or more hectares, yielding about 20 per cent of China's cotton, while rice is sown in about 800,000 hectares, producing about 10 per cent of China's rice. Kiangsu's total grain crop in 1955 was 13.75 million tons.

Being largely alluvial in origin, Kiangsu is poor in hard-rock minerals. Coal is found at Kiawang (formerly called Kiakiawang) on a rail spur north of Süchow on the Shantung border. This coal deposit is an extension of the Tsaochwang deposit farther north in Shantung and yields bituminous coking coal. Iron ore is interstratified with the coal measures and has been mined in the past at Likwoyi, just northwest of Kiawang on the Tientsin-Pukow railroad. Salt is obtained along the coast, predominantly north of the Hwai Ho, in the special Hwaipei salt district near Sinhailien. The salt has traditionally been shipped south along the Yen Ho to Sipa (near Tsingkiang) for marketing. In southern Kiangsu, nonmetallics are found near Küyung and Ihing. Küyung limestone is used for the production of cement at Lungtan, on the Yangtze halfway between

Nanking and Chinkiang. Ihing clay, mined on the west shore of the lake Tai Hu, has furnished the basis for a ceramic handicraft industry at Ihing itself.

Industrial centers are concentrated almost entirely south of the Yangtze River in the Kiangnan lowland. Cotton and silk mills as well as food processing plants are typical of this area. The Kiangnan section is well served by railroads, in contrast to northern Kiangsu where rail lines are entirely absent except for the Lunghai line in the extreme north. Waterways, usable only for small junks, play a major role in the transportation of northern Kiangsu. The chief route is the Grand Canal, navigable for small steamers from the Lunghai railroad south to Kwachow on the Yangtze River. The Yen Ho, another important junk route, links Tsingkiang and Sinhailien. The navigability of waterways in northern Kiangsu is expected to be much improved in connection with the Hwai Ho reclamation project. South of the Yangtze, the chief waterways are the Whangpoo River, Soochow Creek, and the Kiangnan Canal section of the Grand Canal. The Kiangnan Canal was built about 600 A.D. from Chinkiang on the Yangtze to Hangchow in Chekiang. It was 200 miles long and about 150 feet wide. It is still navigable all year for small vessels. Silting has been a major problem in the northern part and vessels, especially during the winter months, use the Wusih-Kiangyin cut-off canal to reach the Yangtze.

Kiangsu contains Shanghai, China's largest city, which is however politically independent of the province. Shanghai is easily described in superlatives. It is the largest city on the continent of Asia and is among the world's five largest metropolises. In June, 1953, its population was 6,204,417. Shanghai is one of the great world ports and is the natural outlet for the huge Yangtze basin. It was an unimportant coastal trading center until the mid-19th century, when the Treaty of Nanking (1842) opened the port to foreign trade and abruptly projected it on the world stage. Its growth under the ensuing Western influence has been phenomenal. Its prosperity is also the result of its favorable geographic position near the Yangtze River estuary, the most important navigation artery along the entire China coast. Shanghai's hinterland covers more than 400,000 square miles and has a population of more than 200,000,000. This tremendous landward empire, combined with the large coastwise trade funneled into the port, has made Shanghai the natural seaward trade focus of central China.

The heart of the city is situated on a tidal flat on the left bank of the Whangpoo River at the mouth of Soochow Creek. Shanghai's commercial core is in the former International Settlement at the river confluence, where broad streets and handsome boulevards are lined by imposing buildings. Here are the well-known thoroughfares of The Bund (along the waterfront) and Nanking Road. The business section is bounded east by the Whangpoo, south by the old Chinese inner city, west by the former hippodrome, now a public park, and north by Soochow Creek. Across Soochow Creek is the industrial section of Hongkew; across the Whangpoo is the right-bank industrial suburb of Pootung. Residential sections surrounding the business center on the southwest and north include the former French Concession and the workers' suburb of Chapei. In recent decades the municipal area has spread on both sides of the Whangpoo toward its mouth at Woosung on the Yangtze River. The municipal area covers about 350 square miles.

The city proper is situated about 15 miles from the Yangtze River. Shipping along the Whangpoo has been maintained in the past only through laborious dredging and a channel of about thirty feet in depth has been provided. Another major obstacle to navigation is presented by enormous sand bars in the Yangtze itself—the Shen Tan (Fairy Flats), situated about twenty miles southeast of Woosung in the Yangtze estuary. A low-water depth of only eighteen feet has forced large ships to wait for high tide at that point.

Except for local cotton and silk resources, Shanghai does not owe its economic dominance to a local raw material basis. In fact its industry has been dependent largely on imported materials. Nearly half of China's imports and exports passed through Shanghai normally before 1949. The chief exports were raw silk, tea, tung oil, eggs, hog bristles, and ores. Imports consisted largely of manufactured goods, food, cotton and woolen goods, petroleum, steel, and chemicals. After 1949, the import of food and consumer goods was greatly curtailed in accordance with the economic policy of the Communists.

In the past Shanghai has concentrated about one-third of China's industries, fixed industrial capital, and industrial labor force. This proportion is likely to decline sharply in the future as new areas are being industrialized. But, contrary to expectations, Shanghai has retained its pre-eminent position after 1949 in the face of the loss of its foreign contacts, the reorientation of China's trade toward the Soviet Union and Eastern Europe, and the hostilities in the Formosa Strait. In many ways, Shanghai's position after 1949 can be compared to Leningrad's role after the Bolshevik Revolution in the Soviet Union. Long supplied by foreign raw materials, Shanghai has increasingly looked landward for resources. A large part of its pig iron, for example, is now imported from Maanshan in Anhwei. Like Leningrad, Shanghai has retained its industrial leadership through the presence of a large skilled labor force. To this day, both Leningrad and Shanghai are the only producers of certain specialty products required by the Soviet and Chinese economies.

Textile industries predominate in the city's industrial structure, with about one-half of all industrial workers employed in spinning and weaving mills. Before 1949 Shanghai had almost half of China's cotton spindles, but the partial shift of spinning capacity to inland cotton centers has lowered this ratio. The city is also China's leading silk and wool textile producer. In addition to flour, oilseed and rice mills, Shanghai also has a well developed paper and chemical industry. It rivals Peking as a publishing center. Heavy industry includes a number of steel mills, operating on the basis of imported pig iron and scrap. These steel mills are associated with machinery plants and specialize in high-grade machine and tool steels. The Kiangnan shipyards are one of China's leading shipbuilding and repair enterprises. Shanghai also produces agricultural implements and has a petroleum refinery supplied with crude oil from Yümen. In keeping with its industrial production, Shanghai is one of China's leading power producers. Its power plant capacity is about 220,000 kilowatt, about 10 per cent of China's total capacity.

Virtually all the leading cities of southern Kiangsu are situated along the Shanghai-Nanking railroad. First along this trunk line is Soochow, a silk-milling center with a 1953 population of 474,000. Soochow is situated east of the lake Tai Hu, on the Grand Canal and near Soochow Creek. It was the capital of the Wu kingdom in the 5th century B.C. After Soochow was declared an open port in 1896, active trade developed in the southern part of the walled town, adjoining the waterways. But the construction of the railroad, which passes north of the town, caused the business section to be shifted to the industrial railroad settlement that developed northwest of the walled town. The proximity of the large economic centers of Shanghai and Wusih dwarfs Soochow as an industrial city. It is known chiefly as an old, unmodified, typically South Chinese city situated in a scenic hill and lake district. It ships raw silk and silk cloth, rice and vegetables and is noted for its embroidery work.

Twenty-five miles northwest is the industrial city of Wusih. The third largest city of Kiangsu, with a 1953 population of 581,000, Wusih has supplanted Soochow as the economic center of the Tai Hu basin. A small walled town until the late 19th century, it then industrialized and made use of modern machine methods, while Soochow retained its ancient handicraft character. Wusih is next only to Shanghai as a textile and food-processing center. Its excellent transportation facilities —railroads, waterways and highways—have made it a natural collecting center of the rich rice, wheat, and silk area of the Tai Hu basin. The secondary agricultural center of Changshu is off the Shanghai-Nanking railroad, twenty-five miles east of Wusih.

Proceeding along the railroad we come to Changchow, another agricultural center of 297,000 inhabitants in 1953. It was called Wutsin prior to 1949. The southeastern suburb of Chishuyen has a large railroad workshop.

At the point where the Shanghai-Nanking railroad reaches the Yangtze River and the Grand Canal intersects the river stands Chinkiang. The city consists of the old town and a western port and commercial section on the Yangtze River. The port settlement, once a British concession, was returned to China in 1927. Chinkiang had a population of 201,000 in 1953. Before the railroad era, Chinkiang was a flourishing transportation center on the Grand Canal, then the chief link between North and South China. As late as the 1870's, it was held that Chinkiang, not Shanghai, would monopolize the trade of the lower Yangtze River. However, Shanghai did prevail and the rise of that competitor together with the gradual shift of trade from waterways to railroads brought about Chinkiang's relative decline. Today the city is important for its food trade; it ships northern wheat and soybeans southwest along the Yangtze and forwards rice to the northern plain.

Nanking, the second largest city of Kiangsu and the provincial capital, is situated on the lower Yangtze River, about 150 miles from the sea. The city dates from the Han dynasty (2d century B.C.) and was variously known a Kinling, Kiangyeh and Kiangning. The name Nanking dates from the Ming dynasty and means "southern capital." Nanking was China's capital under several early Chinese dynasties, but notably after 1928 under the Nationalists. In 1949, the Communists moved the capital to Peking, but in 1952 Nanking became the provincial capital of Kiangsu, succeeding Chinkiang. Nanking is surrounded by the remains of a circuitous 22-mile-long wall that encloses not only the city proper (three miles from the Yangtze) but adjacent rural areas. The wall extends to Nanking's waterfront section of Siakwan, which is the city's railhead, shipping and commercial suburb. A rail ferry links Siakwan with Pukow, terminus of the railroad from Tientsin. A municipal railroad connects Siakwan with the city's southern Chunghwa Gate, terminus of the railroad to Wuhu.

The city's main thoroughfare, Chungshanlu, traverses the walled area from Siakwan to the Chungshan hills, east of Nanking. It passes the Kulou district, an area of parks and residences, and Hsinchiehkow, the central business district. Noteworthy in the eastern hills are tombs of the early Ming emperors and the Sun Yat-sen memorial. Long China's political center, Nanking is of relatively little importance as an industrial city. It has textile industries and has given its name to nankeen cloth and porcelain. The left-bank suburb of Pukow has a large chemical plant producing fertilizer. Nanking's population, in spite of its loss of the political leadership, remains about 1,000,000.

North of the Yangtze River, three urban centers are situated in the immediate vicinity of the river. They are Yangchow, Taichow, and Nantung. Yangchow, called Kiangtu prior to 1949, is situated near the north bank of the Yangtze River opposite Chinkiang. The Grand Canal passes through the city's eastern section. Like Chinkiang, Yangchow had its heyday in the period of the Grand Canal's peak navigation. It flourished particularly under the Sui and Tang dynasties (589-907 A.D.). Today Yangchow, with a population of 180,000, is primarily a rice and salt-marketing center. Rice is traded in the northeastern suburb of Siennümiao, called Kiangtu since 1950. Salt trade is concentrated in Shiherhwei, to the southwest. Taichow and Nantung, to the east, are agricultural centers on the north bank of the Yangtze, the latter known particularly for its cotton industry.

Tsingkiang is the center of north central Kiangsu. Called Hwaiyin prior to 1949, the city has a population of about 100,000 and is a waterway hub of the northern Kiangsu plain. Like other cities along the Grand Canal, Tsingkiang was a great trade center before the railroad era. It has been partly superseded by Pengpu on the Tientsin-Pukow railroad. However, Tsingkiang still fulfills a useful function as an agricultural center of north central Kiangsu, at the focus of the Grand Canal and the Yen Ho. From here the Grand Canal is navigable southward for large junks as far as Yangchow near the Yangtze and northward for smaller junks as far as Tsining in Shantung. Grain and salt (marketed at adjacent Sipa) are the main trade goods.

In northernmost Kiangsu, two major centers are situated along the Lunghai railroad. They are Süchow and Sinhailien. Süchow is one of China's major rail cities, situated at the junction of the Tientsin-Pukow and Lunghai lines. With a population of 300,000, it dominates not only the northwestern panhandle of Kiangsu, but also adjacent parts of Shantung, Honan and Anhwei. A major battle in the Chinese civil war was fought here in November, 1948. Süchow was known as Tungshan from 1912 to 1945.

Sinhailien is an amalgamation of the three cities of Sinpu, Tunghai and Lienyünkang, situated at the eastern end of the Lunghai railroad where it reaches the Yellow Sea. Tunghai, the central section of this conurbation, was formerly called Haichow. It is an old junk harbor at the head of the combined estuary of the Yen Ho and the old Shu Ho. Made unusable because of silting, Tunghai was replaced by the down-river landings of Sinpu and Tapu. In the 1930's a deep-water harbor was built south of the estuary on a site sheltered by hills and offshore islands. The new harbor, at first called Laoyao, later Lienyün or Lienyünkang ("kang" means harbor), succeeded Tunghai as the terminus of the Lunghai line and became the chief Chinese port on the Yellow Sea between Tsingtao and Shanghai. Tunghai has now been virtually abandoned as a river port and the center of administration of the three-city conurbation has been transferred to Sinpu.

ANHWEI PROVINCE

Capital: Hofei; area: 56,000; population: 30,343,637

Like Kiangsu, Anhwei was administered in two sections in the aftermath of the civil war, but Anhwei was reunited in August, 1952, three months earlier than Kiangsu. In November Anhwei recovered small areas temporarily ceded to Kiangsu and the province was restored to its pre-1949 boundaries. The two northernmost hsien of Tangshan and Siaohsien were ceded to Kiangsu in early 1955.

Anhwei may be said to include two distinct natural divisions: the North China plain in the north and the Yangtze valley proper in the south. The northern section, coinciding with the Hwai Ho river system, is typical of the North China plain with its cold, dry winters and hot, rainy summers, calcareous alluvial soils and shakiang soils, and the winter wheat-kaoliang crop association. The southern section, sheltered by low-lying hills, is more typical of Yangtze valley conditions, with more uniform annual precipitation and less severe winters, noncalcareous valley alluvium ringed by podzolic and lateritic upland soils, and the wheat-rice crop association.

Anhwei's 1955 total grain production was 11,170,000 tons, or about 6 per cent of China's total. Wheat is the chief winter grain both in the north and in the south, while rice is grown in the summer in the Wuhu plain of the south, particularly in the Chao Hu lake basin north of the Yangtze River. Lesser grains are summer kaoliang in the north and winter barley in the south. Soybeans and sweet potatoes are also grown in the North China plain section.

Cotton is cultivated chiefly in the northern half of Anhwei, but the province as a whole produces only about 5 per cent of the nation's cotton crop. Silk is produced only in the southeast zone bordering on Kiangsu. Anhwei is however one of China's leading tea-producing provinces. The chief producing area in the extreme south is centered on Tunki, which produces a green tea, and Kimen, which grows the black keemun tea. A lesser area in the central uplands is Liuan, known for the sunglo leaf.

Anhwei has East China's chief coal-mining area around Hwainan. This is situated both north and south of the Hwai Ho, with the main mining operations proceeding on the south bank. Hwainan is a new city set up after 1949 on the site of the riverside coal harbor of Tienkiaan. Prior to 1949, mining operations were centered south of Hwainan, at Shunkengshan and Kiulungkang. Later, in connection with an extension of mining operations, a rail spur was driven 10 miles west to a new mining area at Pakungshan. Hwainan coal is shipped by rail to the growing Yangtze port of Yükikow, opposite Wuhu. In 1957, Hwainan's coal output is planned to reach 6.85 million tons.

In addition to Hwainan, Anhwei has two lesser coal mines: at Liehshan and Suitung. Liehshan is located in northernmost Anhwei, about twenty-five miles northwest of Suhsien. In the past, coal mined here on a small scale has been shipped down the river Sui Ho to Fulitsi, a station on the Tientsin-Pukow railroad. Suitung is situated twenty miles southeast of Süancheng in southeastern Anhwei. Here coal measures found on the flanks of the southern Anhwei uplands dip under the alluvium of the Yangtze delta in Kiangsu. The coal is of anthracite rank in the more compressed western part of the Suitung field, but is predominantly bituminous in the east.

In addition to coal, Anhwei is also well supplied with iron ore. Two major contact metamorphic deposits are found along the south bank of the Yangtze River: near Tangtu and Fanchang. The Tangtu deposit is situated on the Kiangsu border. Large-scale operations were initiated here by the Japanese, who laid a short rail spur from the main Tawashan (Tayaoshan) deposit to the riverside smelting center of Maanshan. After an eight-year suspension, six small blast furnaces built by the Japanese at Maanshan were restored in 1953. Maanshan's pig iron now meets almost half the metal needs of the Shanghai steel industry, thus reducing the need for long-haul shipments of pig iron from North China and Manchuria. The Fanchang deposit, west of Wuhu, has been in operation since 1918. Here a narrow-gauge line has been laid from the main Taochung deposit to the riverside loading port of Tikang. Annual production at each of these two deposits has averaged 200,000 to 300,000 tons. Copper mining is being developed at Tungkwanshan near Tungling.

Anhwei's leading urban centers are situated along the Yangtze River and on railroads linking Yangtze River ports with the North China plain. The main railroad is the Tientsin-Pukow line, from which a branch joins the river port of Yükikow. Three minor waterways usable by junks branch off from the Yangtze River, the province's chief navigable artery. These waterways are the Yüntsao River, which joins the lake Chao Hu to the Yangtze and permits junks to ascend as far as Hofei, the provincial capital; and on the right bank, the Shuiyang River as far as Süancheng and the Tsingi River as far as Shihtai. In the north, junk traffic is possible along the Hwai Ho, where navigability is being improved in connection with the Hwai Ho reclamation project. In the past large junks were able to ascend the Hwai Ho as far as Chengyangkwan, at the mouths of the Pi Ho, a right tributary, and the Ying Ho, a left tributary. Among the flood-prevention reservoirs thus far completed in northern Anhwei are the Fotzeling reservoir on the upper Pi Ho (completed 1954) and the Meishan reservoir on the upper Shih Ho (completed 1956).

The two principal Anhwei cities along the Yangtze are Wuhu and Anking. Wuhu is on the river's south bank at the mouth of the Tsingi River. A city of 242,000 persons (1953), it was the capital of South Anhwei from 1949 to 1952. The city is linked by rail with Nanking and Shanghai and by the Yüntsao River with the lake Chao Hu and the Hofei area. Wuhu is thus admirably situated as a collecting center for the surrounding agricultural districts. It is in fact one of China's leading rice markets. Opposite the city, on the Yangtze's left bank, is the rail terminus and river port of Yükikow.

Anking, on the left bank of the Yangtze, was formerly called Hwaining. A former capital of Anhwei, it lost its political position largely because of poor connections with the rest of the province. Its trade is much less significant than that of Wuhu, downriver, or Kiukiang, upriver in Kiangsi Province. The population of Anking exceeds 100,000. About forty-five miles downstream from Anking is the town of Tatung, a stopping place for Yangtze River streamers.

The two provincial centers north of the Yangtze River are Hofei and Pengpu. Hofei, the provincial capital, was formerly called Luchow. It is situated near the lake Chao Hu, center of a major rice-producing area. Once a major transportation center on routes linking North and South China, it has been partly superseded by Pengpu. Its population is about 100,000. A textile mill, to be completed in 1957, will process the cotton grown around Hofei.

Pengpu, on the Hwai Ho, developed in conjunction with the Tientsin-Pukow railroad. Situated at the crossing of the railroad and the Hwai

Ho, here navigable for large junks, Pengpu is the grain-marketing center of northern Anhwei. A branch line connects Pengpu with Shuikiahu on the Hwainan-Yükikow coal railroad. Pengpu's population was 300,000 in 1953. To the east is Linhwaikwan, another important port on the Hwai Ho.

In southernmost Anhwei is the isolated, hill-rimmed Tunki area. Here natural conditions are typical of the more southerly tea-rice region. In fact, the area's natural outlet is southeastward along one of the headstreams of the Tsientang River. This is the leading tea area of Anhwei. Noteworthy places in addition to Tunki, largest city and administrative center, are Kimen, the tea center, and Sihsien. Sihsien, formerly called Hweichow, was once the regional center but has been replaced by Tunki. So isolated is the Tunki area that a separate Mandarin dialect, the so-called Hweichow speech, has maintained itself.

Chapter 6

THE MIDDLE YANGTZE PLAIN

The Middle Yangtze plain includes the provinces of Hupei, Hunan and Kiangsi. The combined area of these three provinces is about 220,000 square miles, or 6 per cent of the nation's total territory. The total population of the region in 1953 was 78,000,000, or 13 per cent of China's population. The average density of 350 per square mile is thus considerably below that of the North China plain or the Lower Yangtze region.

Traversed from west to east by the Yangtze River, the region consists essentially of the drainage basins of the three major tributaries of the middle Yangtze: the Han Shui basin in Hupei, the Siang Kiang basin in Hunan, and the Kan Kiang basin in Kiangsi.

Mountains of medium elevation suround the region as a whole and divide the component basins from one another. Separating the region from the North China plain are the Hwaiyang Mountains. In the west, the Middle Yangtze basins border on the Szechwan mountains and the Kweichow plateau. In the south, the basins are separated from Kwangsi and Kwangtung by the Nan Ling divide, one of China's major natural barriers. Finally, in the east, are the uplands of Fukien and Chekiang.

The Middle Yangtze plain can be described in terms of three major subdivisions: the Hwaiyang divide in the north, the Middle Yangtze valley proper, and the South Yangtze hills. The Hwaiyang Mountains extend along the Honan-Hupei border from the Nanyang area to the province of Anhwei. In the west it includes the low, strongly eroded Tahung and Tungpeh hills. These uplands are of ancient origin and have gently rounded contours. A large part of their area is taken up by broad valleys. In the east rise the Tapieh Mountains, with elevations exceeding 3,000 feet. They are characterized by abrupt, deeply dissected scarps on the north side and gentle slopes in the south. The Hwo Shan of the central Anhwei uplands is the easternmost outlier of the Hwaiyang system.

The Middle Yangtze valley proper extends from the Ichang gorges in the west to the Anhwei border. The level, alluvial land of the valley reaches up into the surrounding mountains. In two localities, between Wusüeh and Tienkiachen on the Kiangsi-Hupei line and between Pengtseh and Tungliu on the Kiangsi-Anhwei line, the hills approach the river on both banks. Elsewhere the mountains retreat from the river and the valley is as much as 200 miles wide. The Wusüeh-Tienkiachen constriction divides the valley into two sections: the Tungting and Poyang plains, named for the lakes of the same names. The Tungting plain includes central Hupei and northern Hunan. It is the floor of an ancient lake, of which Tungting Lake and many smaller water bodies are the remains. The Poyang Plain occupies a smaller area than the Tungting plain. Poyang Lake was once considerably larger and has been gradually filled in by sediments.

The South Yangtze hills include the southern parts of Hunan and Kiangsi. Their elevation varies from 500 to more than 3,000 feet, with the greater elevations along the provincial borders. The mountain rims enclose the Siang Kiang and Kan Kiang basins like two amphitheatres. The most important ranges along the western margin are the Wuling and Süehfeng mountains. The isolated Heng Shan rises to 4,000 feet in central Hunan overlooking the Siang Kiang valley. The divide between the two river basins is made up by a series of ranges trending NE-SW, including the Mufow, Kiuling, Wukung and Wanyang mountains. Valleys separating these ranges serve as routeways between Hunan and Kiangsi. The isolated Lu Shan, a continuation of the Mufow Mountains, rises to 5,000 feet on the west shore of Poyang Lake. The eastern margins of the South Yangtze hill region are made up largely of the Wuyi Mountains, which form the divide between the Kan Kiang and the southeastern coastal drainage basins.

The Yangtze River is of course the region's principal river. It debouches onto the plain at Ichang and traverses it in a meandering course, trending first southeast to Tungting Lake, then northeast to Wuhan, again southeast to Poyang Lake and turning once more northeast as it enters Anhwei Province. The volume of water varies greatly, being lowest during the winter and highest after the summer rains. Fortunately, the sudden surge of the summer high water seldom produces floods as the surplus is discharged into the natural reservoirs of the Tungting and Poyang lakes. Dikes encase the middle Yangtze course, whose numerous meanders and irregular channel width offer a relatively low carrying capacity. Occasionally neither the natural detention basins nor the riverside embankments are able to contain the raging waters. In recent times two disastrous floods have occurred in 1931 and in 1954. The fight to regulate the river is a continuing one. Among the measures undertaken since 1949 is the construction of the Kingkiang reservoir south of Shasi, one of several flood-detention basins planned along the middle Yangtze River.

Owing to the moderate barrier effect of the Hwaiyang divide, the Middle Yangtze plain is even less exposed to the northern air masses than the lower reaches of the river. As a result of its sheltered position with respect to the cold, dry Polar Continental air, the January temperatures average 40° F (5° C) compared with 35° F in the lower plain. The inland location of the middle plain, far from the moderating effect of the sea, also results in higher July averages of 85° F (29° C) compared with 80° F in the lower reaches. Precipitation is abundant and distributed relatively evenly through the year. Of an annual average of 45 inches, about 43 per cent falls in the three summer months June, July, August, 25 per cent in the spring, 21 per cent in the fall and 11 per cent in the winter.

The Middle Yangtze plain depends for its precipitation largely on turbulence associated with the polar front. Because of the varying intensity of the interaction of the southeastern Maritime Tropical air and the northern Continental air, both flood years and drought years have been produced in the past. Strong southeastern monsoons usually advance as far as the North China plain, which then receives abundant precipitation, while the Middle Yangtze plain to the south suffers drought conditions. Weak summer monsoons, on the other hand, meet Continental air masses over the Yangtze valley, which then has a rainy year while the Yellow River plain remains dry. This irregular shifting of the polar front zone produces alternate floods and droughts in the two great Chinese lowlands.

The Yangtze valley proper, including the Tungting and Poyang lake basins, has recent noncalcareous alluvium. Podzols are well developed in the Hwaiyang divide, while lateritic soils predominate in the South Yangtze hills. Red lateritic soils cover most of Kiangsi and Hunan, while yellow soils are restricted to western Hunan adjoining the Kweichow plateau. Agriculturally, the clay pans developed on the valley alluvium are associated with rice, the principal summer crop grown on irrigated land. More than half of the arable land is irrigated and terracing is common on the hillsides in the south. In terms of the conventional agricultural divisions, Hupei belongs largely to the Yangtze rice-wheat area, in common with the Lower Yangtze plain, while Hunan and Kiangsi are almost entirely in the rice-tea area.

Rice cultivation is favored throughout the region by high summer temperatures and abundant precipitation. It even yields two crops in

Middle Yangtze Plain

southernmost Kiangsi, where conditions resemble subtropical Kwangtung. Early-ripening types are grown chiefly north of the Yangtze, while late-ripening varieties and rice used for distilling are cultivated south of the river. The highest yields are obtained in the Yangtze valley proper, where the Tungting and Poyang basins have become known as the "rice bowl" of China. Kiukiang and Changsha are the two great rice markets.

Winter wheat is important only north of the Yangtze. Other winter crops, grown chiefly in the terraced hillsides, include beans, corn and sweet potatoes.

Tea, also a hillside crop, has three major production centers within the Middle Yangtze area. They are the Siu Shui area of northwest Kiangsi, the Puchi area of southeast Hupei, and the Anhwa area of central Hunan. The leaves in these areas are commonly cured to produce black tea. Hankow and Kiukiang are the regional tea-marketing and processing centers.

Other important products are cotton, grown in parts of the Poyang and Tungting basins, and ramie and other bast fibers, cultivated chiefly in the South Yangtze hills. Rapeseed and sesame are grown for their oil.

Although much of the region has been cleared of trees, both to make available land and provide fuel, the original subtropical evergreen broadleaf forest cover remains in remote and thinly settled upland areas. The stands yield fir, pine and cypress, as well as bamboo. Although the tung tree is not as important here as in China's Southwest and in the Szechwan basin, the wood oil is produced both in western Hunan and Kiangsi.

The region is rich in minerals, yielding not only coal and iron ore, but nonferrous metals. High-grade coking coal is mined at Pingsiang in Kiangsi. This deposit, together with the iron ore reserves of Tayeh, provides the raw material base for the growing iron and steel center of Hwangshih on the Yangtze River. The nonferrous mining centers are Sikwangshan (antimony), Sihwashan (tungsten), Shuikowshan (lead, zinc, silver). Important nonmetallic sites are Yingcheng for gypsum and Kingtehchen for kaolin.

The region's industrial centers are situated along the Yangtze River and the railroad lines. These run in general perpendicular to the river and include the Peking-Hankow-Canton line, the Kiukiang-Nanchang line and the latitudinal Chekiang-Kiangsi railroad.

The middle Yangtze is accessible to vessels of 5,000 tons in the summer and 2,000 tons in the winter as far as Hankow. Above Hankow, 2,000-ton and 1,000-tons ships can reach Ichang in the two seasons, respectively. From the Yangtze, large motorized junks can ascend the Han Shui. The tributary rivers of the Tungting and Poyang basins are also navigable in the lower reaches.

The big industrial centers are the three-city conurbation of Wuhan in Hupei, Changsha in Hunan and Nanchang in Kiangsi. The principal industries are cotton and ramie mills, porcelain manufacturing (Kingtehchen), flour, oilseed and tea factories. Hwangshih is the regional metallurgical center.

The population is particularly dense in the Yangtze valley proper, where it reaches 750 per square mile. Lower densities are found along the Siang Kiang and Kan Kiang valleys—about 300 to 400 per square miles. The most sparsely settled areas are the peripheral South Yangtze hills. Relief is a major determinant of population distribution.

The ethnic make-up of the population is almost entirely Chinese, speaking Mandarin dialects. In Kiangsi, it is the Lower Yangtze variety of Mandarin that predominates, while in Hupei and Hunan the Upper Yangtze variety is spoken. In southernmost Kiangsi are Hakka-speaking Chinese, and the specific Kan dialect is associated with the Kan Kiang valley. In Hunan, the Hunanese dialect is associated with the Siang Kiang valley. The only non-Chinese minorities are in Hunan. They are the Miao and Tung in the western mountain margins.

HUPEI PROVINCE

Capital: Wuchang; area: 72,000; population: 27,789,693

Hupei Province occupies a central position in China proper. It is crossed both by the Yangtze River, the nation's chief waterway and east-west transportation artery, and by the Peking-Hankow-Canton trunk railroad. The two national routes meet in the Wuhan conurbation.

The province is about two-thirds lowland (in the east) and one-third upland. The low-lying, lake-studded alluvial plain is bounded by the Hwaiyang divide along the Honan border and by the Mufow Mountains along the Kiangsi line. It continues at water level in the Tungting basin of northern Hunan. In the west, the lowland makes way for the rugged red sandstone outliers of the Szechwan mountain rim.

Through these western uplands the Yangtze River makes its way in precipitous gorges before debouching onto the plain at Ichang. The meandering river proceeds generally eastward through the Hupei lowland past Wuhan, where it receives on the left the Han Shui.

Most of the province is characterized by the rice-wheat crop association. Rice is the main summer crop. Wheat, the winter grain, is sown chiefly in the northern part of the province and milled at Hankow. Other winter crops are barley, rapeseed and broad beans. Among the summer crops are cotton, soybeans and corn. Cotton is grown in the central part of the province and milled into textiles at Wuchang. A distinctive hillside crop is tea. It is cultivated in the uplands west of Ichang and especially on the slopes of the Mufow Mountains near Puchi.

Iron ore is the province's only major mineral resource. It is mined near Tayeh, where operations began in 1891. The mines, situated at Tiehshan and Siangpishan, are linked by a twenty-mile railroad with Hwangshih on the Yangtze River. The high-grade magnetite deposit has yielded from 500,000 to 1,000,000 tons a year in the past, chiefly for export down the Yangtze River to Japan. In the future, the entire output of the mines is expected to be smelted in the new iron and steel plant of Hwangshih.

Some coal is mined in the vicinity of the Tayeh iron ore deposit, but in negligible amounts. Among nonmetallics, Hupei occupies a key position as China's chief gypsum producer. About 90 per cent of the nation's output originates at Yingcheng, northwest of Wuhan. Limestone deposits near Hwangshih are processed into cement and lime.

Nearly all provincial centers are situated along the Yangtze River. They are the Wuhan tri-cities, the iron and steel city of Hwangshih, and the river ports and commercial centers of Shasi and Ichang. A fifth regional center is Siangfan on the middle Han Shui.

Wuhan is the foremost metropolis of central China, dominating the Middle Yangtze plain. This tri-city conurbation consists of Hankow, the largest component, Hanyang and Wuchang. With a 1953 population of 1,500,000, Wuhan is China's seventh largest municipality. Hankow, which accounts for about two-thirds of the total population, is a major manufacturing and commercial center. Its development, which paralleled that of Shanghai, began in 1858 when it was one of the first Chinese inland cities to be opened to foreign trade. The city is situated on the left bank of the Han Shui where it joins the Yangtze. The old Chinese part of town extends along the Han, while former foreign concessions line the Yangtze. These concessions, once held by Germany, Russia, Britain, Japan and France, now constitute the manufacturing and business center of the city. The chief industries are machinery, chemicals, cement and textiles. The city owes much of its development to the Peking-Hankow-Canton railroad, which here crosses the Yangtze by ferry. Plans call for a railroad bridge across the Yangtze, the first throughout the river's middle and lower course. A bridge from Hankow to Hanyang across the Han Shui was completed in 1954. Construction on the bridge across the Yangtze between Hanyang and Wuchang started late in 1955.

Hanyang, situated on the right bank of the Han Shui, has been known in the past as an iron and steel center and arsenal city. Built at the turn of the 20th century, the metallurgical plant was long the chief iron and steel producer in China proper. After early activity, the plant's production lagged in the 1930's and the installation was finally dismantled and shipped to Chungking in the face of the Japanese advance in 1939. The site of the former steel plant is now occupied by a cotton mill. There is also a railroad-tie plant.

Wuchang, the third member of the Wuhan cities, is situated on the right bank of the Yangtze opposite Hanyang and Hankow. With a population of 400,000, it is primarily the administrative and cultural center of the municipality. Here is the seat of the Hupei provincial government, a government mint, and universities. Residential and business sections are situated within the old city wall. Industrial plants and the waterfront are outside the walls. The industries here include cotton, silk and paper mills, railroad repair shops and a shipyard. The oldest of the Wuhan cities, Wuchang has preserved much more of the traditional Chinese character than either Hankow or Hanyang. The Hwangholow, a tower on the bank of the Yangtze, is one of the city's sights. Wuhan university is situated in the suburb of Lokiashan, east of the city.

Hwangshih, on the right bank of the Yangtze, about fifty miles southeast of Wuhan, is a new industrial center. The product of China's industrialization drive, the city was formed in 1950 out of the two riverside towns of Shihhweiyao, former iron-ore loading port, and Hwangshihkang, cement center. (Hwangshih means "yellow stone," the cement rock.) A large iron and steel plant is being built in Hwangshih on the site of two 450-ton blast furnaces dismantled by the Japanese during the Second World War. The new steel plant, intended to rival the Anshan facilities in Manchuria, will be based on the near-by Tayeh iron ore and Pingsiang coking coal. Long limited to the shipping of iron ore, largely to Japan, and the intermittent production of pig iron, Hwangshih is scheduled to become the integrated iron and steel center of central China. Formerly accessible only by way of the Yangtze River, the city has been linked by a rail spur with the Hankow-Canton line. This rail connection will facilitate both the shipping of coking coal from Pingsiang and the marketing of Hwangshih's production. Full-scale operations are not expected to start before the second five-year plan.

West of Wuhan are the Yangtze River ports of Shasi and Ichang. Shasi is a water transportation center on the north bank of the Yangtze. It is linked with Hankow, in addition to the river itself, by a junk route utilizing a maze of waterways and lakes north of the Yangtze River. South of Shasi, the Taiping and Owchih canals link the Yangtze with the Tungting basin of northern Hunan. These excellent water routes have made Shasi a natural agricultural market for the surrounding water-logged region. A city of more than 100,000, it markets chiefly cotton and grain. Shasi has superseded the older Kiangling, situated five miles west, as the local commercial center. South of Shasi, between the Taiping and Owchih canals, is the Kingkiang flood-detention basin, built in 1952-53. Covering an area of 350 square miles, this dike-enclosed reservoir is controlled at its northern end by the flood inlet gate of Taipingkow, on the Yangtze, west of Shasi. The Kingkiang basin is named for the King Kiang, a local name for the Yangtze River in the section north of Tungting Lake.

Ichang is noteworthy as the head of navigation on the middle and lower Yangtze River. It is situated at the eastern end of the Yangtze gorges leading to Szechwan, where navigation is restricted to 500-ton vessels. The city has a population of 100,000 and ships tung oil, sesame, and grain.

Siangfan, the agricultural and commercial center of the Han Shui valley, is another twin city with a combined population of 100,000. It consists of the north-bank town of Fancheng (seat of the combined municipality) and the south-bank town of Siangyang. Siangfan, in addition to handling the trade of northwestern Hupei, is also the natural outlet for the Nanyang basin of Honan.

HUNAN PROVINCE

Capital: Changsha; area: 79,000; population: 33,226,954

The province of Hunan coincides approximately with the drainage basin of Tungting Lake. The lake, situated in the northern part of Hunan, fluctuates in volume between the high-water stage in the summer and the low-water stage during the winter. Moreover, silting has somewhat reduced the lake's area in recent years. At comparable seasons of the year, the lake had an area of 1,800 in 1937 and an area of 1,450 in 1946. The lake is linked with the Yangtze River in the northeast at the town of Yoyang. In addition, the western part of the lake is joined to the Yangtze by a number of channels, including the Taiping and Owchih canals.

The lake receives the four main rivers of Hunan. They are the Siang Kiang, the Tze Shui, the Yüan Kiang and the Li Shui. Each of these rivers is navigable for junks, the Siang taking the largest vessels, and each river is associated in its lower reaches with a major trade center. These lower river cities are Changsha, the provincial capital, on the Siang, Yiyang on the Tze, Changteh on the Yüan and Tsingshih on the Li.

Topographically, the province consists of the alluvial basin of Tungting Lake and the valleys of its tributary rivers. These lowlands are enclosed on the west, south and east by hills of reddish sandstone, rising rarely to more than 3,000 feet. Level land is restricted to the alluvial lowlands. Terracing is widespread on the hillsides.

Hunan is almost entirely in the rice-tea agricultural area of China. Rice is the universal summer crop wherever the land can be irrigated. The Tungting basin and the lower Siang valley are one of China's "rice bowls," with the trade center at Changsha. In 1951, Hunan produced 7,500,000 tons of rice, or nearly 15 per cent of China's total.

Tea is the principal upland crop. In 1955, Hunan produced 18,750 tons of tea, or nearly 17 per cent of the nation's total. The tea is grown in the hill ranges separating the major stream valleys. The best known variety is the Anhwa, which is produced in the Tze Shui valley and shipped via Hankow.

Cotton is cultivated chiefly west of Tungting Lake, near Changteh and Tsingshih. Cotton production in 1951 was 5 per cent of the national total. Rice acreage in the lowlands is usually planted in wheat, barley or rapeseed during the winter. Hillside crops, in addition to tea, are corn, soybeans and sweet potatoes. As part of its effort to increase food production, the Peking regime is encouraging the expansion of sweet potatoes, a high-yield crop, on higher ground. The 1955 area and planned output in Hunan were 400,000 hectares and 3,500,000 tons.

Distinctive provincial crops, other than tea, are ramie and tung oil. Ramie is grown chiefly in the vicinity of Liuyang and Liling on the east side of the Siang valley. Tung oil is produced chiefly in the western hills of the province. One of the best known grades of tung oil originates in the area of Hungkiang in the valley of the Yüan Kiang. The so-called Hung oil is shipped down the Yüan to Changteh and from there to Hankow for further distribution.

Fir, pine and bamboo stands in the uplands of Hunan yield lumber that is floated down the Yüan Kiang to Changteh and the Siang Kiang to Changsha. From these two cities, the lumber is rafted to Wuhan for milling.

Hunan is a conspicuously rich mineral province, in particular in nonferrous metals. The province leads China in the production of antimony and mercury. Lead and zinc, tungsten, tin, manganese, gold, molybdenum and sulfur are also produced.

The two largest antimony centers of China are Sikwangshan, northeast of Sinhwa, and Panki, southwest of Yiyang, both in the Tze Shui basin. Sikwangshan, the more important of the two producers, has been set up as a special industrial and mining ch'ü. It produces about 13,000 tons of antimony metal a year, or 70 per cent of China's output. The Panki mine and near-by Kiangkiachung produce more than 1,000 tons of metal. Hunan as a whole produces about 90 per cent of China's antimony. The concentrate from Sikwangshan is smelted at Changsha.

Hunan's tungsten mines in the southern part of the province are second only to those in Kiangsi. The tungsten is sometimes associated with tin, molybdenum and bismuth. Hunan produces about 10 per cent of China's tungsten.

In the tungsten area, coal mines are served by spurs of the Hankow-Canton railroad close to the Kwangtung border. These coal mines are Tzehing, on a spur from Sükiatung; Yangmeishan, on a spur from Paishihtu; and Kowyatung, on a spur from Pingshek (Kwangtung). Tungsten mines, thus far not connected to the railroad, are Yaokangsien, twenty miles south of Tzehing, and Sianghwaling, north of Linwu.

China's chief lead-zinc mine outside of Manchuria is Shuikowshan, thirty miles south of Hengyang. This center, insignificant by world standards, also produces silver as part of the mixed ores. The mine and concentrating mill is linked by a short railroad with Sungpai, where a zinc smelter is situated. Lead concentrates are shipped down the Siang Kiang to a smelter at Changsha.

Manganese is mined at Shaoshanchung, twenty miles west of Siangtan. In the past, Hunan has accounted for about 90 per cent of China's manganese production.

Hunan's mercury deposits are a continuation of the Kweichow field. The mercury mine is on the Kweichow border at Howtzeping, northwest of Fenghwang. This district accounts for about two-thirds of China's mercury output.

The province is also one of China's leading gold producers, with mining centers found both in the western uplands near Taoyüan and Yüanling and in the eastern uplands near Pingkiang. During the Second World War, Hunan produced as much as 1,200 kilograms a year. Silver production as a by-product of the Shuikowshan mixed ores has reached 40,000 kilograms a year. Another by-product at Shuikowshan is sulphur, which is obtained from the lead and zinc sulphides mined there.

The main provincial centers have arisen along the main north-south railroad, crossing Hunan between Canton and Hankow, and along the main navigable rivers. The cities along the railroad are at the same time ports on the Siang Kiang. They are Changsha, Siangtan, Chuchow and Hengyang.

Changsha, the provincial capital, had a 1953 population of more than 500,000. It is a major port on the Siang Kiang, accessible to 500-ton vessels. Situated in the heart of Hunan's "rice bowl," Changsha is one of China's leading rice-marketing centers. It also exports tea, lumber, ramie and nonferrous metals. Antimony, lead and silver are processed here. The city is noted for its handicrafts, including embroidery and porcelain. Changsha ("long sand") is named for the elongated sandy island of Shuiluchow in the Siang Kiang. Changsha was known as an ancient literary and educational center on the north-south water route of the Siang Kiang. On the left bank of the river opposite the city stands the hill of Yolushan, bearing ruins of an ancient Chinese college.

South of Changsha lies Siangtan, Hunan's second largest city. Siangtan was formerly noted as a regional trade center, shipping rice, tea, tung oil, cloth and paper. Since 1949, it has become an important industrial center, producing electrical goods, wire, machine tools, cement, and chemicals (ammonium sulphate fertilizer). The city also has a cotton mill. In connection with this industrial expansion, the population of Siangtan has risen from 80,000 in 1949 to 160,000 in 1953. Just south of Siangtan is Isuho, a local rice trade center.

Chuchow, east of Siangtan, is a rail center on the Hankow-Canton railroad. It is the junction for the Chekiang-Kiangsi railroad, going east to Nanchang and Hangchow. It is also the contemplated junction for the planned Hunan-Kweichow line, westward past Siangtan, Sinhwa, Chihkiang to Kweiyang. The construction of the Hunan-Kweichow railroad was started during the Second World War by the Japanese, but the completed section was destroyed subsequently. The initial spur from Chuchow to Siangtan, including the Siang Kiang bridge, was rebuilt in 1953. Chuchow has locomotive and car repair shops. A coal-washing plant processes coal from Pingsiang and Tzehing.

The southernmost of the cities along the railroad leading to Canton is Hengyang. This is the head of navigation of the Siang Kiang for large motorized junks. Above Hengyang only smaller junks can ascend the upper Siang Kiang and the Lei Shui, at whose mouth Hengyang is situated. The city is also a key rail hub, where the Hunan-Kwangsi line takes off toward the southwest. Several major roads meet at Hengyang, which was formerly called Hengchow.

Five of Hunan's regional centers are situated off the Siang Kiang and the Canton-Hankow railroad. They are Shaoyang, Yiyang, Hungkiang, Changteh, and Tsingshih.

Shaoyang is the trade center of the upper Tze Shui valley. It is situated at the point where a major highway from Hengyang crosses the stream. The city is noted for its bamboo. From Shaoyang, the Tze Shui drops rapidly toward the rivermouth city of Yiyang. The Siaoki and Tungping rapids along the stream are regarded as potential sources of hydroelectric power.

Hungkiang and Changteh are the trade centers of the upper and lower Yüan Kiang valley, respectively. Hungkiang is noted chiefly for its tung oil and lumber trade. Changteh is the processing center for products shipped down the Yüan Kiang, as well as for the agricultural output of the western Tungting basin. The city has a population of more than 50,000.

Finally, Tsingshih handles the trade of the Li Shui basin in northwestern Hunan. A city of about 50,000, it is linked by canals with the Yangtze port of Shasi.

Hunan is the only province of the Middle Yangtze plain region with non-Chinese minority groups. These include the Miao, Yao and Tung, all members of the Miao-Yao ethnic group, as well as Chinese Moslems.

The West Hunan Miao Autonomous Chou takes in the uplands of northwestern Hunan. It has a population of 1,500,000, of whom about 20 per cent are of the Miao nationality. Set up in August, 1952, the area produces timber, tung oil, and gallnuts used for tanning. It contains small coal and iron mines, as well as the mercury deposits near Fenghwang. Transportation with the rest of Hunan is maintained by junk traffic along the Li Shui and the Yüan Kiang, as well as a highway from Changteh, completed in 1954. The area's administrative center was established in a small Miao village called Soli, just north of the Chinese town of Kiencheng, a hsien seat. In connection with the establishment of the autonomous government, the administrative institutions of Kiencheng were transferred to Soli village and Soli was renamed Kishow, which means "auspicious beginning."

The Tungtao Tung Autonomous Hsien was established in southwestern Hunan in May, 1954. Situated on the Kweichow and Kwangsi borders, it adjoins the Sankiang Tung Autonomous Hsien of northern Kwangsi.

Tungtao hsien has a population of 80,000, of whom 50,000 are of the Tung nationality.

The Kianghwa Yao Autonomous Hsien was set up in southwest Hunan in November, 1955. Its population of 108,000 includes 39,000 of the Yao group.

KIANGSI PROVINCE

Capital: Nanchang; area: 67,000; population: 16,772,865

Topographically, Kiangsi is very similar to Hunan. Like its western neighbor, Kiangsi consists of a central lowland, dominated by the Poyang Lake basin in the north and by the Kan Kiang valley in the south, enclosed by uplands on the west, south and east. Only in the north does the province open directly on the Yangtze valley proper.

Poyang Lake, which like Tungting Lake is a natural flood reservoir for the Yangtze River, has an area of about 1,000 square miles. Like Tungting Lake, Poyang has a high-water stage in the summer, when its depth reaches sixty to seventy feet. In the winter, the lake becomes quite shallow. It is connected with the Yangtze by a narrow arm that joins the stream at Hukow, east of Kiukiang. Again, like Tungting Lake, Poyang receives one major river, the Kan Kiang, and several minor ones. These are the Siu Shui, which enters Lake Poyang from the west, and the Sin Kiang and the combined Po Kiang and Chang Kiang, which enter the lake from the east.

The Kan Kiang traverses the province from south to north and serves as its major navigable waterway. Small junks can travel as far as Kanchow, and even beyond that city up the two headstreams. Larger junks are prevented by rapids from going beyond Kian.

Most of Kiangsi falls in the conventional rice-tea area. The extreme south, adjoining Kwangtung, is part of the double-cropping rice area. The richest rice-growing region is the Poyang basin, with its trade center at Kiukiang. Tea is the hillside crop, with the best Kiangsi varieties originating in the Siu Shui basin on the southern slopes of the Mufow Mountains. It will be recalled that the high-grade Puchi tea of Hupei is produced on the northern slopes of the same hill range. Like rice, tea is marketed and processed at Kiukiang.

Cotton is a secondary crop, restricted largely to the northeast shore of Poyang Lake near Tuchang and to the Siu Shui basin. Cotton is is marketed and processed at Kiukiang.

Another fiber widely grown throughout Kiangsi is ramie. Production centers are at Wantsai, whose fiber is widely known throughout China, and Ichun in western Kiangsi, and at Ihwang and Fuchow in eastern Kiangsi.

In southernmost Kiangsi, where the long growing season permits the cultivation of two crops of rice, subtropical crops include sugar cane, tobacco, and tangerines. The surrounding uplands yield bamboo and other woods. These are floated down the Kan Kiang and its tributaries to mills at Nanchang.

Coal and tungsten dominate the province's mineral resources The principal coal center is Pingsiang, situated near the Hunan border on the north slopes of the Wukung Mountains. Pingsiang, the largest coal producer south of the Yangtze, produces a good coking coal. It has shared the fortunes of the iron and steel centers in the Wuhan area, flourishing until the 1920's and virtually closing down thereafter. In the absence of a coking coal market, Pingsiang has also supplied fuel to the railroads of south China. Future expansion of Pingsiang is envisaged with the development of a major iron and steel center at Hwangshih on the Yangtze. The coal mines proper are at Anyüan, on a rail spur southeast from Pingsiang, and at Kaokeng, on a rail spur from Chüankiang east of Pingsiang.

China's leading tungsten producer is Sihwashan in southernmost Kiangsi. Sihwashan is situated just northwest of Tayü, which was formerly called Nanan. Tungsten is also mined near Anyüan and Lungnan in the extreme south of the province. The tungsten, which occurs in loose detrital deposits on hill slopes, is commonly in association with tin and bismuth, as well as molybdenum.

Other minerals include manganese, found in the Loping area, and kaolin, named for Kao Ling (high hill), a height near the noted porcelain center of Kingtehchen.

The regional centers are situated either along the Kan Kiang in southern Kiangsi or along the two railroad lines in northern Kiangsi. The east-west railroad was completed by 1935 from Chekiang province to Nanchang. At that time, Pingsiang was also connected with the Hankow-Canton railroad at Chuchow. The gap between Nanchang and Pingsiang was closed in 1937. The north-south railroad connects Nanchang with the Yangtze at Kiukiang. Long-range plans call for the continuation of this line southward along the Kan Kiang into Kwangtung. In 1955, construction was begun on the Yingtan-Amoy railroad, which serves part of eastern Kiangsi before entering Fukien.

Nanchang, the provincial capital has a population of more than 200,000. It is situated on the right bank of the Kan Kiang, at the head of the river's delta on Poyang Lake. The railroad termini of the Kiukiang and Chekiang-Kiangsi lines are on opposite banks of the river. Near the right-bank railhead a new industrial district has sprung up, with factories producing oils and fats, paper, textiles, machinery, chemicals and farm implements.

Kiukiang, Kiangsi's port on the Yangtze River, is the principal outlet for the province's products: rice, tea, tobacco, cotton, and ramie cloth. Like many Chinese cities caught in the tempo of modern commercial life, Kiukiang consists of the old town in the east and a commercial waterfront section at the head of the railroad from Nanchang. South of Kiukiang is the popular hill resort of Kuling in the Lu Shan.

In northeastern Kiangsi are the cities of Kingtehchen and Shangjao. Kingtehchen, a 110,000-population city on the south bank of the Chang Kiang, is the world-famous porcelain center of China. It was based originally on the kaolin resources of Kao Ling, a hill to the east of the city, for which the white clay was named. The original deposit has been largely exhausted through the centuries of porcelain making and Kingtehchen now obtains its clay from Kimen in southern Anhwei. Shangjao is the regional agricultural center of northeastern Kiangsi, on the railroad leading to Chekiang.

Fuchow is an agricultural center south of Poyang Lake. An important road hub, it was raised to the status of provincial city in 1954. Previously it was called Linchwan.

Southward, along the Kan Kiang, are the cities of Kian and Kanchow. Both are road and water transportation centers along the main Kwangtung-Kiangsi route. Kian serves as the regional center of south central Kiangsi and Kanchow for the southern subtropical section of the province. Kanchow handles shipments of lumber, tungsten, sugar and tobacco. It is the seat of the special administrative ch'ü of South Kiangsi.

Chapter 7

THE SOUTHEAST COASTAL UPLANDS

The Southeast uplands include the coastal provinces of Chekiang and Anhwei. The combined area of the two provinces is about 85,000 square miles and their population 36,000,000. This amounts to more than 2 per cent of China's total area and 6 per cent of the nation's population, respectively. The average density of the Southeast uplands is 400 persons per square mile.

In contrast to the predominantly low-lying regions considered thus far, the Southeast uplands, with the exception of a few coastal delta plains, have a rugged topography. Resistant rocks, such as granite, porphyry and other hard formations, have withstood erosion over the years. In general, there is a distinct structural alignment from northeast to southwest. This trend parallels the coast and reflects the axis of the ancient rock folds of which today's ranges are the remnants.

Along the Chekiang-Anhwei border, the Tienmu Mountains rise to more than 5,000 feet in the highest points of Chekiang. These rugged border ranges are separated by the Tsientang River valley from a series of parallel coastal ranges. Near Linhai, the Kwotsang Mountains rise to more than 4,500 feet. The mountain ranges enclose a number of inland basins, such as those of Chühsien-Kinhwa, Chuki, and Chenghsien, and coastal plains, including those of Ningpo-Shaohing.

The southern part of the Southeast uplands includes two basic mountain ranges, trending NE-SW. They are the Wuyi Mountains along the Fukien-Kiangsi border, rising to 3,500 feet, and the Taiyün Mountains, nearer the coast. The principal plains along this part of the coast are those of Foochow, Chüanchow, and Changchow.

The rocky and intricately embayed coast line reflects the rugged inland topography. This is a coast of subsidence with drowned valleys and offshore islands ranging in size from several miles to mere rocks. The coast offers many excellent natural harbors, but these have poor connections with the hinterland and have never developed into major commercial ports. They do play a useful role in coastwise trade.

One of the most interesting coastal features is the large funnel-shaped Hangchow Bay, at the extreme north of the region being considered here. The bay, which narrows from about sixty miles at its mouth to less than two miles near Hangchow, is famous for its tidal bore. The abrupt tidal front, caused by the rapid narrowing and shallowness of the channel, may reach six to ten feet in height.

Outstanding coastal indentations south of Hangchow Bay are Siangshan Bay, which penetrates thirty miles inland; intricate Sanmen Bay, noted for fisheries and salines; Sansha Bay, virtually enclosed by two peninsulas; and Amoy Bay, with the island of Quemoy. The most extensive island group is the Chushan Archipelago off Hangchow Bay.

The region is characterized by a typical trellis drainage pattern, in which the main streams have cut narrow valleys perpendicular to the trend of the mountain ranges and tributaries follow the broad valleys between parallel ranges. The rivers divide the region into distinct economic subareas, each dominated by its river-mouth city. From north to south these cities are Hangchow at the mouth of the Tsientang River, Ningpo at the mouth of the Yung Kiang, Linhai at the mouth of the Lin Kiang, Wenchow at the mouth of the Wu Kiang, Foochow at the mouth of the Min Kiang, Chüanchow at the mouth of the Tsin Kiang, and Amoy at the mouth of the combined Kiulung River and Lung Kiang.

The Southeast uplands have a hot and wet subtropical climate with some of the heaviest rainfall in China. The average rainfall is 60 inches along the coast and up to 80 inches in the inland mountains. The July temperature is uniformly high, averaging about 85° F (29° C). The January temperatures, however, vary with latitude, being lowest in the north—about 40° F (5° C)—and highest in the south—about 60° F (15° C). In view of the mountain barrier against the Polar Continental air in the winter, cold air penetrates rarely into the region and snow is all but unknown. The coast is especially exposed to typhoons, which occur most commonly in August and September. They are rare from January to April. As much as 4 to 8 inches of rain may fall in a single day.

Because of the predominantly mountainous relief, agriculture is restricted to narrow plains along the coast, river valleys and inland basins. The principal areas are Ningpo-Shaohing, Wenchow, Kinhwa-Chühsien, Foochow, and Changchow. Terracing is practiced in the mountains wherever soil and climate conditions permit tilling.

In terms of distinct crop associations, most of the region falls in the rice-tea area, except the extreme south where double cropping of rice is possible. Irrigated rice takes about 60 per cent of the sown area. The first crop is usually sown in April and harvested in June. The second crop is sown either after the first harvest where the growing season is longest or between the rows of the first crop in June. In the second case the new crop is harvested in October.

Chief among other food crops are sweet potatoes. Wheat, corn, and millets are cultivated on a small scale in the uplands. In view of the fact that rice can be grown only in plains and river valleys constituting only 5 per cent of the total area, sweet potatoes are a major local subsistence crop.

The warm, humid climate has made the Southeast uplands China's main tea producer. Tea is grown especially in the Wuyi Mountains for export through Foochow. Well-known grades are also cultivated in Chekiang. Hangchow, Wenchow and Foochow are all major tea-trade centers. Other characteristic agricultural products are subtropical fruit, sugar cane and tobacco.

The Southeast uplands are favorably situated for the development of a forest industry. The extensive uplands are unusable for agriculture and are covered with luxuriant tree growth. Three main potential lumbering centers are: The Tienmu Mountains and Tsientang valley with outlet through Hangchow, the Wu Kiang valley with outlet through Wenchow, and the Min Kiang and Tsin Kiang valleys with outlets at Foochow and Amoy. In addition to construction timber, largely fir and pine, the region also produces camphor, tung oil and lacquer.

Fishing is the most distinctive activity along the coast. The coastal margins are overcrowded with a population that cannot obtain its livelihood from the restricted agriculture. The surplus manpower together with the rocky indented character of the shore line, the abundance of islands and coves have given the region a major place in China's fishing industry.

The Southeast uplands are generally poor in mineral resources. Coal is mined in small amounts near Changhing in Chekiang and marketed chiefly in the Shanghai area. Fukien is said to have very large iron ore reserves, but these have not been exploited. Alum is mined at Fan Shan on the Chekiang-Fukien border near the sea and fluorite is found at Wuyi in Chekiang. Lithographic stone and kaolin are also mined. In connection with the fishing industry, a large salt industry has developed along the coast, notably in the Antung salt district on the south shore of Hangchow Bay.

Except for the Chekiang-Kiangsi railroad, which traverses the inland basins of northwest Chekiang, and the Yingtan-Amoy line, the Southeast uplands are devoid of rail lines. The Hangchow-Ningpo railroad, completed in 1937, was destroyed during the Second World War and was rebuilt in 1955. A major share of transportation thus falls on the waterways, and especially the coastwise routes. Ningpo, Wenchow, Foochow and Amoy are the main maritime ports. Although it is situated on the sea, Hangchow is not accessible to ocean-going vessels because of silting. It is used only by river and canal junks. Since 1949, maritime trade along the southeast coast has greatly suffered from hostilities between mainland China and Formosa. Foochow and Amoy, in particular, have been virtually interdicted by Formosa garrisons on the islands of Matsu off Foochow and Quemoy in Amoy Bay. The principal inland waterways are the Tsientang River, the Wu Kiang, and the Min Kiang. Northernmost Chekiang is served by the southern end of the Grand Canal system.

As might be expected, the greatest population density of more than 800 persons per square mile is found in the coastal agricultural lowlands. Inland river valleys have densities of about 300 to 400, and the upland areas 100 to 150. Although the region is virtually homogeneously Chinese from the ethnic viewpoint, it represents extraordinary linguistic diversity. The rugged relief and poor communications between valleys have resulted in a large number of local dialects. For example, Ningpo, Wenchow, Foochow, Chüanchow, and Amoy dominate linguistic subareas of their own. Language maps of China generalize the complex situation by grouping the Chekiang dialects under the Wu (Shanghai) speech, the northern Fukien dialects under the Min (Foochow) speech, and the southern Fukien dialects under the Amoy-Swatow speech.

Except for Kwangtung, Fukien has produced most of the Chinese overseas emigration. The ports of Ningpo, Wenchow, Chüanchow and Changchow were early centers of China's foreign trade. Starting in the late Ming dynasty and early Manchu dynasty (17th century), Chinese began to emigrate through these ports to seek their fortunes abroad—and to find them.

Two thousand years ago, most of the Southeast uplands were occupied by aborigene tribes. As a result of the Chinese southward advance, these peoples were driven into the mountains. Today most of their descendants have been assimilated. Only two small groups, neither of which has its own autonomous area, have retained distinguishing ethnic characteristics. They are the Tan people, who are largely boatmen along the lower Min Kiang, and the Yü people, a branch of the Yao, settled in the uplands of the upper Wu Kiang.

CHEKIANG PROVINCE

Capital:Hangchow; area: 39,000; population: 22,865,747

Northernmost Chekiang, north of Hangchow, is a continuation of the densely populated, intensively cultivated Lower Yangtze plain. The rest of the province is more typical of the Southeast uplands, with rugged mountain ranges enclosing coastal plains and inland basins.

Rice is cultivated throughout the province wherever water is available for irrigation and clay pans develop on the alluvial soils of flood plains and deltas. In the Lower Yangtze plain section of Chekiang, rice is associated with winter wheat and with silk and cotton. Cotton is also cultivated on the south shore of Hangchow Bay, chiefly around Yüyao, from where it is shipped to Shanghai and Ningpo. Mulberry for silkworms is also grown along the middle valley of the Tsientang River and along the Tsaongo River, which enters Hangchow Bay from the south. The towns of Tunglu, Siaoshan, and Shaohing are known for their silk production. Jute is an important bast fiber. Chekiang produces about half of China's jute.

Tea is a major crop in the uplands, where it is usually grown on hillside terraces. Several well-known leaf types are produced in Chekiang. They are the Lungtsing leaf, produced southwest of Hangchow, the Pingshui leaf, produced near Shaohing, and the Wenchow leaf, produced in the Wu Kiang valley. The province is a major green-tea producer, but has increasingly shifted to black tea, an export variety. Provincial tea output in 1954 was 20,000 tons, having risen from 13,000 tons in 1950.

Fruits make up an important part of the province's exports. Peaches, plums, and loquats are grown in the Ningpo-Fenghwa area. In the southern part of the province, near-subtropical conditions make possible the production of citrus fruit, with centers in Tientai, Linhai, and Wenchow. Hwangyen, southeast of Linhai, is nationally known for its oranges.

Lumbering and fishing are major nonfarm occupations. Most of the lumber originates in the basins of the Tsientang River and the Wu Kiang and is exported via Hangchow and Wenchow. Tung oil is produced in the Tsientang valley and processed at Kienteh. The fishing industry is best developed in the Chushan Archipelago; other fishery areas are Sanmen Bay and the area around Yühwan Island. Chekiang has about 300,000 fishermen, many of whom are based at Tinghai, chief town of the Chushans. Other major fishing centers, not only of Chekiang but all China, are Puto (Shenkiamen), also in the Chushans, and Ningpo, on the mainland. Chekiang's 1955 fish catch was 386,000 tons.

Chekiang's mineral resources are limited. Coal is mined northwest of Changhing, at the Kiangsu-Anhwei line. The mines are at Hoki and Tienyang, both of which are situated on a railroad spur leading northwest from Changhing. Other coal deposits, as yet unexploited, are found near Kienteh in association with iron ore. An important mineral site is the alum deposit of Fan Shan, set up in 1954 as the Mingfan mining ch'ü. It is situated where the Chekiang-Fukien line meets the sea south of Pingyang. It accounts for 70 per cent of China's alum output. Chekiang also has a major fluorite deposit at Wuyi, whose output was exported to Japan via Kinhwa prior to the Second World War. Tsingtien, on the Wu Kiang upstream from Wenchow, produces a high-grade lithographic stone. Finally, Chekiang has a large salt production, concentrated on the south shore of Hangchow Bay. The special Antung salt-producing ch'ü has been set up there.

Chekiang's regional centers are situated in the coastal plains and inland basins. They are served either by rivers navigable for large junks or by the Shanghai-Hangchow-Nanchang railroad, which traverses the northwestern half of the province. The chief navigable rivers are the Tsientang River, the Yung Kiang, the Lin Kiang, and the Wu Kiang. The Tsientang River is navigable from Hangchow to Tunglu and at high water as far as Lanchi. From Kienteh, small junks can make their way up the Hwei Kiang as far as the Tunki area of southern Anhwei. This is the natural access route to the southern part of that Yangtze valley province.

The Yung Kiang is navigable for ocean-going vessels between Ningpo and Chinhai, its outer port. A navigable canal that can be regarded as an extension of the Grand Canal runs from Ningpo to Hangchow, paralleling the south shore of Hangchow Bay and serving the Ningpo-Shaohing agricultural lowland.

The Lin Kiang is navigable only for junks between Linhai and its outer port of Haimen. Haimen is a key harbor along Chekiang's coastwise shipping routes. Finally the Wu Kiang, a major timber-floating route in its upper reaches, is navigable for junks from Wenchow past Tsingtien to Lishui.

Hangchow, the provincial capital, was known as Linan under the Southern Sung dynasty (1127-1280), when it was the capital of southern China. The city, which has a 1953 population of about 700,000, is situated on the north bank of the Tsientang River at the head of Hangchow Bay. Although the city is situated on the coast, it has virtually no coastwise trade. Its port functions are restricted to navigation on the lower Tsientang River and the Grand Canal, which here reaches its southern terminus. Neither the Grand Canal nor the canal's extension to Ningpo are connected with the Tsientang, whose high tides would flood the canals. Hangchow, in a charming natural setting on the east shore of West Lake and at the foot of wooded hills, attracts tourists and vacationists. Modern commerical and industrial activities are centered in the northern suburb of Kungchenkiao, situated on both sides of the Grand Canal. Since 1953, Kungchenkiao has been the seat of Hangchow hsien. Hangchow's industry and trade are largely devoted to silk and silk cloth, as well as the processing of tea and jute.

North of Hangchow, in the Lower Yangtze plain section of Chekiang, are the agricultural centers of Huchow and Kashing. Huchow, formerly called Wuhing, is situated south of the lake Tai Hu. A city of 63,000, it is served by a branch of the Grand Canal and by the Hangchow-Nanking highway. Its chief products are silk and rice. Halfway between Hangchow and Huchow is the noted hill resort of Mokanshan, situated on a spur of the Tienmu Mountains. Kashing, another major silk and rice center of northern Chekiang, is situated at the junction of the Grand Canal, the Whangpoo River and the Hangchow-Shanghai railroad. Kashing has a population of 78,000 (1953).

Kinhwa, a rail town with a population of more than 100,000, is the regional center of central Chekiang. It is situated in the Kinhwa-Chü-hsien basin, one of the province's rice-producing areas. Kinhwa, which owes its regional importance to the Chekiang-Kiangsi railroad, supplanted the old waterway hub of Lanchi on the Tsientang River. A rail spur now connects Kinhwa and Lanchi. Another rail spur, linking Kinhwa with Wuyi, the fluorite center, has not been restored since the Second World War.

Three other regional centers are situated along the Chekiang coast. They are Shaohing, Ningpo and Wenchow. Shaohing is an agricultural center in the Shaohing-Ningpo lowland on the south shore of Hangchow Bay. It is served by the canal from Sihing (opposite Hangchow) to Ningpo. Shaohing, which has a population of 130,000, is noted for its rice wine.

Ningpo, a city of 240,000, is one of China's principal fishing ports. Situated on the Yung Kiang, it can be reached by ocean-going vessels from its outer harbor of Chinhai. Ningpo has been one of China's foreign trade centers since the Tang dynasty (618-907) and was one of the original treaty ports opened in 1842. Its exports include cotton, tea, and fish products. The city is connected by rail with Hangchow.

Wenchow, with a population of 200,000, is the trade center of southern Chekiang. It is situated on the south bank of the Wu Kiang. Export products include tea, timber, tobacco, and citrus fruit.

FUKIEN PROVINCE

Capital: Foochow; area: 46,000; population: 13,142,721.

Fukien has no extensive lowlands comparable to the coastal plains of northern Chekiang. The southern province is essentially an upland region typical of the southeast coast. The uplands gradually descend in a series of parallel NE-SW ranges toward the sea. The main streams, cutting perpendicularly through the hill ranges, form small delta plains at their mouths. The principal coastal plains of Fukien are the lowlands around Foochow, Chüanchow, and Changchow and Amoy.

Rice is by far the principal food grain in Fukien, with double-cropping common in the south. Sweet potatoes are a major staple food in non-rice-growing areas. Total food crop production in Fukien rose from 2,850,000 tons in 1949 to 3,850,000 tons in 1953. An output of 4,100,000 tons was planned for 1955.

Tea is a hillside crop in the Min Kiang basin of northern Fukien. The province is noted for the bohea leaf, named for the Bohea Hills, a Western corruption of the name of the Wuyi Mountains. Bohea tea is exported through Foochow. Fukien's tea acreage expanded from 17,000 hectares in 1949 to 29,000 in 1954 and its output from 2,500 tons in 1949 to 4,800 tons in 1954.

Like Chekiang, Fukien is a major fruit producer. Its subtropical fruit includes citrus grown around Foochow, the longans of Putien, the pomelos of Changchow, and bananas south of the Tsin Kiang. Orange production rose from 9,000 tons in 1948 to 29,500 tons in 1954.

Sugar cane is a characteristic crop of southern Fukien, particularly in the Chüanchow and Changchow areas. In 1954, Fukien produced 800,000 tons of cane. Another distinctive crop is tobacco, which is produced in the Engteng area. Engteng is situated in the upper reaches of the Han Kiang, here known as the Ting Kiang. The tobacco, which provides the livelihood for virtually the entire hsien of Engteng, is shipped to Swatow in Kwangtung.

Lumbering and fishing play a major role in the provincial economy. Timber is floated down the Min Kiang and its tributaries for milling at Foochow. Other river basins, such as the Tsin Kiang and the Kiulung River, are also rich in forest resources. Camphor and lacquer are distinctive forestry products. The coastal fisheries of Fukien are concentrated around Santuao in Sansha Bay, off the mouth of the Min Kiang, at Pingtan Island, and in the bays of Hinghwa, Chüanchow and Amoy. About 170,000 tons of fish were caught in 1953 compared with about 70,000 tons in 1949.

Fukien's mineral resources are largely unexploited. Coal is found near Shaowu, Kienow and Lungyen. The province is said to have very extensive iron ore reserves near Anki, Tehwa and Hwaan, but these are not being exploited. Tehwa also has kaolin deposits that have given rise to a small porcelain industry. Salines are common along the coast.

In July, 1955, it was announced in Peking that the Army's railway corps had completed construction of the Litang-Tsamkong railroad in the Kwangsi-Kwangtung border region. The next assignment of the corps was to be the construction of the Yingtan-Amoy line, connecting the main port of Fukien with Yingtan, a station on the Hangchow-Nanchang railroad in Kiangsi Province. Work on the line, the first rail transportation link of Fukien, began in the summer of 1955. The 1956 construction plan calls for completion of the line as far as Yungan. The Amoy terminus is to be reached in 1957. In addition to providing a much-needed transportation route for the economy of southern Fukien, the railroad is evidently designed to supply Chinese armed forces stationed along the Fukien coast opposite Formosa.

Fukien had no railroads prior to the construction of the Yingtan-Amoy line and transportation is largely restricted to roads, waterways and coastal shipping. The Min Kiang is by far the most important inland navigation route. Large junks can ascend the river as far as Nanping, a lumbering center with a population of 50,000. At Nanping, three headstreams join to form the Min Kiang proper.

Fukien's regional centers are all situated along the coast. They are, from north to south, Foochow, Chüanchow, Amoy and Changchow.

Foochow, the provincial capital, has a 1953 population of 553,000. The walled city is about two miles from the north bank of the lower Min Kiang. Its commercial riverside suburb is linked by the Wanshow ("ten thousand ages") and Kiangnan bridges with Nantai, former foreign settlement and business center located on a large island in the Min Kiang. Ocean-going vessels must anchor at the Pagoda, nine miles downstream. Near-by Mamoi is a former Chinese naval base and shipbuilding center. Foochow is the natural outlet of the Min Kiang basin and exports tea, timber, leather and lacquerware. It was Foochow lacquerware that, together with porcelain and silk, became identified with the traditional Chinese export trade.

Chüanchow, formerly also called Tsinkiang, was one of China's leading ports during the Sung and Yüan (Mongol) dynasties (11th to 13th centuries). It lost its importance in connection with the silting of its port on the Tsin Kiang and the rise of Foochow and Amoy. However, Chüanchow is still the natural outlet for the Tsin

Kiang basin. It has a population of more than 100,000. Its industry includes sugar refining (on the basis of local sugar cane), oilseed milling, and gunny bag manufacture. Chüanchow is noted for its large overseas Chinese population.

Amoy is Fukien's second largest city, with a population of 150,000. It is situated in Amoy Bay on the southwest shore of Amoy Island, which is 10 miles across. West of the city, beyond the inner harbor, is the island of Kulangsu, a former foreign settlement and residential section. Both Amoy and Foochow are among the original treaty ports opened to foreign trade in 1842. Amoy has an excellent natural harbor, whose growth was limited by the lack of hinterland transportation until construction of the Yingtan-Amoy railroad. Amoy exports the products of the Lung Kiang and Kiulung River, including sugar, tobacco and bamboo paper. Like Chüanchow, Amoy has yielded a large part of the Chinese overseas emigration.

Changchow, formerly also called Lungki, is located on the north bank of the Lung Kiang. It was the former commercial center of the Lung Kiang and Kiulung River basins, but has been supplanted by Amoy. It is known for its satin and sugar production. Because of shallowness of the Lung Kiang, most vessels must anchor at the outer port of Shihma, nine miles downstream from Changchow.

CAPTER 8

THE KWANGTUNG-KWANGSI HILLS

As the name implies, the region contains the two southern provinces of Kwangtung and Kwangsi on the South China Sea. They have a combined area of 168,000 square miles, which is more than 4 per cent of China's total area, and a population of 54,000,000, or about 10 per cent of the nation. The average population density is 320 persons per square mile. The two provinces are sometimes called Liangkwang ("the two Kwangs") or Lingnan ("south of the mountains"), a reference to the mountain area along the northern boundary of the provinces. The region includes the island of Hainan, administratively part of Kwangtung Province.

The northern mountain border plays a key role in shaping the physical geography of the region. The mountains, collectively known as the Nan Ling or Nan Shan ("southern mountains"), trend generally east-west and form a watershed between the tributaries of the Yangtze and the rivers flowing to the South China Sea. At the same time, the mountains are a major climatic divide, sheltering the region to the south from cold northern air masses in the winter.

South of the divide are the Kwangtung-Kwangsi hills proper, a hilly area with little level land and few well-defined ranges. In the west the hills adjoin the Yünnan-Kweichow plateau and in the east they continue in the Southeast uplands. The hills are dissected by the region's three main rivers and their tributaries—the Si Kiang (West River), Pei Kiang (North River), and Tung Kiang (East River). A characteristic feature of the northern Kwangsi hills is a mature karst topography in limestone, with deep sink holes, subterranean channelways, and weirdly dissected limestone pinnacles and spires.

Along the coast of the South China Sea, the hills enclose the Canton delta, the largest area of level land. The delta, built up by the alluvial sediments of the three main rivers, is also known as the Yüeh Kiang (Canton River) or Chu Kiang (Pearl River) delta, for the names of the combined stream. The delta, similar in some respects to the Yangtze

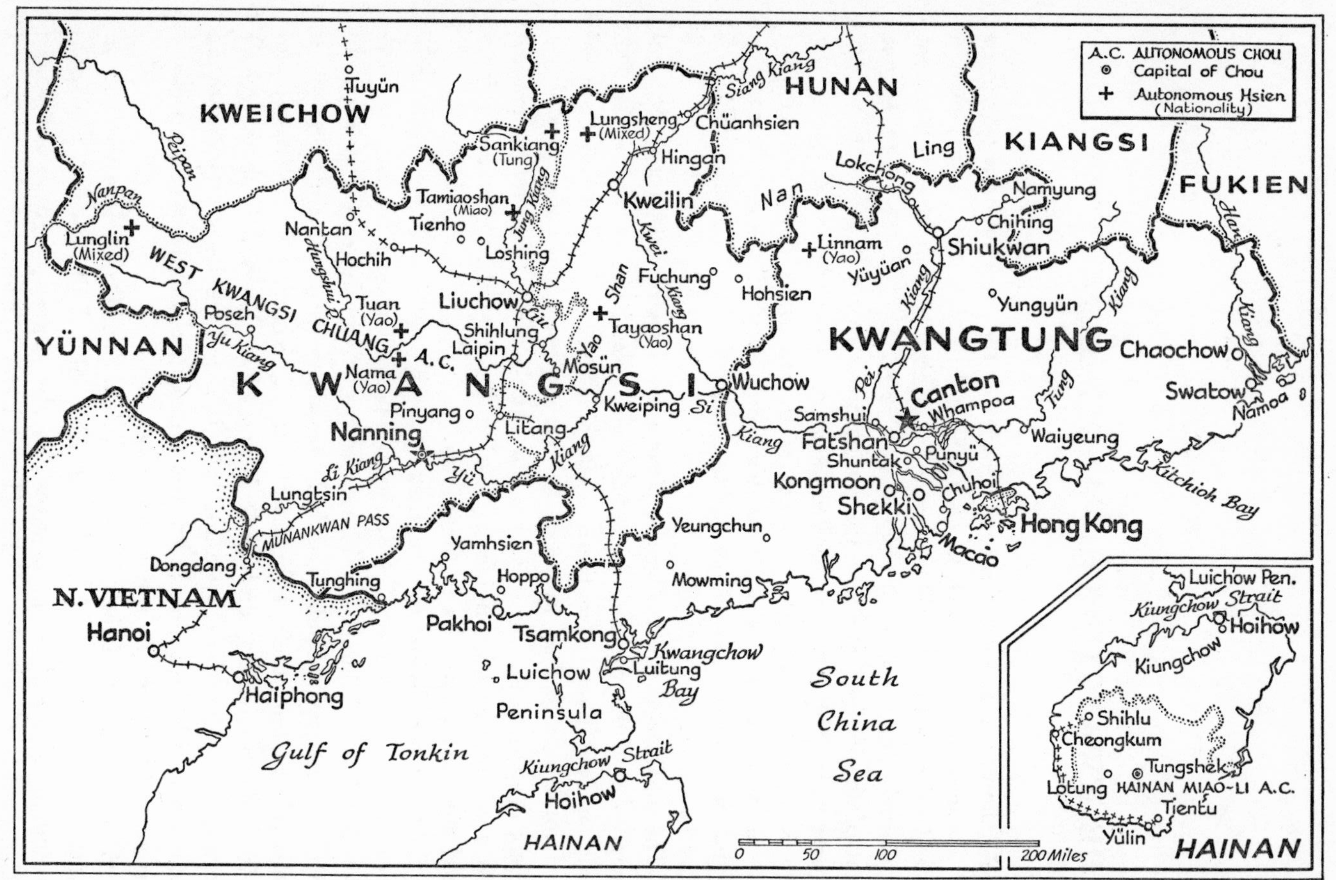

Kwangtung and Kwangsi

delta around Shanghai, is the economic focus and population center of the Kwangtung-Kwangsi region. Unlike the Shanghai area, however, the Canton area is not entirely level. Numerous low hills of red sandstone have been enveloped by the advancing alluvium of the delta.

Another subregion along the coast is the prominent Luichow (Leichow) Peninsula, very frequently misspelled in English as Liuchow. The peninsula, which projects southward toward Hainan Island, is an ancient basaltic lava flow that has been eroded virtually to base level. With Hainan, the peninsula forms the eastern side of the Gulf of Tonkin, an embayment of the South China Sea.

Hainan itself is, next to Formosa, the largest island off the Chinese coast. It was once connected with the Luichow Peninsula until faulting produced the present Kiungchow Strait. Hainan is low-lying in the north, but mountainous in the south, where it rises to 5,000 feet in the Wuchi (Five Finger) Mountains.

The coastline of the Kwangtung-Kwangsi region is irregular, but less so than that of the southeast coast. Promontories, protected bays and offshore islands abound. Ocean fishing has not developed extensively because of the warm water temperature, but some of China's most important harbors are along this coast: Swatow, Canton(more precisely, its outer port of Whampoa), Tsamkong. Pakhoi, and on Hainan, Hoihow and Yülin.

The Kwangtung-Kwangsi region is bisected by the Tropic of Cancer, so that about half the region is situated in the tropics. Its climate is best described in terms of three seasons. The cool season, from November to February, is dominated by the northeast monsoon, which brings relatively dry, cool weather with pleasant days. This is followed by two months of relatively warm, muggy weather. The true summer lasts from June to October and is associated with considerable heat and excessive humidity. During this season, average July temperatures are about 85° F (29° C), the same as in the Southeast uplands. January temperatures, however, are considerably higher than along the southeast coast, varying from 60° F (15° C) inland to 70° F (20° C) on Hainan. Winter is virtually absent and snow is found only on the higher peaks. Vegetation grows luxuriantly all year round, producing a strikingly green landscape.

Rainfall exceeds 65 inches along the coastal ranges and in the higher inland hill ranges. Areas in the rain shadow are likely to receive only 45 to 50 inches. Rainfall is concentrated in the warm and hot seasons when the region is under the dominance of the southern and southwestern monsoon. Only about eight inches fall during the winter season from November through February. Part of the summer rainfall, especially from June through September, is associated with typhoons.

Soils fall in two categories: High-yield noncalcareous alluvium in flood plains and deltas and humus-deficient reddish laterites in the uplands. In western Kwangsi, along the edge of the Yünnan-Kweichow plateau, yellowish laterites predominate.

Tillage agriculture is largely restricted to the level flood plains and delta land, or about 10 per cent of the total area. Terracing is practiced on the hill slopes. Thanks to the uniformly high temperatures and abundant precipitation, agriculture is virtually a year-round affair.

Irrigated rice is the dominant food grain, yielding two successive crops on the mainland and three crops on Hainan. The first sowing generally takes place in March, the first harvest and second sowing in July and the second harvest in November. In the northern part of the uplands, the second crop is generally planted between the rows of the first, about two months before the first harvest, to accommodate two crops within the shorter growing season. The principal rice areas are the lowlands of the Canton delta, the Luichow coastal plain and the major river valleys.

The Canton delta is also an important silk-growing area. Sericulture is practiced in association with pond fisheries, the fish being fed on the by-products of silkworm breeding and fertile mud from the pond bottoms supplying fertilizer for the mulberry trees. In northern Hainan, silkworms are bred on the leaves of the camphor tree.

Characteristic subtropical crops are sugar cane and fruit. Bananas, pineapples, oranges and tangerines, litchi and betel nuts are produced. Other tree crops of interest are tung oil, as well as camellia, cassia and anise oil. Lumbering, mainly for firewood, is of some importance in parts of Kwangsi.

The Kwangtung-Kwangsi region is moderately well endowed with mineral resources, but mining is still in its early stages. Some coal is found in scattered localities and is mined chiefly in the vicinity of railroads. Hainan has one of China's leading iron deposits. Mining was carried on here by the Japanese but has not been resumed since the Second World War. Like the rest of South China, the Kwangtung-Kwangsi region is rich in nonferrous metals. Tungsten, in association with bismuth and molybdenum, is mined in northern Kwangtung in an extension of the Hunan-Kiangsi deposits. Kwangsi is China's second tin producer. The region's reserves of manganese are said to be the largest in China, with Kwangtung alone accounting for 60 per cent of the nation's total.

The region's dissected relief has offered considerable obstacles to railroad construction. Two main lines have been built. One is the southern section of the Hankow-Canton railroad, completed in 1936; the other, the Hunan-Kwangsi railroad, was completed to the Vietnamese border in 1951. Among major branch lines are the initial section of the Kwangsi-Kweichow railroad, the Tsamkong branch, and the Canton-Kowloon railroad to Hong Kong.

Railroad transportation is supplemented by one of China's best highway nets, coastwise shipping lines and inland waterways. The region's three main rivers are all navigable in their lower courses. River steamers can ascend the Si Kiang as far as Wuchow and junks can penetrate deeply into Kwangsi Province. Three historic routes link the region with the north. They are the Meiling route linking Kwangtung and Kiangsi, the Cheling route between Kwangtung and Hunan, and the Kweilin route between Kwangsi and Hunan. These routes are now used either by railroads or modern highways.

The population of the Kwangtung-Kwangsi region is distributed quite irregularly. The greatest concentration of up to 1,000 persons per square mile is found in the Canton delta, the main river valleys and the coastal lowlands. A far more sparse settlement is found in the interior uplands. The inhospitable character of the uplands and the limited agricultural possibilities have long turned the attention of the people toward the sea. These early maritime interests resulted in mass overseas emigration after the 17th century. The average overseas Chinese is a Cantonese.

Linguistically, the Kwangtung-Kwangsi region is rather complex. The Upper Yangtze River (or Southwestern) Mandarin dialect is spoken by the Chinese of northern Kwangsi. Southern Kwangsi, roughly south of the Tropic, is part of the Cantonese language area, which extends eastward to include the Canton delta. Northern Kwangtung is dominated by the Hakka dialect, while the Swatow dialect, akin to the Amoy, is spoken in eastern Kwangtung.

Non-Chinese minorities are most numerous in Kwangsi, where the Chuang Autonomous Chou takes in the western half of the province. In addition to the Chuang, who number about 6,000,000, the principal ethnic groups include the Miao, Yao, Tung and Li. The non-Chinese population of the two provinces is about 8,000,000, about 15 per cent of the total population.

KWANGTUNG PROVINCE

Capital:Canton; area: 84,000; population: 35,000,000

Kwangtung extends westward in a panhandle to the Vietnamese border. From 1951 to 1955, this area of 6,000 square miles, including the port of Pakhoi and the administrative center of Yamhsien, was ceded to Kwangsi, giving that province an outlet to the Gulf of Tonkin. The provincial area was thus temporarily reduced from 84,000 to 78,000 square miles and the population from about 35,000,000 to 34,770,059.

Kwangtung Province includes the drainage basins of the lower Si Kiang, the Pei Kiang, Tung Kiang, and in the extreme east, the lower Han Kiang. The combined delta of the first three in the Canton area is the economic focus of the province. Unlike the deltas of the Yellow River and the Yangtze, this is not a broad plain, but a fragmented area of alluvium cut by hills and wide distributaries. The population density on this restricted, hill-studded plain is truly amazing. About 10,000,000 persons live on 3,000 square miles. The economic pressure for intense land use is such that parts of the delta have been diked off before the normal work of sedimentation is complete. Major embankment projects carried out after 1949 include the Sheklung-Shektan embankment along the lower Tung Kiang and the Kiupak dike on the lower Si Kiang south of Samshui.

Irrigated rice is the leading food crop and yields two harvests a year. In Hainan, where the area under rice was 140,000 hectares in 1955, three crops are produced on the same land during the year-round growing season. Kwangtung requires about 9,000,000 tons of food crops for self-sufficiency. Before the Second World War, production was usually just short of that amount and 500,000 tons of rice annually had to be imported from Thailand and South Vietnam. In 1949, only 6,000,000 tons were produced, but production rose and by 1952 the province became self-sufficient in food. Since that time, Kwangtung has been a rice-surplus area. The total output of food crops in 1954 was 9,406,000 tons. The 1957 goal is 12, 290,000 tons, including 9,937,000 tons of rice.

The Canton delta, which is the chief rice-growing area, is also a major silk producer. In 1935, 2840 tons of raw silk were produced, but by 1949 output had dropped to 384 tons. By 1952 it was still only 50 per cent of pre-war production. The most intensive breeding of silkworms is found in the areas of Fatshan and Shuntak, where cocoon crops are gathered six or seven times during the year. A total cocoon crop of 10,000 tons, or one-eighth of China's total was planned for 1955.

Kwangtung is one of China's great sugar cane provinces. In 1952, 65.000 hectares were under cultivation, in 1955 84,000 hectares and by the end of the five year-plan in 1957 this was to be expanded to 100,000 hectares. At the same time, cane sugar production was to rise from 300,000 tons in 1952 to 600,000 tons in 1957. The principal producing areas are in the Canton delta near Punyü and Shuntak, in the Tung Kiang valley near Waiyeung, and on Hainan.

Oranges, tangerines, bananas and pineapples are distinctive fruits in Kwangtung, which in 1954 had 30,000 hectares planted in fruit trees. Bananas are grown south of Canton in the delta. The banana crop was 45,000 tons in 1955.

Among other crops are tea, tobacco and peanuts. Tea is grown on hillsides, both in the northern hills adjoining Hunan and in the Canton delta. Namyung, in northern Kwangtung is noted for tobacco. The area under peanuts is to be expanded, chiefly in southwestern Kwangtung and on Hainan. The increase in acreage, from 12,000 hectares in 1952 to 33,000 hectares by 1957, is expected to triple the output of peanut oil to 100,000 tons.

Several tropical products are distinctive of Hainan, the only truly tropical part of China. They include coconuts, coffee, natural rubber, and figs.

Fisheries play a major role in the coastal economy. Fisheries are found in Kitchioh Bay, off the mouths of the delta distributaries, and Kwangchow Bay. Three special fishing hsien have been set up in the main districts. They are Namoa, in eastern Kwangtung; Chuhoi (formerly called Chungshankong and Tongkawan), in the Canton delta, and Luitung, on an island in Kwangchow Bay east of the Luichow Peninsula. A major fishing center is Yamchow Bay, at whose head is the town of Yamhsien. Other fishing ports in the western panhandle are Hoppo, known for pearls, and Pakhoi. Kwangtung's fishing population is 560,000. The total catch in 1953 was 338,000 tons, including 110,000 of freshwater fish. This was more than 25 per cent of China's total fish catch. The province's saltwater catch has been rising as follows in recent years:

1949	150,000 tons
1953	228,000 "
1954	270,000 "
1955 Plan	300,000 "

Kwangtung's small coal reserves are largely unexploited. Coal is mined in the Wu Shui basin on a head stream of the Pei Kiang, which is traversed by the Hankow-Canton railroad. The mines are in the area bounded by Shiukwan, Lokchong and Yüyüan. Other deposits, as yet unexploited, are in western Kwangtung between Mowming and Yeungchun.

Hainan's rich iron ore resources, uncovered by the Japanese, are situated at Shihlu and Tientu. Shihlu is situated in western Hainan, 20 miles northeast of Cheongkum. The mine, which is part of the Li-Miao Autonomous Chou, is situated at 2,700 feet. Formerly copper was mined in this area. The iron ore deposit with reserves of several hundreds of millions of tons was discovered to the east of the copper deposit. The ore is largely hematite with a 63 per cent metal content. Tientu is situated in southern Hainan, in the coastal hills, 10 miles northeast of Yülin. The reserves of Tientu are about one-ninth of those of Shihlu. The Japanese linked both Shihlu and Tientu by rail with the Yülin port area, but the lines had not been rebuilt by 1955. During their wartime exploitation the Hainan mines yielded about 1,000,000 tons of iron ore a year.

The coastal strip ceded by Kwangtung to Kwangsi in 1951 and returned to Kwangtung in 1955 is said to have about 60 per cent of China's manganese deposits. The manganese is concentrated in the Yamhsien-Fangcheng area.

In northern Kwangtung, on the Hunan-Kiangsi line, is the continuation of the tungsten field of those two provinces. The principal mines are near Chihing, Lokchong and Yungyün. Associated with the tungsten are bismuth, molybdenum and tin.

With the exception of Shiukwan on the Canton-Hankow railroad, Kwangtung's regional centers are situated along the coast, notably in the Canton delta. There, in addition to Canton, are the cities of Fatshan, Kongmoon and Shekki. The metropolis of western Kwangtung is Tsamkong, and Pakhoi is the chief town of the western panhandle. Swatow and Chaochow dominate the Han Kiang valley and eastern Kwangtung. Hoihow is the chief city of Hainan.

Canton, the metropolis of the province, has a population of 1,600,000. The city is actually called Kwangchow. Canton is a Western corruption of the name of Kwangtung Province. The city was the first Chinese port opened for foreign trade. After early contacts with Hindu, Persian and Arab traders, Canton was first visited by Portuguese in 1516, followed by the British, Dutch and French. Its foreign trade prospered briefly after foreign concessions were granted in the mid-19th century.

But the phenomenal growth of British Hong Kong soon eclipsed Canton as a foreign trade center. Since the completion of the railroad to Hankow in 1936, Canton has looked increasingly landward.

The city is the focal point of the river trade of the Kwangtung-Kwangsi region. From here 2,000-ton vessels can travel up the Si Kiang as far as Wuchow. Junks can penetrate deeply into Kwangsi, using the wide-flung headstreams of the Si Kiang. Junks also travel up the Pei Kiang and the Tung Kiang and are the chief means of transportation within the combined delta itself. In addition to the trunk railroad going north, Canton is linked locally by rail with Samshui and with Kowloon in Hong Kong.

Canton is situated on both banks of a wide delta distributary. The main section of the city, on the north bank, includes the old city (walled until 1921) and the new sections of Saikwan (west), Namkwan (south) and Tungkwan (east). The former foreign residential and business concession was on an island in the river off Saikwan. Across the river are the industrial suburbs of Honam (south) and Fati (southwest). Other industries are concentrated at Saitsun, a northern suburb along the main line to Hankow. Canton's modern industries include machinery plants, cotton, silk and jute mills, cement, newsprint, and matches. Traditional handicrafts are lacquerware and ivory engravings.

Still within the eastern city limits is Whampoa, Canton's outer port. Now accessible to 5,000-ton vessels, Whampoa is expected to be able to admit 10,000-ton ships once port improvement work has been completed.

In the delta south of Canton are Fatshan, Kongmoon and Shekki. Fatshan, formerly also called Namhoi, is noted particularly for its silk industry and porcelain handicrafts. The city, situated on the Canton-Samshui railroad and on a delta arm of the Pei Kiang, has a population of about 200,000.

Kongmoon, another delta center, was formerly also called Sunwui. It is situated on the west bank of the main delta arm of the Si Kiang. A city of 50,000, it is know for its fruit and timber trade. The railroad running southwest from Kongmoon and serving the Toishan area was still out of commission in 1955. The regional center of Shekki, formerly also called Chungshan, dominates the delta district north of the Portuguese colony of Macao.

The regional center of northern Kwangtung is Shiukwan, formerly called Kükong and Shiuchow. Shiukwan is a major transportation hub on the main railroad to Hankow, the junction of the headstreams of the Pei Kiang, and on highways to Hunan and Kiangsi, the so-called Cheling and Meiling roads. It has a population of about 200,000.

The port of Swatow in easternmost Kwangtung is the natural outlet of the Han Kiang basin. Its sphere of influence includes both eastern Kwangtung and southwest Fukien. A city of 200,000, Swatow was opened to foreign trade in 1858 and became a major port for Chinese overseas emigration. It trades largely in sugar and tropical fruit. Inland from Swatow and once linked to the port by a railroad is the city of Chaochow, also spelled Teochow according to the local dialect. Chaochow, formerly called Chaoan, has a population of 170,000 and handles the local trade of the Han Kiang valley. The railroad to Swatow was still not restored by 1955.

Rapidly developing as the regional center of western Kwangtung is the city of Tsamkong, also spelled Chankiang according to the Mandarin. This city and its surrounding area were leased to France in 1898 and became the territory of Kwangchowwan (Kwangchow Bay). The city was returned to China after the Second World War and its French name Fort-Bayard and former Chinese name Siying were changed to Tsamkong (Chankiang). The city was reached by a railroad from Litang in 1955 and plans are under way to develop Tsamkong into a deep-sea harbor.

Pakhoi is Kwangtung's port on the Gulf of Tonkin. It is situated on a peninsula that shelters its harbor. A city of about 50,000, Pakhoi is of limited importance because of lack of interior communications. It serves mainly the Hoppo hinterland. It was part of Kwangsi from 1951 to 1955.

The main city of Hainan is Hoihow, situated on the northern coast of the island opposite the Luichow Peninsula. A shallow-water port, with a population of about 50,000, Hoihow has replaced the formerly island center of Kiungchow or Kiungshan, just south of the port.

Kwangtung's minority peoples include the Li, Miao and Yao, closely related nationalities of the Miao-Yao and Thai ethnic groups. They are organized in two autonomous areas: the Li-Miao Autonomous Chou in Hainan and the Linnam Yao Autonomous Hsien in northwest Kwangtung.

The Hainan Li-Miao Autonomous Chou was first set up in the mountains of southern Hainan in July, 1952, with its administrative center at Loktung. In the summer of 1953, the chou annexed the island's southern coast, doubling its population to 540,000 and moving its capital to a new site fifteen miles east of Loktung. The new capital was at first called Chungchong and then renamed to its present designation of Tungshek. The Li-Miao chou includes all of China's Li population, 330,000 strong. The Miao component numbers only about 30,000.

The Linnam Yao Autonomous Hsien was set up in January, 1953, in the northwestern hills adjoining the Hunan and Kwangsi borders. The seat of the autonomous hsien was established at Samkong, subsequently renamed Linnam, 10 miles southwest of Linhsien, on the main Shiukwan-Liuchow road. The population includes 245,000 Yao people.

In addition to these two autonomous areas, Kwangtung Province also administers the islands in the South China Sea claimed by China. These are the Tungsha, Sisha, Chungsha and Nansha groups. The northernmost Tungsha group, also called Pratas, consists of an island at Lat. 21 degrees 42 minutes N. and Long. 116 degrees 43 minutes E. and two coral reefs to the northwest. The island has guano deposits and is the site of a meteorological station charged with the tracking of typhoon paths.

The Sisha group, also known as the Paracel Islands, extends from Lat. 15 degrees 46 minutes to 17 degrees 5 minutes N. and from Long. 110 degrees 14 minutes to 112 degrees 45 minutes E. These islands also have rich guano deposits. Twice a year, in the spring and fall, they are visited by fishermen from Hainan. The Chungsha group, also known as Macclesfield Bank, just southeast of the Sisha, consists merely of a group of underwater reefs and sandbanks.

Finally, the Nansha group, which has no collective Western designation, extends from Lat. 4 degrees to 11 degrees 30 minutes N. and from Long. 109 degrees 30 minutes to 117 degrees 50 minutes E. The main islands are Taiping (Itu Aba) and Nanwei (Spratly). The islands yield guano, tropical fruit and fish.

KWANGSI PROVINCE

Capital: Nanning; area: 84,000; population: 19,000,000

In 1951, Kwangsi annexed a coastal strip of 6,000 square miles from Kwangtung and thus gained access to the Gulf of Tonkin. The newly acquired area includes the administrative center of Yamhsien and the port of Pakhoi. The strip was returned to Kwangtung in June, 1955.

Kwangsi coincides essentially with the upper basin of the Si Kiang. The Si Kiang is the most important of the three rivers forming the combined Canton delta in Kwangtung Province. It is formed through the confluence of four main headstreams: the Hungshui River, the Liu Kiang, the Yü Kiang and the Kwei Kiang.

The Hungshui River, the most important headstream, rises in two branches on the Yünnan plateau at an elevation of 6,000 feet. The branches, known as the Peipan and Nanpan (Northern Pan and Southern Pan), join on the Kwangsi-Kweichow border and the combined stream flows through nonnavigable mountain gorges to a junction with the Liu Kiang at Shihlung. Although the Hungshui is the longest headstream of the Si Kiang system, precipitous limestone gorges render it unsuitable for navigation throughout its course.

The Liu Kiang, in turn, rises in two branches in southeastern Kweichow. The eastern branch, known as the Jung Kiang, is navigable for junks below Jungshui. Just before the Liu Kiang joins the Yü Kiang at Kweiping, it traverses the gorges variously known as Twantan and Tateng. This 20-mile stretch of rapids, formed where the Liu Kiang skirts the southern outliers of the Yao Shan, is a substantial hazard to navigation.

With both the Hungshui River and the Liu Kiang thus handicapped to a greater or lesser extent, the Yü Kiang is the headstream that carries most of the upriver navigation in the Si Kiang basin. The Yü Kiang also rises in two branches—the Yu Kiang or Siyang River, descending from southeastern Yünnan, and the Li Kiang or Tso Kiang, entering from North Vietnam. Although the Li Kiang is navigable for small junks as far as Lungtsin near the Vietnamese border, it is the Yu Kiang that carries most of the traffic. The Yu Kiang is navigable in virtually its entire length to Poseh near the Yünnan border.

Finally, the Kwei Kiang, which joins the Si Kiang at Wuchow, is navigable for large junks as far as Kweilin. The Kwei Kiang has its source in the vicinity of the Siang Kiang, the chief river of Hunan. About 2,000 years ago a canal was built across the low divide separating the two source streams. The canal, which at one time provided continuous navigation between South China and the central and northern parts of the country, has fallen into disuse.

The topography of the province of Kwangsi rises from the coastal lowlands in the south toward the Yünnan-Kweichow plateau in the northwest. Agriculture is favored in the south and east where more level land is available. The southeastern half of Kwangsi is part of the double-cropping rice area. In the northwestern uplands, rice is the summer crop in the few valleys that offer sufficient level bottom land. In the mountains the chief crops are corn, barley and millet, and these form the staple diet of the non-Chinese minorities.

Sugar cane is a distinctive crop in the south, with production centered on Nanning. Subtropical fruits are raised in the warmer districts and tea is grown on hillsides near the Hunan line.

Forestry is of considerable importance in the Yü Kiang basin. There is a large production of firewood. Sandalwood and cork are among the forest products. The northern limestone mountains are largely bare of any tree growth. Only in the extreme north near the Hunan border is there some lumbering activity. The wood is floated down the Liu Kiang and the Yü Kiang to the Si Kiang and markets in the Canton delta.

Other tree crops of interest are tung oil and cassia. The seeds, blossoms and leaves of cassia, also known as Chinese cinnamon, yield an oil that is used in soaps and cosmetics. The Chinese word for cassia is "kwei", and the occurrence of this particle in such geographic names as Kweilin, Kwei Kiang and Kweiping points to cassia production in the northeastern quadrant of Kwangsi. Another oil, that of the aniseed, is produced largely along the Yu Kiang between Lungtsin and Poseh. Normal cassia oil production in Kwangsi and adjoining parts of Kwangtung is 10,000 tons a year.

Like Kwangtung, Kwangsi has moderately extensive mineral deposits whose exploitation is still in its initial stages. Coal is found near Hingan and Chüanhsien near the Hunan border and near Tienho and Loshing, northwest of Liuchow. Iron ore has been found near Mosün, Kweiping and Hohsien.

The principal tin deposits are found near Hohsien and Fuchung in northeastern Kwangsi. The province's tin output is second only to that of Yünnan, but while Yünnan's production is concentrated at Kokiu, Kwangsi has a large number of scattered mines. Tin deposits have also been reported in the Hochih-Nantan area near the Kweichow border.

Antimony deposits representing a continuation of the Hunan field are mined in the Nantan-Hochih and the Mosün-Pinyang areas.

While east-west transportation in Kwangsi relies largely on the navigable headstreams of the Si Kiang, north-south connections are supplied by the Hunan-Kwangsi trunk railroad. The railroad was started in 1939 as a military line from Hengyang to Laipin. It was destroyed during the war and rehabilitated by 1947. The southern section from Laipin to the Vietnamese border at Munankwan (called Chennankwan until 1953) was completed in 1951. Two major branches leave the main line at Liuchow and at Litang. The Kwangsi-Kweichow railroad at one time during the Second World War ran from Liuchow to Tuyün. After the war, the line was rehabilitated only as far as Hochih. The railroad from Litang to Tsamkong (in Kwangtung) was completed in June, 1955.

Kwangsi has four regional centers of importance. Three are situated along the Hunan-Kwangsi railroad. They are Kweilin, Liuchow and Nanning. The fourth is a river city on the Si Kiang.

Nanning, formerly also called Yungning, is the capital of Kwangsi and the metropolis of the Yü Kiang basin. A city of 200,000, it lies at the crossroads of routes to Yünnan through the Yu Kiang valley and to Vietnam through the Li Kiang valley. The surrounding district is one of the more fertile agricultural basins of Kwangsi, producing in particular sugar cane and fruit.

Northward along the railroad is Liuchow, a city of 200,000. Liuchow is a transportation center commanding a dominating position in northern Kwangsi. It is the junction of the railroad toward Kweichow and the trade center of the Liu Kiang basin. The city is situated in picturesque surroundings in a hairpin bend of the Liu Kiang itself.

The northernmost railroad center in Kwangsi is Kweilin, at the junction of the Hunan-Kwangsi line and the Kwei Kiang. The name of the city, meaning "cassia woods", is a reflection of the original vegetation of the area. Kweilin is a former provincial capital and has a population of about 150,000.

The river city controlling the trade of eastern Kwangsi is Wuchow, formerly also called Tsangwu. This city of 200,000 is situated at the junction of the Kwei Kiang and the Si Kiang and handles virtually the entire river trade of the Si Kiang basin. Tung oil and timber are among the main export items.

About one-third of Kwangsi's population consists of non-Chinese minorities. The total minority population of 6,300,000 includes 5,400,000 Chuang, 440,000 Yao, 180,000 Miao, 140,000 Tung and 8,000 Chinese Moslems. These minorities are organized in one autonomous chou and seven autonomous hsien.

The West Kwangsi Chuang Autonomous Chou was originally formed in December, 1952, with an area of 42,000 square miles and a population of 6,200,000. In the fall of 1953, the chou was expanded eastward so that the present area is 52,000 square miles and the population is 8,400,000. The mountainous character of the western part of Kwangsi covered by the chou is reflected in the relatively sparse population density of 160 per square mile. By contrast, the eastern, lower-lying and predominantly Chinese section has a population density of 300. The Chuang Autonomous Chou thus covers more than half of the province and incorporates two of the largest provincial cities—Liuchow and Nanning, which is the capital of the chou as well as the provincial capital. In addition to the dominant Chuang minority numbering 5,400,000, the Chuang Autonomous Chou includes Yao, Miao and Tung groupings, some of which are organized in autonomous hsien within the autonomous chou.

The Sankiang Tung Autonomous Hsien, formed in February, 1952, occupies the confluence area of the San Kiang and the Jung Kiang. The hsien is a southern continuation of the Tungtao Tung Autonomous Hsien in southwestern Hunan. The hsien seat is Sankiang, formerly called Kuyi.

The Tamiaoshan Miao Autonomous Hsien, formed in February, 1952, adjoins the Tung hsien on the south. The hsien is situated in the Ta Miao Shan (Great Miao Mountains), a hill range along the Kwangsi-Kweichow border. The hsien has a population of 160,000, of whom nearly half are of the Miao nationality. The hsien seat is at Jungshui, on the Jung Kiang.

The Lunglin Autonomous Hsien, the third within the Chuang chou, includes a number of nationalities in the most remote western part of Kwangsi on the Kweichow and Yünnan borders. The hsien, whose seat is at Lunglin (formerly called Silung), was formed in the summer of 1953.

Two additional autonomous hsien inhabited by the Yao nationality were set up in the Chuang chou in September, 1955. They have their seats at Tuan and Nama in the middle Hungshui River basin.

Two autonomous hsien of Kwangsi are situated outside of the Chuang chou. They are the Lungsheng Multi-nationality Joint Autonomous Hsien and the Tayaoshan Yao Autonomous Hsien. The Lungsheng Autonomous Hsien, formed in July, 1951, is in northernmost Kwangsi and adjoins the Sankiang hsien on the east.

The Tayaoshan Yao Autonomous Hsien is situated in the Ta Yao Shan (Great Yao Mountains), a hill range east of Liuchow. The hsien, which was formed in February, 1952, has its seat at Kinsiu.

CHAPTER 9

THE YÜNNAN-KWEICHOW PLATEAU

The region contains the provinces of Yünnan and Kweichow in southwestern China. The combined area is nearly 230,000 square miles, or 6 per cent of China, and the population 33,000,000, or nearly 6 per cent of the nation's total. This yields an average density of 145 persons per square mile.

The plateau is a spur of the great Tibetan tableland. High, rugged surfaces dissected by deep valleys and crossed by mountains make up most of the region. The average elevation decreases from about 6,000 feet in Yünnan to 4,000 feet in Kweichow. The region may be divided into three related sub-regions: the plateau of Kweichow, the plateau of Yünnan and the canyons of western Yünnan.

The Kweichow plateau consists of a high upland core dissected along its periphery by river valleys. The central core represents the undissected portion of an old plateau surface, serving as the divide between the Yangtze and Si Kiang drainage basins. Karst topography is found along the southern margins of the plateau bordering on Kwangsi.

The Yünnan plateau occupies the eastern part of the province and rises generally 2,000 feet above the Kweichow plateau. Here the westernmost headstreams of the Si Kiang rise. The plateau has in part been faulted into grabens, some of which are occupied by lakes. Karst topography is also present in wide tracts. Continuing geological activity is evidenced by occasional earthquakes.

The deep north-south canyons of western Yünnan are carved by some of the great rivers of southeast Asia. Here are the virtually inaccessible upper courses of the Salween, the Mekong, the upper Yangtze River, and the Red River of North Vietnam. The gorges are separated by narrow, abrupt mountain ranges. They are the Kaolikung Mountains along the Burmese border, separating the Irrawaddy from the Salween; the Nu Shan, between the Salween and the Mekong; and the Yünling Mountains between the Mekong and the upper Yangtze. Farther south, the Wuliang Mountains separate the Mekong and the Black River, a tributary of the Red River, while the Ailao Mountains separate the Black River and the Red River. In western Yünnan also, faulting has produced lake-filled basins, notably that of the Erh Hai, and earthquakes are a constant threat. The worst recent earthquake occurred in March, 1925, in the area of Tali.

Although the Yünnan-Kweichow plateau lies next to the tropics, the climate is distinctly temperate because of the high altitude. Several mountain barriers north of the plateau place it beyond the effective reach of the cold northern monsoon and winters are largely devoid of major frosts. The average January temperature is 50° F (10° C), with temperatures decreasing from south to north. The dry winter season lasts from November until April.

From April until October, the region is under the influence of the southwest monsoon, with rains at frequent intervals from the middle of May until the end of October. Despite the high humidity, the climate is not oppressive on the plateau because temperatures remain moderate. The average for July is 77° F (25° C). Actually the summer maximum does not occur in July, but in May just before the start of the rains. The May average may rise up to 80° F. Total annual rainfall is 50 to 60 inches.

Cultivation is confined to upland plains, locally called "pa-tzu" (literally, "dike, embankment"), a few open river valleys and occasional terraced hillsides. Rice is the chief summer crop in irrigated land, while corn, barley and millet are raised in the summer on dry fields. Wheat is the dominant winter grain. Other products of the region are sugar cane, tea, and oak-fed silk cocoons.

The region contains some of the richest timber reserves of China, but lack of transportation routes has limited lumbering operations to local needs. Tung oil is also a major forest product.

The chief mineral resources are nonferrous metals, notably tin and copper in Yünnan and mercury in Kweichow. Coal deposits are scattered throughout the region, although mining is still on a small scale.

The rugged terrain has deprived the region of waterways, except on the northern margins of the Kweichow plateau. Few railroads exist and transportation must thus rely largely on roads. The chief railroad outlet before the Second World War was the French-built rail line from Haiphong and Hanoi in Vietnam to Kunming. A section of the railroad between Pisechai and Hokow was destroyed during the war. Rehabilitation of the Vietnamese section of the line was begun in 1955 and presumably the Chinese adjoining section will also be rebuilt.

Yünnan and Kweichow

While the Kunming-Haiphong line thus provides an outlet to the sea, inland connections are contemplated between Yünnan and Szechwan. The Chinese are speeding plans to build a railroad connecting Kunming and Neikiang (on the Chungking-Chengtu line). Other railroads still in the planning stage would link Kweichow with Hunan, Kwangsi and Szechwan. Work on the Szechwan-Kweichow link was being pushed in 1956.

Compared with other parts of China proper, the Yünnan-Kweichow plateau is sparsely populated. Population is concentrated chiefly in the upland plains along means of transportation, whether railroads or highways. The least settled sections are the peripheral parts of the Yünnan and Kweichow plateaus.

Chinese settlement of the region began 2,000 years ago, but the two provinces were not made an integral part of China until the fourteenth century. Chinese colonizers pushed the original tribal inhabitants into the mountains and occupied the best level land. The non-Chinese peoples thus retained their distinct languages and cultures, transforming the plateau region, and notably Yünnan, into one of China's most diverse ethnic areas.

The Chinese, who speak the southwestern variety of Mandarin, make up about 70 per cent of the population, the ratio being slightly larger in Kweichow and slightly smaller in Yünnan. Non-Chinese minorities, numbering about 10,000,000, are found around the periphery of the region. The principal minorities are the Miao, Puyi, Thai, Minchia and others. The non-Chinese groups are organized in four autonomous chou and fourteen autonomous hsien that are listed and described in the provincial sections of this chapter.

KWEICHOW PROVINCE

Capital: Kweiyang; area: 66,000; population: 15,037,310

Kweichow Province is drained in its northern half by the Wu Kiang, a right tributary of the Yangtze River, which traverses the province from west to east. The southwestern quadrant, characterized by karst topography, is drained by the Peipan Kiang, left headstream of the Hungshui River. The Yüan Kiang of Hunan Province and the Liu Kiang of Kwangsi both rise in southeastern Kweichow. None of these rivers is navigable. Only the lower Wu Kiang is accessible to small junks.

Rice, wheat and corn are grown chiefly in the eastern part of the province and their total production renders Kweichow virtually self-sufficient in food. The richest rice yields are obtained in the basins of the Wu Kiang and the Yüan Kiang. Silkworms are bred on oak leaves in the Tsunyi area. Tung oil is a distinctive forest product.

Coal deposits are scattered through the northern and central parts of the province. In the north, coal is found in the Tungtze-Tsunyi and Tating areas. The coal is of coking grade and could supply the iron and steel industry of Chungking once the Kweichow-Szechwan railroad is built. In central Kweichow, coal measures extend from the area of Langtai and Anshun past Kweiyang to the area of Tuyün.

Kweichow's noted mercury deposits extend in an arc-shaped belt from the southwestern part to the eastern part of the province. In the nineteenth century Kweichow produced as much as 1,000 tons of metal, meeting China's demands and leaving a surplus for export. At that time the largest mines were in the southwest at Paimatung, 10 miles west of Kaiyang, and at Nanmuchang near Hingi. Since then these producers have declined and production has shifted to eastern Kweichow and adjoining Hunan. The main Kweichow mine is now at Wanshan, 15 miles south of Tungjen. Wanshan was formerly the seat of Shengki hsien.

In the absence of navigable waterways and railroads, Kweichow must depend on highways for its transportation. The present highway focus and planned railroad hub is Kweiyang, from where roads go west to Yünnan, north to Szechwan, east to Hunan, and south to Kwangsi.

Only two urban centers have been raised above the hsien level in Kweichow, indicating the province's economic backwardness. These two cities are Kweiyang, the capital, and Tsunyi.

Kweiyang is situated virtually at the geographical center of the province and has thus become its natural transportation focus. A city of about 300,000 persons, Kweiyang is divided by the city wall into a new city and an old city. The old city has traditionally traded with Kwangsi, Yünnan and Hunan, while the new city has its interests in Szechwan.

Tsunyi is situated on the main highway from Kweiyang to Szechwan. It is the commercial center of northern Kweichow and has a population of 70,000. A phospate fertilizer plant is in operation here. At a meeting held here in January, 1935, by the Communists on their long march to the Northwest, Mao Tse-tung assumed the party leadership.

Kweichow includes seven autonomous hsien organized largely on the basis of the province's Miao, Puyi and Yi minority population. The Miao are found predominantly in the southeast, the Puyi in the southwest in the valley of the Peipan Kiang, and the Yi in the northwest.

The Shuichia, 150,000 strong, live in the south but have no autonomous area.

Four Miao autonomous hsien have been organized in southeastern Kweichow. They are Lushan hsien, which in the summer of 1953 apparently succeeded the original Kaili autonomous hsien (created in 1950); Taikiang hsien, established in the summer of 1953 and formerly called Taikung; Tanchai hsien, established in the summer of 1953 and formerly called Pachai; and Leishan hsien, established in 1954 and formerly called Tankiang.

Two hsien south of Kweiyang are based on a mixed Miao and Puyi population. They are the Hweishui Puyi-Miao Autonomous Hsien, established in the summer of 1953 and formerly called Tingfan; and the Lotien Puyi Autonomous Hsien, established in 1954 and formerly called Lohu.

The seventh hsien, established in 1954, is the triple nationality Weining hsien, which combines the Yi, Chinese Moslem and Miao minorities of northwestern Kweichow, the Yi group predominating.

YÜNNAN PROVINCE

Capital: Kunming; area: 162,000; population: 17,472,737

Yünnan Province consists of two distinct sections: the eastern plateau with small upland plains and a relatively dense population, and the western canyon section, inaccessible and sparsely settled.

Important crops are rice, grown mainly on the eastern plateau, wheat, barley and corn. Sugar cane finds favorable conditions in southeastern Yünnan in the valley of the Nanpan Kiang. A well-known black tea is produced in the area of Puerh, formerly also called Ningerh.

Coal is distributed throughout the province. However, mining has reached any importance only at Kwangtung (formerly called Ipinglang), which has been set up as a special mining ch'ü, and at Kunyang.

Yünnan plays a major role in the mining of nonferrous metals. It is the leading producer of tin, which is mined and smelted at Kokiu. The metal was formerly shipped via Mengtsz and the railroad to Haiphong in Vietnam and on to Hong Kong for further refining. It accounted for about two-thirds of Yünnan's exports by value.

Other major mineral products are copper, iron and salt. Copper is mined primarily near Hweitseh, which was formerly called Tungchwan. The mines flourished in the seventeenth century when about 6,000 tons of copper a year were produced. But production dropped subsequently as imported copper could be delivered more cheaply to the market centers. In view of China's resent drive for self-sufficiency, it may be expected that output will be spurred once the Kunming-Neikiang railroad is completed. In preparation for expanded production a special Tungchwan mining ch'ü was established in 1954 about twenty miles southwest of Hweitseh on the projected rail route. Lead and zinc are also mined in the Hweitseh area.

Salt is obtained in brine wells in the Yenhing-Kwangtung area. The principal wells are at Langtsing, west of Yenhing, and at Yüanyungtsing and Aliutsing on the road between Yenhing and Kwangtung. Iron ore is mined chiefly in the Tungshan mine at Imen, southwest of Kunming.

A rudimentary rail net handles much of the transportation in the Kunming area. The provincial capital is linked by rail with Chanyi and along the preserved section of the Haiphong railroad as far as Pisechai. From Pisechai, a branch serves the tin-mining area of Kokiu.

A grandiose rail construction plan before the Second World War called for the building of a line across Yünnan from Kunming to Burma, where it would link up with the Burmese rail net at Lashio. Construction began in 1940, but was suspended in face of the Japanese advance into Burma. Only a short section from Kunming to Anning was completed. Instead, transportation to Burma is being maintained by the well-known Burma Road. This is the main highway artery of Yünnan, serving together with its branches most of the important provincial centers. Chanyi, the rail terminus in eastern Yünnan, is connected by road with the near-by provinces of Kweichow and Szechwan.

Kunming is situated on the north shore of the lake Tien Chih. A major transportation center, it has grown from a population of about 250,000 in 1949 to 500,000 in 1953. The city acquired a number of industries during the Second World War, including a copper smelting plant for the Tungchwan mines. Power to the city and its industries is supplied by the Shihlungpa hydroelectric plant, built in 1912 at Haikow, where the Tanglang River leaves the lake Tien Chih.

The regional transportation center of western Yünnan is Siakwan. This road hub on the Burma Road has largely supplanted the older city of Tali, situated to the north on the shore of the lake Erh Hai. Tali is noted for its marble quarries.

Kokiu, the tin city, is the third Yünnanese city above the hsien level. Its commercial needs are handled largely by the near-by rail city of Mengtsz.

Yünnan is perhaps China's most complex ethnographic province. Of the provincial population of more than 17,000,000, the non-Chinese minorities make up 6,000,000. As many as twenty-eight nationalities are represented in the provincial legislature, but only the fifteen most important groups (including the Chinese) are represented in the National People's Congress. As of January, 1956, the province included four autonomous chou and seven autonomous hsien. The autonomous chou, situated along the borders of Vietnam, Laos and Burma, are: the Hungho Hani Autonomous Chou, the Hsi-shuang-pan-na Thai Autonomous Chou, the Tehung Thai-Chingpo Autonomous Chou, and the Nu Kiang (Salween River) Lisu Autonomous Chou.

The Hungho Hani Autonomous Chou is situated in the wedge formed by the Red River and the Vietnamese border. The Hani group was originally organized into the Hungho Autonomous Hsien in the fall of 1953. Hungho (formerly called Yisa) is a hsien town on the right bank of the Red River, whose Chinese name is Yüan Kiang or Hung Ho. The name of the Hani was originally rendered as Aini and Haoni. In January, 1954, the autonomous hsien was expanded into an autonomous chou with an area of 4,000 square miles and a population of 400,000, of whom 60 per cent are Hani. The capital of the chou was moved downstream from Hungho to Yüanyang (formerly called Sinkai).

The Hsi-shuang-pan-na Thai Autonomous Chou is situated in southernmost Yünnan astride the Mekong River on the borders of Laos and Burma. The chou, which was set up in January, 1953, has an area of 9,600 square miles and a population of 200,000, of whom 70 per cent are Thai. Hsi-shuang-pan-na is the Chinese transcription of the traditional Thai name of the area Shih Shong Baan Naa, which means "twelve rice lands", a reference to the twelve minor administrative units that make up the chou. The capital, Yünkinghung, is situated on the right bank of the Mekong River, on a highway from Kunming. It was originally known as Kianghung, later renamed to the Chinese name of Cheli, and in October, 1954, reverted to its present Thai designation, meaning "capital of the dawn".

On the Burma border, astride the Burma Road, is the Tehung Thai-Chingpo Autonomous Chou. This chou, set up in July, 1953, has an area of 8,000 square miles and a population of 400,000. Of that population, 175,000 are Thai, 97,000 are Chingpo, and 100,000 are Chinese. The Lisu, whose autonomous chou is farther north, form a minority in the Thai-Chingpo chou. The capital, situated on the Burma Road, was originally called Mangshih, but was renamed Lusi when it became the seat of Lusi hsien.

The Nu Kiang Lisu Autonomous Chou lies in the Salween-Mekong canyon country on the northern Burma border. It was formed in August,

1954, through merger of the four Lisu autonomous hsien of Kungshan, Fukung, Pikiang and Lushui, formed one year earlier. It has an area of 3,500 square miles. About 75 per cent of the total population of 120,000 are Lisu, with Nu, Tibetans, Yi and Minchia making up the minority. The chou capital is at Pikiang, formerly called Chihtzelo, on the Salween River.

Of the seven autonomous hsien, five are situated along the borders of Yünnan, while two, inhabited by the Yi, are in the area of Kunming.

The Tehtsin Tibetan Autonomous Hsien is situated on the Mekong River in northwesternmost Yünnan. It borders on the Chamdo district of Tibet and has its seat at Tehtsin, formerly called Atuntze. The autonomous hsien was set up in the fall of 1953.

In southwesternmost Yünnan, between the Mekong River and the Burma border, are two autonomous hsien based on the Lahu nationality. The Lantsang Lahu Autonomous Hsien, set up in April, 1953, lies on the right bank of the Mekong River, which is called Lantsang by the Chinese. The hsien seat is at the town of Lantsang, formerly called Munai. About 46 per cent of the total population of 200,000 is Lahu, with the rest being made up by Kawa, Chinese and other groups. To the southwest, on the Burma border itself, is the Menglien Thai-Lahu-Kawa Autonomous Hsien. This triple-nationality hsien was established in 1954.

North of the Lahu nationality area is a joint Thai-Kawa autonomous hsien with its seat at Kengma. The hsien, set up in October, 1955, has a population of 70,000.

In southern Yünnan, wedged between the Thai and Hani autonomous chou, is the Kiangcheng Hani-Yi Autonomous Hsien. The hsien, set up in 1954, has a population of 30,000. It lies in the mountains bordering on Vietnam and Laos.

The two Yi autonomous hsien in the Kunming area were set up in the second half of 1953. They are at Milo, southeast of Kunming, and at Oshan, southwest of the provincial capital.

CHAPTER 10

THE SZECHWAN BASIN

SZECHWAN PROVINCE

Capital: Chengtu; area: 210,000; population: 65,685,063

Even before Szechwan's annexation of Sikang Province in 1955, Szechwan was the most populous province of China. The merger of Sikang almost doubled the area of Szechwan but added only 3,381,064 persons to the 62,303,999 already reported in the June, 1953, census. The population of the enlarged province represents about 11 per cent of the nation's total.

The Szechwan basin is so called largely in relation to the high encircling mountains. The detailed topography of the region is thoroughly hilly and the basin as a whole lies at a higher elevation than the Middle Yangtze plain, though considerably below the Tibetan plateau to the west.

The high barrier ranges encircling the basin make isolation a distinctive aspect of the regional geography. The ranges are best defined in the west and north. In the northwest rises the 10,000-foot-high Min Shan, a spur of the Tibetan plateau that separates Szechwan from Kansu and Tsinghai to the north. The Min Shan is a meeting place of fold mountains trending both east-west and north-south and is subject to earthquakes. A destructive quake occurred here in August, 1933.

Eastward the northern barrier of the Szechwan basin drops sharply to the upper Kialing valley, where the mountains are breached by the newly-built Chengtu-Paoki railroad. The ranges rise once again east of the valley in the Tapa Mountains, another rugged barrier on the Szechwan-Shensi border. The Tapa Mountains, made up largely of limestone, rise to more than 8,000 feet.

Along the eastern border with Hupei a complex system of limestone uplands is broken by the noted Yangtze gorges. These gorges, three in number, start in the five-mile-long Chütang Gorge at Fengkieh in easternmost Szechwan. This is followed by the thirty-mile-long Wu Hsia (Wu Gorge), cutting through the Wu Shan on the Szechwan-Hupei border. The easternmost Siling Gorge, twenty miles in length, lies in Hupei and ends just above Ichang.

In the west, the Kiunglai Mountains separate the Szechwan basin from the Sikang plateau and constitute the easternmost of a series of parallel north-south ranges that form the divides for deeply entrenched valleys. These ranges, which make up the dissected Sikang plateau, are the Kiunglai Mountains between the Min Kiang and the Tatu River, the Tasüeh Mountains between the Tatu and the Yalung River, and the Shaluli Mountains between the Yalung and the upper course of the Yangtze River itself.

The Szechwan basin proper thus lies enclosed by high barrier mountains rising to 8,000 and 10,000 feet. The central part of the basin, which lies at an elevation of 1,000 to 2,000 feet, can be described as an amphiteatre descending toward the Yangtze valley. The Szechwan basin is also known as the Red basin. This term, first used by the German geographer Ferdinand von Richthofen, refers to the reddish coloring of the soft sandstones that underlie much of the region and to the predominantly reddish-purplish soils.

Erosion has dissected the central part of the Szechwan basin to such an extent that level land is confined to rounded hilltops and flood plains. Accordingly, three subregions can be distinguished: the parallel folded hills of eastern Szechwan, the Fang Shan hills of central Szechwan, and the Chengtu plain of western Szechwan.

The folded hills of the eastern basin trend generally northeast-southwest between the Chü Kiang and the Yangtze River. Six parallel hill ranges can be distinguished in this area, extending about 125 miles in length.

The Fang Shan hills are separated from the folded hill area by the lower Kialing River. Unlike the uplands to the east, the Fang Shan has not been folded. It consists of horizontal strata of soft red sandstone that have been deeply eroded by streams. This has resulted in steep-sloped, level-topped, virtually square hill mesas. The name Fang Shan in fact means "square hills".

The Chengtu plain is the principal economic subregion of the basin. It is a gently sloping alluvial fan formed by the waters of the Min Kiang as it emerges from the western mountains at Kwanhsien. The plain has an average elevation of 2,000 feet. It slopes to the south and has an area of 1,700 square miles. The thickness of the alluvium has been estimated at 200 feet, with one foot being added every 100 years.

The name Szechwan means "four rivers". The identity of these four rivers is not generally agreed upon. Some sources list the Yangtze and three of its left bank tributaries—the Min Kiang, the To Kiang and the Kialing River. Others list four tributaries of the Yangtze—either the Min Kiang, To Kiang, Kialing River and Fow Kiang, or the Min Kiang, To Kiang, Kialing River and Wu Kiang.

Since 1955, the upper Yangtze River (also called the Kinsha) forms the western border of enlarged Szechwan Province. Flowing in one of the deeply entrenched canyons of the Sikang plateau, the upper Yangtze flows south, briefly enters northern Yünnan, and receives the Yalung River, another north-south canyon stream. Throughout its encased course in the Sikang plateau, the Yangtze has a strong gradient, dropping from 10,000 feet to 1,000 feet at Ipin where it enters the Szechwan basin. Within the basin itself, the gradient is gentle and the river is at once navigable for 500-ton vessels. Only the gorges on the Hupei border present an obstacle to shipping, requiring careful navigation.

Upon entering the Szechwan basin at Ipin, the Yangtze River receives the Min Kiang. This tributary rises at 10,000 feet in the Min Shan, descends rapidly through canyon-like gorges and emerges at Kwanhsien to form the Chengtu plain. The noted Tukiangyen irrigation system, devised in the third century B.C., spreads the waters in channels over the Chengtu plain and reunites them into the main Min Kiang channel at Pengshan. At Loshan, where the Min Kiang receives the Tatu River, its main tributary, the river becomes navigable for large junks down to its mouth at Ipin.

The To Kiang, which joins the Yangtze at Luchow, is of less economic importance. It is linked in its upper course with the Chengtu plain irrigation system and is navigable only in its lower reaches for large junks.

The Kialing River, which joins the Yangtze at Chungking, rises in two main branches in southern Kansu. It receives its two main tributaries at Hochwan, the Chü Kiang on the left and the Fow Kiang on the right. Both the Kialing and its affluents are navigable for junks.

The only important right-bank Yangtze tributary is the Wu Kiang, which descends from the Kweichow plateau and enters the Yangtze at Fowling. Only the lower reaches below the plateau are navigable to any extent.

The topographic isolation of the Szechwan basin, in particular the presence of towering ranges along its northern margins, give the region a temperate, moist climate in spite of its inland position. The northern mountains are an effective barrier against the Polar Continental air in the winter. The average January temperature of 50° F (10° C) is several degrees above that of the Lower Yangtze plain, situated on the coast but exposed to the northern air. Severe frost and snow are uncommon.

Summers tend to become quite warm. The average for July is 85° F (29° C), or about five degrees above the July average of Shanghai. The high summer temperatures are partly explained by the adiabatic heating undergone by southern tropical air masses descending from the Kweichow plateau into the Szechwan basin.

These southern air masses bring abundant precipitation, the chief rainy months being June, July and August. Total precipitation varies from 35 to 45 inches. Even the winter months are humid; fogs and mists are common. The characteristic frequency of near-surface condensation of moisture is partly explained by the enclosed situation of the basin, which limits the free circulation of air.

The mild and genial character of the climate is typical only of the basin proper. The surrounding mountains and, in particular, the 10,000-foot-high Sikang plateau are characterized by altitudinal zonation typical of highland climates.

The highly colored Tertiary sandstones that underlie the Szechwan basin have given rise to the characteristic purplish soils of the region. These soils, limy to neutral, are relatively immature since the rate of erosion of the soft sandstones is quite rapid. South of the central basin, yellow lateritic soils predominate along the margins of Kweichow Province. The mixed coniferous and deciduous forests of the surrounding mountains are associated with podzolic soils, while the high plateau of the west bears a mantle of thin, immature highland soils.

In the Szechwan basin proper, the mild humid climate and an eleven-month growing season produce favorable conditions for agriculture. Although relatively little land is available, more than 20 per cent of the total area is under cultivation. A large part of the land has been made arable through terracing of hillslopes.

The principal summer food crop in the lowland is rice, which yields in the Chengtu plain some of the highest outputs per unit of land. In 1954, 3,400,000 hectares of Szechwan's land were in rice. During the winter, wheat is the dominant lowland crop. In the hills and other areas where irrigation water is not available, kaoliang, millet and corn are grown, along with sweet potatoes. The total expected food crop in 1955 was 19 million tons, largest of any province in China.

Rape is the leading oilseed of Szechwan and is cultivated chiefly along the banks of the Yangtze River. Soybeans and peanuts prosper in the basins of the Kialing River and the To Kiang.

Among the fibers, cotton, jute and silk are produced. Cotton is limited to the Fow Kiang and To Kiang valleys. Shehung (formerly called Taihochen) is the leading cotton center of the Fow Kiang valley. In 1955, 260,000 hectares were planted in cotton. Lungchang and Jungchang on the Chungking-Chengtu railroad are known for their jute production.

Szechwan is one of China's leading silk producers, with four principal areas within the province itself. The largest output of cocoons is found in northern Szechwan around Nanchung and Santai. In second place is the Chungking area, which is the center of modern spinning mills. Weaving is developed principally at Chengtu and Mienyang, which have a small cocoon crop. The fourth area, around Loshan, has a large cocoon crop but uses largely handicraft processing methods. The raw silk is then shipped to weaving mills at Chengtu and Loshan.

Sugar cane and citrus fruit are distinctive subtropical crops. Szechwan is one of China's leading sugar cane growers. Production is concentrated in the To Kiang valley, with mills at Neikiang and Tzechung. Citrus fruit, particularly oranges, are grown in extensive plantations in eastern Szechwan.

Tea and tobacco are hillside crops in the western margins of the basin. Most of the tea is grown in the area of Yaan, Mingshan and Loshan and is shipped in pressed form from Yaan to east Tibet. Tobacco is produced near Hochwan in the Kialing River basin and near Kintang in the Chengtu plain.

One of the leading commodities of Szechwan is tung oil, which is one of the major export items of the province. The oil is concentrated for shipment at Chungking and Wanhsien after having been collected at such local centers as Fowling, Hochwan and Ipin. The tung oil of Siushan is well known. Other forestry products are mushrooms and medicinal herbs.

Goats and hogs are the principal livestock reared in the province's agricultural areas. Szechwan's hog bristles are well known as an export commodity and goatskins are made chiefly in the northern part of the province. In the Tibetan highlands of the northwest and west, yak and sheep graze on the mountain pastures.

Szechwan is richly supplied with mineral resources. Coal underlies most of the province and in terms of reserves Szechwan follows after Shansi and Shensi. The coal measures are usually at great depth and are accessible only where anticlines have raised them near the surface. There are four major coal basins. One mining district is at Pehpei on the Kialing River north of Chungking and still within the Chungking city limits. The coal is mined in the folded hill ranges east

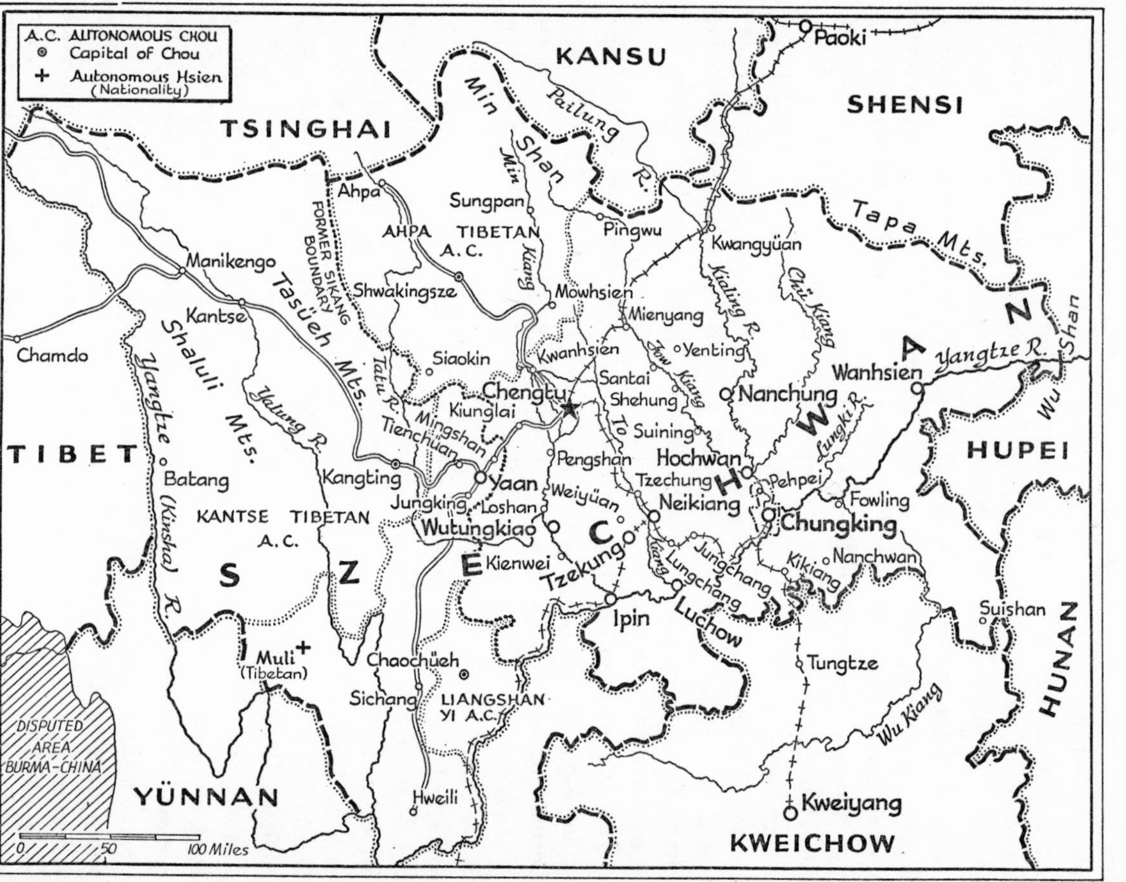
A.C. AUTONOMOUS CHOU
Capital of Chou
Autonomous Hsien (Nationality)
KANSU
SHENSI
TSINGHAI
TIBET
HUPEI
HUNAN
KWEICHOW
YÜNNAN
S Z E C H W A N
Paoki
Min Shan
Pailung R.
Min Kiang
Sungpan
Pingwu
Kwangyüan
Tapa Mts.
Ahpa
AHPA TIBETAN A.C.
FORMER SIKANG BOUNDARY
Manikengo
Tasüeh Mts.
Shwakingsze
Mowhsien
Mienyang
Kialing R.
Chü Kiang
Kantse
Shaluli Mts.
Chamdo
Siaokin
Kwanhsien
Yenting
Jow Kiang
Yangtze R.
Wanhsien
Wu Shan
Yangtze (Kinsha) R.
Yalung R.
Tatu R.
Chengtu
Kiunglai
Mingshan
Tienchüan
Santai
Shehung
Nanchung
Lungki R.
To
Suining
Batang
Kangting
Pengshan
Hochwan
Pehpei
Tzechung
Yaan
Weiyüan
Neikiang
Fowling
Jungking
Loshan
KANTSE TIBETAN A.C.
Wutungkiao
Chungking
Kiang
Jungchang
Nanchwan
Kienwei
Tzekung
Lungchang
Kikiang
Ipin
Luchow
Suishan
Muli (Tibetan)
Chaochüeh
Tungtze
Sichang
LIANGSHAN YI A.C.
Wu Kiang
DISPUTED AREA BURMA-CHINA
Hweili
Kweiyang
0 50 100 Miles

Szechwan

of the Kialing River and brought by rail spurs to riverside loading stations. The mines, which include Sanhweipa and Taikiatsing, are linked by rail with the riverside stations of Paimiaotze and Hwangtungshu, opposite Pehpei.

Coal is also mined in the lower reaches of the Min Kiang and the To Kiang near Kienwei, Pingshan and Lungchang. The deposits are being exploited at Kiayang, between Kienwei and Pingshan, and at Shihyang, near Lungchang.

Coal measures also extend in western Szechwan from Yaan in the southwest through Pengshan and Chengtu to Kwangyüan in the north. These are not being exploited.

A fourth coal basin, developed during the Second World War, is the Nantung district, named for the hsien of Nanchwan in Szechwan and Tungtze in Kweichow. The Nantung basin, situated south of Chungking, has mines at Wansheng and Puho on a rail spur east from Sankiang. The coal, of coking quality, supplies the steel mills of the Chungking area.

The five-year plan calls for the development of a new coal basin, expected to become the chief producer in Southwest China. This basin, producing coking coal, is being developed in the southern Chungliang Mountains near the Chungking-Chengtu railroad.

Szechwan appears to be a potential petroleum producer and exploration has been pushed in recent years. Deposits have thus far been discovered in four areas: the Tzekung-Fushun area, in association with salt deposits; at Penglaichen in the Fow Kiang valley; at Yenpo, twenty miles south of Chungking, and near Tahsien. Natural gas is associated with the oil deposit south of Chungking, and is also obtained near Lungchang.

In addition to these fuels, Szechwan also has deposits of iron ore, copper, gold, salt, asbestos and mica. The main iron ore deposit at Tutai (near Kikiang) is in the same general area as the Nantung coking coal. The iron ore, largely hematite, is shipped by rail to the Chungking steel mills. Another iron ore deposit, which yields siderite, a low grade ore, is located at Lienkiehchang, thirty miles northwest of Weiyüan. Hematite is also found in the area of Fowling and Pengshui.

Copper is mined in Szechwan near Penghsien, and in former Sikang at Tienchüan northwest of Yaan and Jungking southwest of Yaan.

Gold deposits are also concentrated along the western mountain edge of the province. Lode deposits are found in former Sikang between Tienchüan and Mienning. Placers are mined at Pingwu, in the upper reaches of the Fow Kiang; at Sungpan and Mowhsien, in the upper reaches of the Min Kiang; and at Siaokin (formerly called Mowkung), on the Siao Kin (Little Gold) River, a headstream of the Tatu River.

One of the best-known mineral resources of Szechwan is salt, which is obtained from deep brine wells. Half of the wells are concentrated at Tzekung, a new city formed by the merger of Tzeliutsing and Kungtsing. Tzekung produces about 50 per cent of Szechwan's salt. About 20 per cent of the production is contributed by the salt center of Wutungkiao, on the Min Kiang and another 20 per cent by wells in the Kialing River basin in the area bounded by Yenting, Suining and Nanchung.

Asbestos and mica are mined in former Sikang Province.

Economic development of Szechwan was greatly speeded during the Second World War when industrial enterprises from the east were evacuated in the path of the Japanese advance. Many of the industries were re-established in Szechwan, in particular at Chungking and Chengtu.

Before the war, transportation had to rely on the available navigable rivers and on roads. There were no railroads. The first rail construction during the war yielded the mining spurs in the Pehpei coal basin north of Chungking. In addition the coking coal basin of Nantung and the Kikiang iron ore were connected by rail with the river loading station of Miaoerhto, just east of Kiangtsingcheng on the Yangtze River. Starting in 1956, the Kikiang line is to be extended southward toward Kweiyang in Kweichow Province.

Construction was also begun during the war on the long-planned and much-needed Chungking-Chengtu railroad, but because of a shortage of steel no rails were laid. Construction was pressed by the Communists after 1949 and the railroad was officially opened in July, 1952. The line, connecting the two great cities of Chungking and Chengtu, is of tremendous importance for the economic development of the province. Thanks to it, products from interior sections of the province can now be transported speedily to Chungking for transshipment to the Yangtze River.

The completion of the Chungking-Chengtu railroad established a major internal link within Szechwan but did not provide a railroad link to the rest of China. Soon after Chengtu had been reached, construction began on the line from Chengtu to Paoki. The railroad is scheduled to be completed in 1956. This line will not only bring modern transportation to northern Szechwan but provide the first rail link between the province and the rest of China. In addition, plans are going forward to build a second inter-provincial railroad. This is the line between Neikiang and Kunming via Tzekung, Ipin and the upper Yangtze valley. Construction from the Neikiang end is scheduled to start in the last quarter of 1956.

In the meantime, road construction in the western mountains has improved transportation in the Tibetan-populated areas. Among the major road-building projects have been the Chengtu-Ahpa highway, ultimately to be extended into southern Kansu, and the great Tibetan highway, of which the eastern section through Yaan, Kangting, Kantse, Manikengo (former Yülung) and the Kangto ferry of the upper Yangtze serves the former Sikang section of Szechwan. At Manikengo, the Tsinghai highway branches off toward Yüshu.

The central section of former Sikang is served by the lesser Kangting-Patang (Batang) road, while southern Sikang is traversed by the Yaan-Sichang-Hweili highway.

In keeping with its economic importance, Szechwan has an unusually large number of cities above the hsien level. Their distribution has been determined largely by existing transportation routes and regional trade functions. Four cities are situated along the Yangtze River, the main water artery. They are Ipin, Luchow, Chungking and Wanhsien.

Chungking, Szechwan's largest city and wartime capital of China, is situated at the confluence of the Yangtze and the Kialing River. The city proper is situated on a rocky mile-wide promontory between the two rivers, but the city limits extend far along the two river banks. Within the city limits are the coal mines of Pehpei, twenty-five miles north of the city center. Also within the city limits is the health resort of Nanwenchüan with hot springs on the right bank of the Yangtze south of Chungking. Another health resort, called Peiwenchüan, is at the northern city limits, between Pehpei and Hochwan.

Chungking's population exceeded 1,000,000 while the city was China's wartime capital. Subsequently it dropped slightly. By 1953, it had risen once again to 1,620,000, exceeding the wartime peak by 50 per cent. Situated in the southeastern part of the Szechwan basin, Chungking is a focal point of transportation routes. The Kialing River traffic joins the Yangtze here, the newly constructed railroad goes northwest to Chengtu and on to Paoki, and the main Kweiyang highway goes south to Kweichow Province.

During the Second World War, iron and steel-making equipment was dismantled in the Hanyang-Hwangshih area of the middle Yangtze valley and moved upstream out of the path of the Japanese advance. In 1940, an iron and steel plant, now called the No. 101, was set up at Tatukow, ten miles southwest of the city center. The plant has a 100-ton blast furnace, two open-hearth furnaces and rail mills. Until the completion of the heavy rail mill at Anshan in 1953, the No. 101

plant was the nation's chief rail producer. Two lesser steel plants, the No. 102 and No. 104, are also mentioned in the literature. Other industries at Chungking include cotton and silk mills, including the large No. 610 cotton mill, and chemical plants, including fertilizer plant and a plastics factory based on gallnuts. The electric power capacity required by Chungking's industries will be considerably enlarged in 1956 with completion of the Shihtzetan hydroelectric station on the Lungki River, northeast of Chungking.

The three other Yangtze River cities transship their local products. Ipin (formerly called Suifu and Süchow), at the mouth of the Min Kiang, is the uppermost point accessible to Yangtze steamers. Its natural function as trade center at the gateway to Yünnan will undoubtedly be spurred with completion of the projected Szechwan-Yünnan railroad. A short distance downstream is Luchow (formerly Luhsien), at the mouth of the To Kiang. Until construction of the Chungking-Chengtu railroad, Luchow was the outlet for the products of the To Kiang basin, including the salt of Tzekung and the sugar of Neikiang. It still performs a major trade function on the main road linking Szechwan and Yünnan via northwestern Kweichow, but will ultimately be eclipsed by the railroad between the two provinces. The easternmost Yangtze port in Szechwan is Wanhsien, which handles the products of the eastern mountains, notably tung oil and goatskins. Wanhsien is the chief center between Chungking and Ichang (Hupei).

Two cities are the regional centers of the Kialing River basin. They are Nanchung (formerly Shunking), on the right bank of the Kialing River and the navigation head during the winter low-water stage, and Hochwan, at the confluence of the Kialing and its two tributaries, the Chü Kiang (left) and the Fow Kiang (right). Nanchung has a large silk mill.

Szechwan's second city is Chengtu, metropolis of the Chengtu plain. An old-style walled town, it is the capital of Szechwan and has a population of about 800,000. Wartime industrialization and postwar rail construction have brought engineering, textile and railroad maintenance industries to the ancient city. Chengtu is a focus of trade routes linking the Szechwan Basin with eastern Tibet, southern Kansu and southern Shensi.

On the railroad from Chengtu to Chungkiang is Neikiang, Szechwan's sugar capital. Neikiang is the site of one of China's largest sugar cane mills. The city is slated for the functions of a major rail center as soon as the Neikiang-Kunming railroad will get under way. West of the sugar city are the two salt centers of Tzekung and Wutungkiao, both of which are directly under province jurisdiction. Tzekung has a borax plant.

The principal city and former capital of the Sikang section incorporated into Szechwan in 1955 is Yaan. Yaan succeeded Kangting in 1950 as the capital of Sikang. Yaan is the tea center of western Szechwan and a highway hub on the eastern margins of the Tibetan plateau. Its population rose from 25,000 in 1950 to 70,000 in 1955.

Szechwan's predominantly Chinese population speaks the southwestern variety of the Mandarin. The greatest population density of 1,000 persons per square mile is found in the Chengtu plain and a lesser concentration in the central part of the Szechwan Basin. Sparse settlement is characteristic of the surrounding mountains, with the lowest population density on the margins of the Tibetan plateau.

To speed the introduction of the Communist system of government, the Peking regime briefly administered Szechwan in four parts, following the practice used in Kiangsu and Anhwei. The four provincial sections and their capitals, which existed from 1950 to 1952, were: East Szechwan (Chungking), South Szechwan (Luchow), West Szechwan (Chengtu), and North Szechwan (Nanchung).

Prior to the annexation of Sikang, Szechwan had only one minority region, the Ahpa Tibetan Autonomous Chou, in the northwestern part of the province. This Tibetan chou was set up in December, 1952, with headquarters at Mowhsien. In 1954 the chou capital was moved to Shwakingsze, a Tibetan lamasery on the Chengtu-Ahpa highway. The chou has a population of 500,000, of whom 380,000 are Tibetans. The minority is made up of the Chiang nationality, Chinese and Chinese Moslems.

With the addition of Sikang, Szechwan gained three additional autonomy areas: The Kantse Tibetan Autonomous Chou and the Liangshan Yi Autonomous Chou, and the Muli Tibetan Autonomous Hsien.

The Kantse Tibetan Autonomous Chou was set up in November, 1950, one of the earliest nationality areas established by the Communist regime. The capital of the chou was set up in Kangting, the former administrative center of Sikang. The chou, which has an area of 70,000 square miles and a population of 500,000, covers almost the entire Tibetan plateau section of western Szechwan. About 95 per cent of its population are Tibetan, but only 25 per cent are herders.

The Liangshan Yi Autonomous Chou was established in October, 1952, in the Ta Liang Shan (Great Liang Mountains), on the left bank of the Yangtze River. The chou, which has a population of

700,000, nearly all Yi tribesmen, and an area of 5,000 square miles, has its capital at Chaochüeh.

The Muli Tibetan Autonomous Hsien was established in February, 1953. The hsien has a population of about 100,000.

In summary, Szechwan has a non-Chinese population of about 2,000,000 out of a total population of 66,000,000. Of these 2,000,000, about 800,000 are Tibetan, 600,000 are Yi, and the rest Chiang, Miao (along the Kweichow border) and Chinese Moslems.

CHAPTER 11

THE LOESSLANDS

The loesslands are taken to include the two provinces of Shansi and Shensi. Their combined population is 30,000,000, or 5 per cent of China, and their total area 134,000 square miles, or 3.5 per cent of the nation. The average population density thus is 225 per square mile.

The region is essentially a dissected plateau, varying in elevation from 1,500 to 6,000 feet. It is covered by a mantle of yellow wind-laid silt, known as loess. The thickness of the loess cover averages 500 feet and ranges to a maximum of 1,000 feet. The greatest deposits are found in northern Shensi and in the adjoining parts of eastern Kansu. The source of the loess is generally thought to lie in the Ordos Desert of Inner Mongolia, outside the Great Wall and just north of the area of greatest loess accumulation. From there the northerly winter monsoon winds are thought to have blown the fine lake and river sediments over the bordering region.

Both Shensi and Shansi, which are separated by the middle course of the Yellow River, can be divided topographically into a number of subdivisions. The economic and population center of Shensi is the Wei Ho valley. This narrow, elongated plain lies at an average elevation of 1,000 to 1,300 feet along the north foot of the Tsin Ling divide. The Wei Ho valley, also known as the Kwanchung plain, extends from Paoki in the west to Tungkwan on the Honan border. It is about 170 miles long, forty miles wide and covers an area of 6,000 square miles.

In the north, the relief gradually rises to the North Shensi plateau, which is a structural basin buried in loess. The plateau here lies at an average elevation of 2,600 to 3,300 feet between the Liupan Mountains of eastern Kansu and the Yellow River. In the north the Great Wall separates the plateau from the Ordos Desert of Inner Mongolia. A series of hill ranges crowned by the Great Wall rise to 5,500 feet in the Paiyü Mountains. Streams descending from these heights have deeply dissected the loess plateau of northern Shensi.

South of the Wei Ho valley, the great Tsin Ling divide separates that central Shensi plain from the upper reaches of the Han Shui, tributary of the Yangtze River. The Tsin Ling divide rises abruptly above the Wei Ho valley, reaching an elevation of 13,500 feet in the Taipai Mountains. Its gentler southern slopes descend to the Han Shui valley. The upper Han Shui valley, which centers on the city of Hanchung, is in sharp contrast with the parts of Shensi north of the Tsin Ling divide. The barrier range prevents the cold winter monsoon from penetrating into the upper Han Shui valley. This produces conditions similar to those of northern Szechwan, from which the Han Shui is separated by the Tapa Mountains.

The Shansi plateau lies between the Yellow River in the west and the Taihang Mountains, which separate it from Hopei Province and the North China plain. The plateau is traversed by the valley of the Fen Ho, which flows southsouthwest to the Yellow River. The Fen Ho valley widens into a number of small basins, including the basins of Taiyüan and Linfen. The Taiyüan basin, 100 miles long and thirty miles wide, is the economic heart of Shansi Province. It lies at an elevation of 2,500 feet. On both sides of the Fen Ho valley lies the dissected Shansi plateau. The eastern plateau rises to 10,000 feet in the Wutai Mountains, while the western plateau is dominated by the Lüliang Mountains between the Fen Ho and the Yellow River. North of the Fen Ho valley, between inner and outer sections of the Great Wall, lies the Sangkan basin, drained by a headstream of the Yungting River of Hopei Province. The center of the Sangkan basin is Tatung.

The Yellow River flows in precipitous gorges along the border between Shensi and Shansi. The stream enters the loesslands from Inner Mongolia at an elevation of about 3,000 feet and leaves it at an altitude of 650 feet. In the interval the river bed drops rapidly in rapid-strewn gorges that render the stream unsuitable for navigation. The Yellow River improvement project adopted by the Chinese National People's Congress in July, 1955, calls for the construction of dams along the section of the river, notably at the Sanmen Gorge, on the Shansi-Honan border.

The Wei Ho in Shensi and the Fen Ho in Shansi, the principal tributaries of the Yellow River within the loesslands, are the economic and population centers of the two provinces. The King Ho, a major left tributary of the Wei Ho, gives rise to an important irrigation system known as Kinghweichü at the confluence of the two rivers.

In climate, the loesslands are intermediate between the aridity of Inner Mongolia and the barely adequate rainfall of the North China plain. Because of the greater average elevation, both winter and summer temperatures on the plateau are lower than in the North China plain. January temperatures are about 15 to 20°F (–9 to –7°C), lower in the north and higher in the south. The city of Sian, which occupies a sheltered site in the Wei Ho valley in the lee of the North Shensi plateau, has an average January temperature of barely under 32° F (–0.5° C). Freezing temperatures occur during four winter months. Summer temperatures vary from 70 F (20° C) in the north to 80° F (27° C) in the south. They are generally somewhat lower than North China plain temperatures taken at the same latitudes. Summer days are quite hot, but mornings and nights are cool.

The bordering Taihang Mountains and the Tsin Ling divide offer an effective barrier to the moisture-laden southeasterly summer monsoon. The average rainfall is about 15 inches, considerably less than in the North China plain. Virtually all the precipitation occurs in the summer; two-thirds is concentrated in the months of June, July and August. Rain falls frequently in heavy downpours, a major factor in the strong erosion of the regional loess mantle.

The typical soil of the plateau is a light-colored chestnut soil, high in lime content and subject to renewal by wind work. Darker chestnut soils and even black earth have developed on more humid mountain slopes. Podzols predominate in the Tsin Ling divide and the upper Han Shui valley, while true alluvial soils occur in the Wei Ho plain.

Except for their northern margins, the loesslands are part of the winter wheat-millet crop association area. Spring wheat is the dominant crop along the northern fringes on the Inner Mongolian frontier. In the main agricultural area, the chief plains are the valleys of the Wei Ho in Shensi and the Fen Ho in Shansi. More than one-third of the cropland is found on terraced hillsides. The principal food grains are millet, kaoliang, barley and wheat. Kaoliang and wheat are cultivated in the plains and valleys, millet on the drier hillsides. Oats are associated with spring wheat in the north.

Cotton prospers in the warmer valleys of the Wei Ho and the Fen Ho, which have become among the major cotton producers of China. Their 1954 output was 180,000 tons, 16 per cent of the nation's crop. Formerly mainly raw cotton was shipped to mills along the coast. Since 1949, cotton-milling capacity has been greatly expanded, notably in the Sian-Sienyang area of the Wei Ho valley. Other irrigated specialty crops are tobacco, melons and grapes.

The raising of livestock assumes increasingly greater importance toward the north as rainfall decreases and more areas are used for

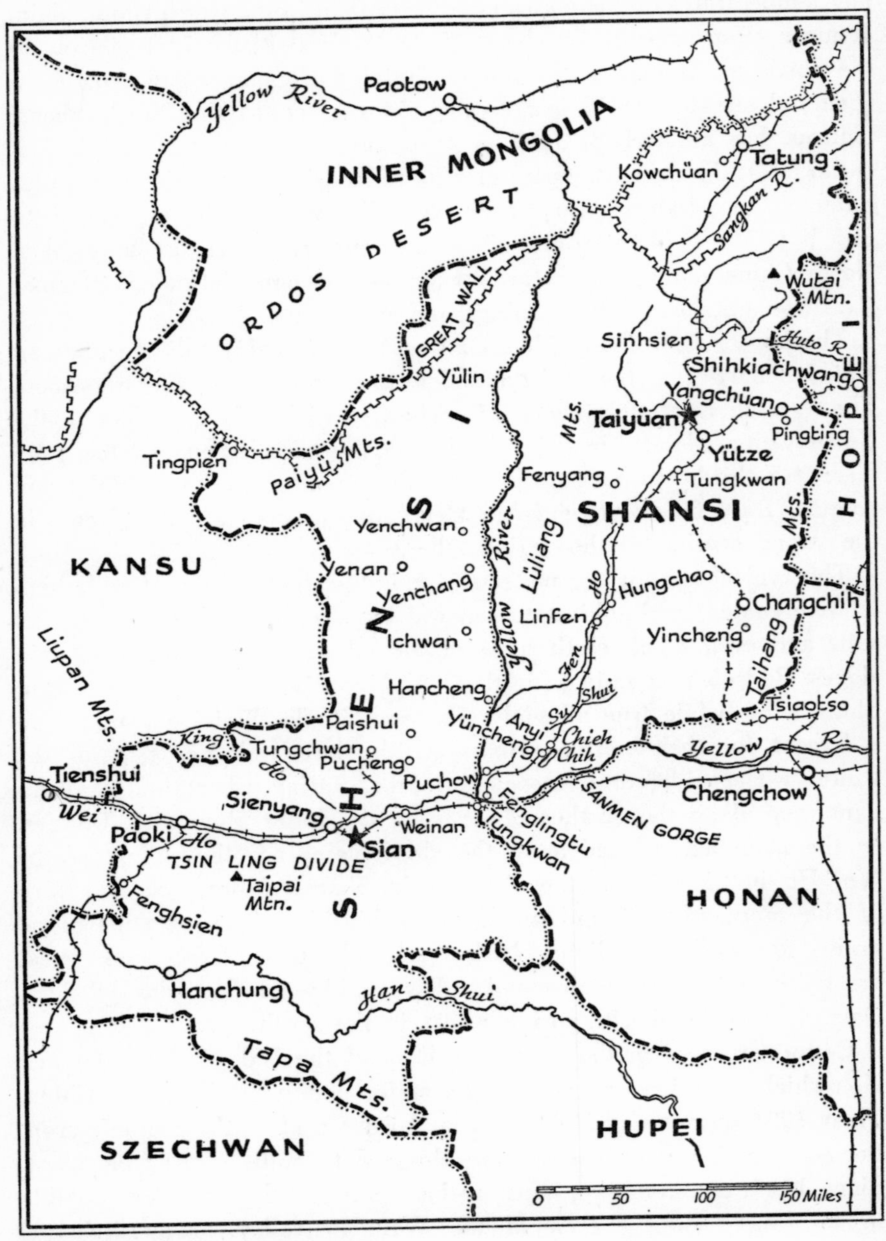

Loesslands (Shansi and Shensi)

pasture. This is the spring wheat zone where a mixed economy of crop tilling and herding prevails. Horses, sheepskins and wool are exported.

The region is well endowed with minerals. Coal is by far the most important mineral resource, with Shansi accounting for 47 per cent and Shensi for 29 per cent of the nation's reserves. However, production has not developed to any great extent because of the region's remoteness from industrial centers. The most important coal-mining center is Tatung. Petroleum, iron ore, gold and salt are also produced.

The region is served by railroads connecting the North China plain with Inner Mongolia and northwest China. Foremost in Shensi is the Lunghai Railroad, while Shansi is traversed from north to south by the Tatung-Taiyüan-Puchow line.

The major cities are Taiyüan and Tatung in Shansi, Sian, Sienyang and Paoki in Shensi.

The loesslands are one of the earliest seats of Chinese culture. According to ancient chronicles, Chinese tribes were settled here as early as the Shang dynasty (1766-1122 B.C.). Sian was China's capital under the important Han dynasty (206 B.C. to A.D. 220). The present population is almost entirely Chinese, speaking the northern (Peking) Mandarin. The Upper Yangtze (Szechwan) variety of Mandarin is used south of the Tsin Ling divide in the upper Han Shui valley.

The population is concentrated in the agricultural valleys of the Fen Ho and the Wei Ho, where the density reaches 400 per square mile. The loess uplands are more sparsely settled, the average density being 50 to 60 per square mile. It was in these sparsely populated uplands that the Chinese Communists consolidated their power after 1935, having established their center at Yenan in the northern Shensi plateau.

SHENSI PROVINCE

Capital: Sian; area: 74,000; population: 15,881,281

Shensi falls into four clearly differentiated natural subdivisions. They are the northern loess plateau, the alluvial Wei Ho plain in the south central part of the province, the great Tsin Ling divide, and the upper Han Shui valley, which has more in common with adjoining Szechwan than with the rest of Shensi.

The Wei Ho valley, also known as the Kwanchung plain, is the economic heart of the province. Here is concentrated most of the agricultural production; here passes the Lunghai Railroad, and here are the major provincial cities of Sian, Sienyang and Paoki. The alluvial plain produces winter wheat and summer millet as the chief food grains, cotton being the principal cash crop.

In 1954, the province as a whole produced 5 million tons of grain on 4.5 million hectares of land. The average yield was 1.1 tons per hectare. The total grain crop included 1.8 million tons of winter wheat. In the same year the cotton harvest amounted to 90,000 tons, or 8 per cent of the nation's total cotton lint output. The area under cotton was 300,000 hectares.

The importance of livestock in Shensi is illustrated by the animal holdings in 1954. There were 2,586,000 large livestock (cattle, horses, mules), 3,004,500 sheep and goats and 1,825,000 hogs.

Coal is mined in Shensi at Tungchwan and, to a lesser extent, at Hancheng on the Yellow River. A branch of the Lunghai Railroad, completed in 1940, leads from Sienyang to Tungchwan, which was formerly called Tungkwan. Petroleum is produced in the northern Shensi field of Yenchang. Other fields, as yet unexploited, are near by at Yenchwan, Yenan and Ichwan. Salt is obtained both from salt lakes near Tingpien in the extreme north and from brine wells near Pucheng in the south. The Pucheng-Paishui area is linked by a narrow-gauge railroad with the Lunghai main line at Weinan.

Until 1934, the Lunghai Railroad stopped at Tungkwan, gateway city at the Shensi-Honan line. Thereafter the railroad was gradually extended westward across Shensi reaching Sian in 1935, Paoki in 1937 and Tienshui in 1945. The only other railroad serving Shensi is the newly built Chengtu-Paoki line, which passes through the southwesternmost section of the province.

Aside from railroads, highways play the major transportation role in Shensi. The Sienyang-Yülin highway is the main route through the northern plateau, connecting the Wei Ho valley with the spring wheat belt adjoining the Great Wall. River navigation is negligible. Pending the completion of major improvement projects, the Yellow River course is entirely unusable for navigation. Small junks can navigate on the Wei Ho below Sienyang and on the Han Shui below Hanchung.

Industrial development in Shensi has been marked since 1949 by the construction of new cotton mills to process the locally grown cotton. Three new mills of 150,000 spindles each were completed between 1952 and 1954. A fourth, of 100,000 spindles, was completed in 1955 and a fifth, also of 100,000 spindles, was scheduled to start operations in 1956.

The principal industrial centers are Sian, the capital, Sienyang, Paoki and Hanchung. With the exception of Hanchung, which is situated south of the Tsin Ling divide in the Han Shui valley, the provincial cities are in the Wei Ho plain along the Lunghai Railroad.

Sian, one of China's oldest capitals, lies in the center of the Wei Ho plain. It owes its administrative and industrial importance largely to its location at the focus of major overland routes linking the North China plain with the Northwest. The development of industries since 1949, which include a large thermal power plant and cotton mills, has resulted in a considerable population rise. The city grew from 500,000 in 1949 to 760,000 in 1953. The city is built in a walled rectangle (2.5 by 1.5 miles), with small walled suburbs adjoining the four main gates. Industrial expansion has affected primarily the western suburb since 1949. The city was the capital of China under the Han dynasty and was then called Changan ("long peace"). It flourished again under the Tang dynasty (618-906) as the western capital of the empire and was known as Siking ("western capital"). In modern times it became known as Sian ("western peace") under the Manchu dynasty, reverted to Changan from 1913 to 1932, to Siking from 1932 to 1943, and has been known as Sian since 1943.

About ten miles northwest of Sian, across the Wei Ho, is the city of Sienyang. Formerly a simple hsien town, Sienyang was raised to the status of city in December, 1952, in connection with the construction of large cotton mills. Sienyang receives its power from the Sian plant, with which it is connected by a transmission line.

Paoki, the westernmost city in the Wei Ho valley, is a major transportation center of the Northwest. It is situated at the crossing of the Lunghai Railroad and the Shensi-Szechwan highway. In 1956, Paoki is due to be reached by the newly constructed railroad from Chungking and Chengtu in Szechwan. The city has large railroad shops and serves as a repair and assembly center for railroad construction equipment used on the major projects of the Northwest. Other industries are concerned with the production of textiles, paper, flour, vegetable oils and tobacco. Paoki developed as a result of the construction of the Lunghai Railroad, superseding Fenghsien, former highway center in the Kansu-Shensi-Szechwan tri-state area. The Paoki-Fenghsien section of the Shensi-Szechwan railroad is due to be the first electrified line in China.

Considerably isolated from the rest of Shensi Province is the city of Hanchung, center of the Han Shui valley south of the Tsin Ling divide. Here rice and silk are the key products. Hanchung, which was called Nancheng prior to 1953, depends on trade along the Han Shui, of which it is head of navigation. The city is being by-passed on the west by the Chengtu-Paoki railroad.

SHANSI PROVINCE

Capital: Taiyüan; area: 60,000; population: 14,314,485

Shansi Province is bordered by the Yellow River on the west and south, the Taihang Mountains on the east, and the outer section of the Great Wall on the north. In the early years of Communist rule, the northern section of Shansi was detached from the province and annexed to Chahar. The detached area, situated between the outer and inner sections of the Grat Wall, was rstored to Shansi in 1952 when Chahar was abolished.

The Shansi plateau, which lies at an elevation of 3,000 to 6,000 feet, is traversed from north to south by a longitudinal depression occupied in part by the Fen Ho, the province's principal river. The depression widens in a few places to form rather extensive upland plains. In the extreme north, between the outer and inner sections of the Great Wall is the Sangkan basin, with its center at Tatung. This basin is drained toward the northeast by the Sangkan River, a headstream of the Yungting River. The central part of the Sangkan basin lies at an elevation of 2,000 to 2,500 feet.

The next upland plain to the south is that of Sinhsien. The Sinhsien basin is drained toward the east by the Huto River, a headstream of the Hai Ho of Hopei Province. The Fen Ho valley proper widens into the Taiyüan basin, in the geographical center of Shansi, and the Linfen plain to the southwest. The Taiyüan basin, 100 miles by thirty miles, is the economic heart of the province. It lies at an elevation of 2,500 feet. The lowest basin of Shansi is the Anyi plain in the extreme southwest at an elevation of 1,300 feet. The area between the lower Fen Ho and the Su Shui, which traverses the Anyi basin, is one of the most important agricultural areas of the province.

In addition to the lower Fen Ho valley and the other basins of the longitudinal depression, agriculture is also of some importance in the Changchih basin on the eastern plateau. Among the food grains, millet and kaoliang are the chief summer crops and wheat the winter crop. Spring wheat and oats are cultivated in the Sangkan basin, where winter temperatures are lower than in the rest of the province.

Cash crops include cotton and tobacco. Vineyards are found in the sheltered Taiyüan basin near Fenyang and are used in the production of "fen-chiu" (Fen liquor), for which Shansi is famous. Each of the cash crops requires irrigation. About 200,000 hectares under cotton yielded about 92,000 tons of cotton lint in 1954. Hungchao is a noted cotton center.

Grain and cotton production in Shansi has greatly fluctuated in recent years, as follows (in million tons):

	Grain	*Cotton*
1951	3.17	.054
1952	3.8	.09
1953	4.26	.077
1954	4.08	.092

The irrigated area has increased from 260,000 hectares in 1952 to 450,000 in 1954.

Shansi greatly exceeds Shensi in its exploitation of mineral resources. The most important coal basin is that of Tatung in northern Shansi. Reserves here are one-tenth of China's total. The five-year plan calls for an output of 6,450,000 tons of coal at Tatung by 1957. The mines are situated at Kowchüan on a rail spur southwest of Tatung. In addition to Tatung, coal outcrops throughout the province with the exception of the extreme southwest. Most of the mines are operated on a handicraft basis. However, modern machinery and methods have been introduced at Yangchüan, on the Taiyüan-Shihkiachwang railroad, and at Changchih, on a dismantled narrow-gauge railroad from Paikwei, just northeast of Tungkwan. Other modern mines are at Kiangtsun and Hopientsun on a rail spur from Sinhsien.

Shansi is one of the oldest ironworking provinces of China. Small deposits are widespread and have been worked by handicraft methods. The deposits in the Yangchüan-Pingting area were formerly exploited by the Paochin company, which erected a small blast furnace at Yangchüan. Another major deposit is south of Changchih at the town of Yincheng, an important ironworking handicraft center.

Shansi has one of China's major inland salt sources. Salt is obtained from the salt lake Chieh Chih in the Anyi basin. The lake, which is fifteen miles long and two miles wide, yields 600,000 tons of salt a year. The producing center is Yüncheng, just southwest of Anyi.

Shansi is relatively well supplied with railroad lines. The backbone of the province is the Tatung-Puchow railroad, which traverses Shansi from north to south. In the north the line connects at Tatung with the Peking-Paotow railroad. In the south the line originally ended at Puchow (formerly called Yungtsi). Subsequently it was extended twenty miles to its present southern terminus of Fenglingtu, in the southwestern corner of Shansi, on the Yellow River opposite Tungkwan (Shensi). The Tatung-Puchow railroad was originally a narrow-gauge line built by Yen Hsi-shan, Shansi warlord. During the Second World War, the Japanese converted the northern section (north of Yütze) to standard gauge to provide direct access to the northern coal mines. Reconstruction of the entire line and conversion of the southern section to standard gauge began in 1955.

The province's chief east-west link is the Taiyüan-Yütze-Shihkiachwang railroad. The line, originally built with narrow-gauge track, was also converted to standard gauge by the Japanese during the war.

Two major narrow-gauge spurs connect the main north-south line with coal-mining centers. They are the spur from Sinhsien to the mines of Kiangtsun and Hopientsun, built before the Second World War, and the branch from Paikwei to Changchih, constructed by the Japanese. The Changchih branch was dismantled subsequently and had not been restored by 1955. Instead construction began in 1956 on a standard-gauge line linking Shansi to the Tsiaotso mining area of Honan.

Execept for small junk traffic on the lower Fen Ho, Shansi's rivers are not navigable. An adequate highway network supplements the railroad system.

Five cities of industrial importance are under the direct jurisdiction of the provincial government. They are Taiyüan, the capital, Tatung, Yütze, Yangchüan, and Changchih.

Taiyüan occupies a central position in Shansi. It is situated at the northern end of the Taiyüan basin, major agricultural area producing wheat and cotton. The city acquired modern industries, such as cotton mills and agricultural implement factories, before the Second World War under the rule of Yen Hsi-shan. Industrialization was greatly intensified after 1949, bringing the city's population from 270,000 at the time of the Communist takeover to 600,000 in 1953. Industrial growth was achieved in particular through expansion of an existing iron and steel plant and the construction of a heavy machine-building plant. The iron and steel plant, in addition to its basic blast furnace and open hearth departments, produces electric steels, sheets, structural and forged items. The Taiyüan iron and steel plant was reported in 1954 to be the largest metallurgical enterprise in China outside of Anshan in Manchuria. The heavy machine-building plant produces rolling-mill and coke-oven equipment and heavy cranes. It is designed to equip industrial construction projects in the Northwest.

Yütze, situated fifteen miles southeast of Taiyüan, was made a provincial city in 1954. It is situated at the junction of the main Shansi north-south railroad and the Taiyüan-Shihkiachwang line. Yütze had some industrial plants before the war, but its importance was greatly enhanced by the construction of the Chingwei textile machinery plant. This enterprise, originally situated in Shanghai, was dismantled after 1949 and rebuilt in the Taiyüan area at Yütze. Construction began in May 1951 and the plant was formally opened in the spring of 1954. It produces spindles and looms for the new cotton mills that have been set up in the cotton areas of Hopei and Shensi.

The industrial metropolis of northern Shansi is the city of Tatung. A rail center of considerable importance, Tatung is situated at the junction of the Shansi main line and the Peking-Paotow railroad. The city is being transformed into a major industrial hub, producing cement, locomotives, mining machinery, as well as coal. Tatung's original cement plant was rebuilt in January, 1955, after having been out of operation for nine years. A second plant of far greater capacity was due to be completed later in 1955. The two cement plants are designed to supply construction projects in the Northwest, in particular at Paotow in Inner Mongolia. Tatung's industries, including its locomotive factory and mining-machinery repair plant, are powered by a 50,000-kilowatt thermal electric plant fed by local coal. Some of the city's industries, in particular, one of the cement plants, are situated in the southwestern coal-mining suburb of Kowchüan. During the five-year plan, Tatung is being developed as the leading coal producer of the Northwest, with 1957 output planned at 6,450,000 tons.

East of Taiyüan, on the railroad leading to Shihkiachwang, is the city of Yangchüan, situated in a coal and iron-ore mining area. Just south of Yangchüan is the ancient Chinese ironworking center of Pingting. This was superseded in modern times by the railroad town of Yangchüan, where the Paochin company erected a small blast furnace before the First World War. A new power transmission line links Taiyüan and Yangchüan.

Another ancient ironworking center is Changchih, in south eastern Shansi. Changchih, which was formerly called Luan, is also situated in a coal and iron-ore mining area. Highways link it to the provinces of Hopei and Honan and a narrow-gauge railroad, built during the Second World War, linked it to the Shansi main line at Paikwei. Changchih, in addition to its iron products, is known for the collection of ginseng roots, wool weaving and liquor distilling.

Chapter XII

MANCHURIA

Manchuria is here taken to include the provinces of Heilungkiang, Kirin and Liaoning, with the eastern section of Jehol, which was incorporated into Liaoning in 1956. The region, as discussed here, does not include the Hulunbuir, Jerim and Jo-oda leagues of Inner Mongolia, nor the northern section of Jehol incorporated into Inner Mongolia in 1956.

Thus defined, Manchuria has a population of 43,000,000 or 8 per cent of China, and a total area of 300,000 square miles, or 8 per cent of the nation's total. The average population density is 140 persons per square mile.

Manchuria is the northeastern region of China and is known to the Chinese simply as "the Northeast." The region borders on the Soviet Union along the Amur and Ussuri rivers and on Korea along the Tumen and Yalu rivers. It consists essentially of a central lowland enclosed by mountains. The major subregions are: the Liaotung peninsula, the East Manchurian uplands, the Manchurian plain, the Khingan mountains, and the eastern Jehol uplands.

The Liaotung peninsula, in southernmost Manchuria, juts out into the Po Hai toward Shantung, with which it has much in common physically. The two peninsulas have a common geological structure interrupted by the downfaulted Po Hai Strait; both have a hilly topography, the eroded remains of mountain masses, covered by the identical mantle of brown podzolic forest soils. The Liaotung peninsula has an average elevation of 600 to 1,000 feet. Its eroded mountain backbone, the Tsien Shan, an extension of the East Manchurian uplands, rises to 1,850 feet south of Penki. At the extremity of the peninsula is the Port Arthur–Dairen municipal district.

The East Manchurian uplands extend in a series of ranges northeast-southwest along the Korean border. They rise to 9,000 feet in the Changpai (Long White) Mountains. The culminating volcanic peak of Paitow Shan contains the crater lake of Tien Chih. The East Manchurian uplands have some of China's most important timber reserves and hydroelectric potential. In addition to the Korean border rivers—the Yalu and the Tumen— the Sungari and its right tributary, the Mutan River, rise in these uplands.

The Manchurian plain is also known as the Sungari-Liao plain, for its two main rivers. It is bounded by the East Manchurian uplands in the east, the Little Khingan mountains in the north, the Great Khingan mountains (largely in Inner Mongolia) in the west, and terminates in the south in the Liaotung peninsula. Its average elevation ranges between 150 and 600 feet. A low watershed of 800 feet separates the plain into the Sungari lowland in the north and the Liao lowland in the south. Unlike the North China plain, which is of depositional origin, the Manchurian plain is a structural lowland with rolling topography. The Sungari, known in Chinese as the Sunghwa, flows northwest until it meets the Nun Kiang (Nonni). It then turns sharply northeast and receives the Mutan River before joining the Amur. In the southern part of the Manchurian plain, the Liao Ho flows east and south to the Gulf of Liaotung, west of the Liaotung peninsula. A narrow strip of coastal lowland, the so-called Liaosi ("west of the Liao") corridor, joins the Manchurian plain at Shanhaikwan with the North China plain and constitutes the only link between the two regions.

The Khingan mountains include the Great Khingan, which is almost entirely in Inner Mongolia, the Ilkhuri Mountains, and the Little Khingan. The Ilkhuri and Little Khingan ranges form the watershed between the Sungari and Amur systems.

The Jehol uplands lie at an elevation of 2,500 to 3,000 feet and form a transition zone between the Manchurian and North China plains and the Mongolian plateau.

Manchuria lies mainly between Lat. 40 and 50 degrees N., corresponding to the northern United States and southern Canada. This suggests similar climatic conditions, but the greater continentality of Asia results in sharper seasonal contrasts. Winters are long and bitter, summers short and hot. Average January temeperatures range from 21° F (–6° C) in the extreme southern Liaotung peninsula to –13° F (–25° C) in the extreme north on the Amur River. Nowhere else in the world are such low winter temperatures found in these latitudes. Snow falls during six to seven months and temperatures are below freezing for four to five months.

By contrast, in the summer temperatures are high throughout the the region. July averages range from 80° F (27° C) in the south to 70° F (21° C) in the north. The growing season is 200 days in the south and

150 days in the north, making it possible to raise only one crop a year. Winter crops are excluded not only by the low temperatures, but also by the thin snow cover, which results in the ground's freezing to a depth of six feet or more.

Precipitation is in effect seasonal, with light winter snowfall, a dry spring and fall and a summer maximum of rainfall. The total amount of precipitation decreases from the southeast (40 inches at Antung) toward the northwest (15 inches at the east foot of the Khingan range), where agriculture becomes precarious without irrigation.

Owing to a natural grass cover in the Manchurian plain, the soils there are among the most fertile in China. There is an extensive development of chernozem in the Sungari plain, passing into chestnut soils toward the south. These are steppe soils corresponding to similar soils in European Russia. Along the drier western margins of the plain, gray steppe soils with saline and alkali patches predominate. Podzolic soils and brown forest soils cover the mountains enclosing the central Manchurian plain.

Manchurian agriculture is characterized by the soybean-kaoliang crop association. Millet, spring wheat, corn, barley and some rice are other crops. Soybeans are by far the most important crop in value of production, in percentage of sown area, and as an export product. It covers 25 to 30 per cent of the sown acreage. In recent times, soybean production has been gradually concentrated in northern Manchuria as more land in the south was being sown in kaoliang and other grains to feed the growing population. Manchuria accounts for about 40 per percent of China's soybean crop. Of this, 30 per cent is exported in the form of oil and beancake.

Kaoliang predominates among the Manchurian grains. Not only does it constitute the chief food crop of the Manchurian peasant, but it is also used for the distilling of the local alcoholic beverage. Kaoliang occupies close to 25 per cent of the Manchurian crop area, being concentrated in the Liao plain. South of Mukden, kaoliang takes up 30 to 40 per cent of the sown acreage. Manchuria's share in China's total kaoliang output is about 35 per cent.

Another major Manchurian grain is millet. The most common among several varieties is the Italian millet or spiked foxtail millet, known as "ku-tzu" in Chinese. The husked millet grain, an important Manchurian food, is known in Chinese as "hsiao-mi-tzu"; this term has been corrupted by the Russians into "chumiza" and is used to designate the millet grown in the Soviet Far East. A less common millet variety grown in Manchuria is the glutinous millet, known in Chinese as "shu-tzu,"which grows in more humid soils than the Italian millet. Millet is widespread throughout Manchuria, but predominates in the southwestern part of the central plain.

Corn is grown primarily in the more humid southeastern part of the Manchurian plain. Unlike millet, which is also exported, corn is consumed entirely within Manchuria. In the southeast it takes up as much as 40 per cent of the sown area. Another grain crop of the southeast is rice, which is grown predominantly by Koreans in the valleys of the East Manchurian uplands. In 1954, Manchuria produced 1.4 million tons of rice.

Spring wheat is associated with soybeans in northern Manchuria. Almost all of Manchuria's wheat crop comes from the chernozem of the Sungari basin, where Harbin is the major milling center. Barley and oats are also grown.

Taking all food crops together, Manchuria produces about 12 per cent of the Chinese total output. Manchurian food production in recent years has been as follows:

1949	13.2 million tons
1950	18.1 million tons
1951	17 million tons
1952	21 million tons
1953	18.6 million tons
1954 Plan	22.3 million tons

Among industrial crops are fibers, such as cotton, hemp and flax, tobacco, sugar beets, and a number of oil-bearing plants, such as castor beans, perilla, sesame and rape.

In the extreme south of the Liaotung peninsula, where conditions are similar to those in the Shantung peninsula, peanuts are produced in the sandy forest soils. Manchuria produces about 6 per cent of China's peanut crop and is second to Shantung in exports.

Cotton is grown chiefly in the Liao plain of southern Manchuria, notably around Liaoyang. Unginned production in 1953 was 190,000 tons, a yield of 693 kilograms per hectare. Manchurian cotton output under the Chinese Communists has gone beyond the peak output under Japanese occupation of about 100,000 tons.

Hemp is grown both for its seed and its fiber, which is made into sacks for soybeans. The production of flax has been greatly expanded in recent years in northern Manchuria. The 1954 plan called for 71,500 tons compared with 48,500 tons produced in 1943 under the Japanese.

Tobacco is grown chiefly in central Manchuria, where 25,500 tons were to be produced according to the 1954 plan. A major expansion program is taking place in sugar beets. This crop was formerly insignificant in Manchuria. Acreage is being greatly expanded, notably in Heilungkiang's chernozem area and the 1954 plan called for a production of 1,030,000 tons of beets. This represents a tenfold increase from 1949, when about 100,000 tons were produced.

Institutionally, Manchuria's agriculture differs considerably from that of most of China. The Communists carried through their land reform program in Manchuria earlier than in the rest of the nation. This fact plus the lower population density per unit of cultivated land have led to a relatively high degree of mechanization in Manchuria. Unlike China proper, Manchuria also offers the possibility of expansion of the cultivated area. It has been calculated that about 30,000,000 hectares, or one third of Manchuria's total area, is suitable for cultivation. At present only 20,000,000 hectares are actually in crops. Most of the unused acreage is in the northern province of Heilungkiang, where efforts are now being made to bring more land under cultivation. Mechanization plays a major part in this expansion program.

Manchuria's mountains have China's most extensive forest reserves. Lumbering plays a major role in the economy of the East Manchurian uplands and the Little Khingan. Timber cut in the eastern uplands is floated down the Yalu, Tumen and Mutan rivers for processing at such centers as Antung, Kirin and Mutankiang. In the Little Khingan, much of the exploitation is centered in the new lumber center of Ichun.

In most of the Manchurian plain, livestock raising is subsidiary to the tilling of crops. The herds include mainly hogs, draft animals and cows. They are fed on the by-products of agriculture. However, along the western margins of the plain bordering on Inner Mongolia, herding is a major part of the economy. Sheep and goats, horses and beef cattle predominate and are fed on steppe pastures.

Fisheries are of some importance along the Yellow Sea coast of Manchuria, where the indented coastline, an abundance of offshore islands and shallow coastal waters offer favorable conditions for fishing. The principal centers are Haiyang Island in Korea Bay, Sinkin (formerly called Pitzewo), Dairen and Port Arthur.

One distinctive occupation in the mountains of Manchuria is the hunting of fur-bearing animals. Foxes, sable and squirrels are hunted in the East Manchurian uplands and in the Khingan mountains.

The mineral resources of Manchuria are inferior to those of the rest of China, but mining developments, particularly under the Japanese, have made the region China's most important producing area. Manchuria has about 8 per cent of China's coal reserves, but produces 30 per cent of the nation's coal. The producing centers are Fushun, Fusin, Pehpiao and Penki-Yentai in Liaoning Province, Liaoyüan (formerly called Sian) in Kirin Province, Hokang, Shwangyashan and Kisi in Heilungkiang Province. During the five-year plan, the greatest production is planned for Fushun (9.3 million tons by 1957) and Fusin (8.45 million tons). Fushun also produces oil shale, which on distillation yields a number of oil products.

Among the metals, iron ore plays a key role in Manchuria. The region has two-thirds of China's iron ore reserves and 60 per cent of the nation's iron ore output, nearly all of which comes from Liaoning Province. The mining centers are Anshan, near-by Kungchangling, Miaoerhkow south of Penki, and Talitze in the Tungpientao district on the Korean border.

Gold is found both in placers and in lode deposits. The placers are worked in northern Manchuria along the Amur and the lower Sungari. Lode deposits are mined near Hwatien and Yenki in Kirin Province.

Manchuria has large reserves of refractory materials, such as magnesite, alunite and fire clays. These materials are of considerable importance in the development of the iron and steel industry at Anshan and elsewhere, but they also constitute a potential source for the production of metallic magnesium and aluminum. The Japanese produced both light metals at Fushun during the Second World War and it can be presumed that this industry will be revived by the Chinese as part of their industrialization program. Reconstruction of the aluminum plant at Fushun was under way in 1955.

Other metallic deposits include copper, lead and zinc, molybdenum (notably in the Chinsi area of Liaoning Province), manganese and pyrites. Salt is obtained along the coast of the Liaotung peninsula.

On the basis of existing mineral resources, Manchuria became China's leading center of heavy industry during the Japanese occupation before and during the Second World War. After 1949 many of the Japanese-built enterprises were gradually restored and expanded. Manchuria continues to dominate in China's heavy industry pending the contemplated build-up of iron and steel and associated enterprises elsewhere in China. Manchuria's industry includes iron and steel enterprises, notably at Anshan and Penki, machinery industries at Mukden, Dairen, Changchun and Harbin, and food-processing and consumer industries in these and other cities. The electric power base is provided in the form of thermal plants in the large centers and hydroelectric installations at Fengman near Kirin and at Shuifeng on the Yalu River.

Manchuria's industrial centers are served by a relatively dense rail

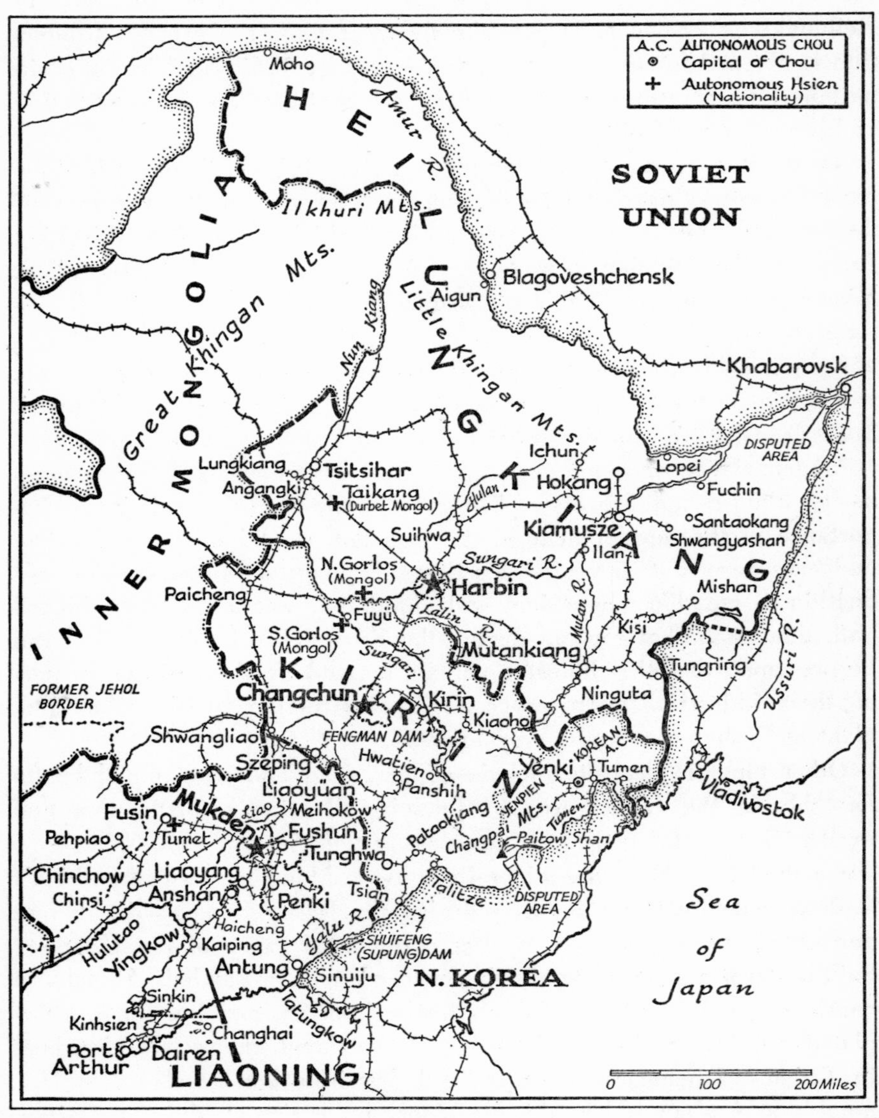

A.C. AUTONOMOUS CHOU
Capital of Chou
Autonomous Hsien (Nationality)
SOVIET UNION
HEILUNGKIANG
INNER MONGOLIA
KIRIN
LIAONING
N. KOREA
Sea of Japan
Moho
Amur R.
Ilkhuri Mts.
Great Khingan Mts.
Little Khingan Mts.
Nun Kiang
Blagoveshchensk
Aigun
Khabarovsk
DISPUTED AREA
Ichun
Lopei
Fuchin
Hokang
Santaokang
Kiamusze
Shwangyashan
Ilan
Lungkiang
Tsitsihar
Angangki
Taikang (Durbet Mongol)
Hulan
Suihwa
Sungari R.
N. Gorlos (Mongol)
Harbin
Mishan
Paicheng
Fuyü
Lalin R.
Mutan R.
Kisi
S. Gorlos (Mongol)
Mutankiang
Tungning
Ussuri R.
FORMER JEHOL BORDER
Changchun
Kirin
Ninguta
Kiaoho
Shwangliao
FENGMAN DAM
Szeping
Hwatien
Yenki
KOREAN A.C.
YENPIEN
Tumen
Vladivostok
Liaoyüan
Panshih
Fusin
Mukden
Liao
Meihokow
Fushun
Pehpiao
Tumet
Tunghwa
Pataokiang
Changpai Mts.
Paitow Shan
Chinchow
Liaoyang
Chinsi
Anshan
Penki
Tsian
Talitze
DISPUTED AREA
Haicheng
Hulutao
Yingkow
Kaiping
Yalu R.
SHUIFENG (SUPUNG) DAM
Antung
Sinuiju
Sinkin
Kinhsien
Tatungkow
Changhai
Port Arthur
Dairen
0 100 200 Miles

Manchuria

network, including about 40 per cent of China's total track mileage. The main lines are the historic Chinese Eastern and South Manchuria railroads, whose T-shaped system formed the only Soviet-Chinese rail link prior to 1955. In that year the completion of the Tsining–Ulan-Bator line through the Mongolian People's Republic offered a second and shorter connection between the two countries.

The Chinese Eastern and South Manchuria railroads were administered jointly by the Soviet Union and China as the Chinese Changchun Railroad from 1945 to 1952. Thereafter the system passed into Chinese hands. The system consists of four main sections: the Harbin-Manchouli line, the Harbin-Tungning (formerly Suifenho) line, the Harbin-Changchun line and the Changchun-Dairen line. Major branches lead from Mukden to Tientsin and Peking and from Mukden to Antung on the Korean border.

Manchuria's main rivers are navigable during the ice-free season, which is about six months on the Sungari River and eight months on the Liao Ho. The Sungari basin is nevertheless the more important navigation system and plays an important role in the transportation of the Sungari plain. The section from Harbin downstream to the Amur is the most heavily traveled. The Amur itself is little used on the Chinese side as its banks are sparsely settled and lie outside the Manchurian plain. The Liao Ho was the chief transportation route of southern Manchuria before the coming of the railroads. Its traffic has declined in recent years and sediments have been choking its channel.

Dairen, at the tip of the Liaotung peninsula, is Manchuria's chief seaport. Of much lesser importance are Hulutao and Yingkow on the Gulf of Liaotung, and Tatungkow, outer port of Antung.

Manchuria's population density is low by Chinese standards. There are about 400 persons per square mile in the relatively closely settled Liaotung peninsula and the Mukden industrial area, but the region's over-all average is 140. Parts of the northern Manchurian plain have as few as 25 persons per square mile. Migration from overpopulated parts of China to Manchuria has been a continuing process in recent decades. Even under the Japanese occupation Chinese workers were recruited for Manchuria's growing industries. The Peking regime is once again stimulating migration from such provinces as Shantung, Hopei and Honan to put Manchuria's virgin lands under the plow.

More than 90 per cent of Manchuria's population is Chinese, speaking the northern (Peking) variety of Mandarin. Among the region's minorities are most of China's 1,100,000 Koreans, of whom about one-half live in the Yenpien Korean Autonomous Chou of Kirin Province.

Along the western margins of the Manchurian plain live about 200,000 Mongols, who are organized in several autonomous banners. Manchuria's population also includes a large part of the 2,400,000 persons reported as Manchus in the June, 1953, census. These persons, presumably descendants of the original Manchus, no longer form a separate cultural group and have been assimilated among the Chinese. They are said to be distributed among the Chinese population throughout Manchuria and have no special autonomous unit of any kind. The only true Manchu-speaking people are members of several small, primitive tribes that form part of the Tungus-Manchu ethnic group. They include the Orochon and Solon tribes in the northernmost part of the Great Khingan, and the Gold tribe, which lives in the marshy lowlands between the Sungari and Ussuri rivers.

LIAONING PROVINCE

Capital: Mukden; area: 50,000; population: 20,000,000

From 1949 until August, 1954, Liaoning Province consisted of the two provinces of Liaosi and Liaotung, respectively west and east of the Liao Ho, and the independent cities of Mukden, Fushun, Anshan, Penki and Port Arthur–Dairen. At the time of consolidation of these areas into Liaoning Province, a strip of territory along the province's northern border, including the cities of Tunghwa, Liaoyüan and Szeping, was ceded to Kirin Province. In 1956, Liaoning Province acquired the eastern section of partitioned Jehol.

As constituted since 1956, Liaoning includes the Liaotung peninsula and part of the East Manchurian uplands in the east, the Liao plain, and the Liaosi corridor in the southwest. In the west the province reaches into the Jehol uplands. Liaoning is the part of Manchuria that is closest to the rest of China and as such was settled by the Chinese earlier than the rest of the region. Its seaboard location and the early construction of a rail net played a major part in the rapid development of the province. During the Second World War the area was a key base of war industries of the Japanese.

Agriculture is concentrated in the Liao plain, which extends largely west of the river. Almost all available land has been put under cultivation. Because of the relatively high population pressure, agriculture is largely of the subsistence type unlike the commercial surplus farming typical of northern Manchuria. As a result, soybeans occupy less than one-fourth of the sown area, while food crops, such as kaoliang and millet, take up more than one-half. Soybeans become more important toward the north. Corn is a leading crop in the southeast, where it covers 40 to 50 per cent of the sown area. The limited cultivation of rice in the same area must also be noted. The production of food crops in 1954 amounted to 5,440,000 tons, a rise from 4,880,000 tons in 1953.

Liaoning produces nearly all of Manchuria's cotton and a large part of its tobacco, sesame and castor beans. Cotton is cultivated chiefly around Liaoyang and toward the southwest, tobacco in the northeast and castor beans in the west and southwest. The unginned cotton crop amounted to 86,258 tons in 1954, a poor cotton year, compared with 160,000 tons in 1953.

A distinctive product of the province is wild silk, which is spun and woven into pongee cloth. The silk, which is produced by a worm feeding on oak leaves, is produced chiefly on the Liaotung peninsula near Kaiping and around Antung. The oak-fed silkworm was introduced into Liaoning by settlers from Shantung, a province with which southeastern Liaoning has much in common.

Another distinctive crop is fruit, especially apples and pears. The apple area on the Liaotung peninsula, again centered on Kaiping, produces about 70 per cent of China's apple crop.

In the realm of mineral resources, Liaoning leads in the production of Manchurian coal and produces nearly the region's entire iron output. Coal resources occur both on the western and eastern edges of the Liao plain. The main mining centers are Fushun and Penki-Yentai on the eastern margin and Fusin and Pehpiao on the western margin. Both Penki-Yentai and Pehpiao produce coking coal. The 1954 plan was 14.5 million tons of coal (not including Pehpiao, then in Jehol).

Iron ore is found in the Anshan-Kungchangling and Penki-Miaoerhkow areas. The small Anshan deposit of high-grade ore was the first to supply the iron and steel plant after its construction in 1918. Later the larger reserves of low-grade ore at Kungchangling were developed 25 miles east of Anshan. The Kungchangling reserves are estimated at 800,000,000 tons with an iron content of 35 to 40 per cent. The iron ore of Miaoerhkow, mined on a rail spur leading east from Nanfen, twenty miles south of Penki, is distinguished by a low phosphorus content, which makes it suitable for use in Bessemer converters. Another deposit supplying the Penki iron and steel industry is that of Waitowshan, situated northwest of Penki and just west of Yaotsienhu railroad station.

Large magnesite reserves in the Liaotung peninsula offer a potential source of refractory materials and metallic magnesium. The deposit, which extends for twenty miles and has a thickess of up to 2,000 feet, is situated between the towns of Haicheng and Kaiping along the Mukden-Dairen railroad. The rail junction of Tashihkiao (now called Yingkow hsien), from which a rail spur goes to the port of Yingkow, is in the area of the magnesite deposit, whose reserves are estimated at 1.4 billion tons.

Another source of refractory materials and light metals are alunite deposits estimated at 120 million tons. The alunite, which contains 40 to 45 per cent alumina, is found chiefly near Yentai, Fushun, Penki and Fengcheng, as well as in the Chinchow area.

Among nonferrous metals, copper is mined in the Fuhsien-Chwangho area of the Liaotung peninsula and lead-zinc ores near Fengcheng and Chinsi. More important is the molybdenum deposit of Yangkiachangtze, on a railroad spur west of Chinsi. The molybdenum deposit, situated near the lead-zinc ore, is estimated at 30 to 40 million tons, with a metal content of 0.5 per cent. During the Second World War, the mine yielded 15,000 tons of ore a month.

Modern industry first penetrated into Liaoning Province at the turn of the century with the construction of railroads. Initially light industry was dominant. Soybeans were produced both in Liaoning and farther north and shipped here for processing into oil and beancake for export. Other factories processed tobacco, grain and other agricultural products. Cotton and silk textiles were produced in the leading cities. But it was the development of heavy industry, notably under Japanese impetus, that gave the province its distinctive economy.

The development of the industrial focus of Mukden-Fushun-Anshan-Penki was greatly aided by the construction of a dense rail net. The Dairen-Mukden-Changchun railroad is the main line crossing the economically most important parts of the province along the eastern margin of the Liao plain. From Mukden, leading rail hub, lines radiate toward the North China plain, Korea and northern Manchuria.

Liaoning Province is one of the most urbanized parts of China. In addition to the five cities that were under the jurisdiction of the Central Government until 1954, Mukden, Fushun, Anshan, Penki and Port Arthur–Dairen, the province includes five additional cities under provincial jurisdiction. They are Antung, Liaoyang, Yingkow, Fusin, and Chinchow.

Mukden, the capital of the province and its largest city, is situated on the right bank of the Hun Ho, a tributary of the Liao Ho. The Manchus had their capital here in the seventeenth century prior to their conquest of China. After the capital was moved to Peking in

1644, Mukden (which is the city's Manchu name, preserved in Western usage) was given the Chinese names of Shengking and, later, Fengtien. Its present Chinese name of Shenyang dates only from 1928. Situated in the southern part of the Manchurian plain and well supplied with transportation routes, Mukden was in a natural position to become the political and economic hub of Manchuria. The city developed particularly under Japanese rule, when its population quadrupled from 421,000 in 1931 to 1,891,000 in 1945. Its population dropped during the Chinese civil war to 1,021,057 in 1948. Under the Communist regime and its emphasis on industrialization and urbanization, Mukden's population has once again doubled and was 2,213,000 in June, 1953. It is China's fourth largest city.

Supplied with convenient raw material sources in the near-by iron and steel centers of Anshan and Penki, Mukden has become one of China's leading machine-building cities. It produces about one-fourth of China's machinery. Machinery makes up 43 per cent of Mukden's output by value. Among the principal machinery plants are factories producing machine tools, electrical goods, pneumatic tools, cables. Among the light industries are oilseeds, flour, textiles, paper, and chemicals.

Mukden consisted originally of the old Chinese city in the east and the new city in the former Japanese railway concession zone. The Chinese city, bounded by a ten-mile-long earthwall now largely in disrepair, contains the inner city with the former Manchu imperial palace and administrative offices. East of the Chinese city is the old Chinese industrial area known as the arsenal district. West of the Chinese city and extending in rectilinear fashion to the railroad station is the new city, which was developed by the Japanese after 1905. Finally, beyond the railroad, in the extreme western part of the city, is the Tiehsi district, known to the Japanese as Tetsunishi. Both Tiehsi, the Chinese name, and Tetsunishi mean "west of the railroad". Tiehsi, which was largely developed after 1937, houses the factories and workers' residences of Mukden's heavy and metal-fabricating industries.

East and south of Mukden, whose municipal district covers an area of 1,200 square miles, are the satellite cities of Fushun, Penki, Anshan and Liaoyang.

Fushun adjoins the Mukden city limits on the east, although the distance between the two city centers is twenty-five miles. Fushun's urban limits were expanded in late 1953 from forty square miles to an area virtually equal to that of Mukden. The population of the expanded city area is 700,000, of whom about 500,000 live in the central city.

Fushun was first developed as a coal-mining center by the Russians in 1902 in connection with railroad construction. In 1905 it passed to the Japanese. The Fushun coal deposit, which occupies an area of 25 square miles, consists largely of one inclined bed, 130 to 165 feet thick, compressed between granites and gneisses. At the point where the coal measures outcrop, they are overlain by more than 300 feet of oil shale. The coal reserves are estimated at 950,000,000 tons and the oil shale at 5,000,000,000 tons. The coal is of bituminous rank, but is suitable for coking only when mixed with high-grade coking coal. The coal is mined by open-cut methods in the western part of the deposit (Laohutai mine) and by underground methods in the east. Fushun has been Manchuria's leading coal-mining center since its beginnings, but its percentage share in the total coal output has steadily declined through the development of other mines. Under the Japanese, Fushun reached a peak output of close to 10 million tons. Production subsequently declined and the 1957 plan has been set at 9.3 million tons. The mining and distilling of oil shale began in 1929. The Chinese Communists have rehabilitated the No. 1 and No. 2 shale oil plants, one of which produces ammonium sulfate fertilizer as a by-product. Synthetic fuel is also being produced at Fushun through the hydrogenation of coal. Another industry associated with coal is that of carbon black, which is produced from the methane gas of the coal deposit. Other industries at Fushun are special steels for ballbearings, produced from Penki pig iron, mining and other heavy machinery, electrical equipment, cement, refractories and chemicals. A large power plant is fed by coal fines. An aluminum plant built by the Japanese for the processing of alunite was being rehabilitated in 1955. Fushun is situated on the south bank of the Hun Ho. Upstream work was begun in the second half of 1953 on the Tahofang reservoir. This project, due for completion in 1956, is designed to regulate the flow of the Hun Ho and the lower Liao Ho. The Tahofang reservoir will be second in size to the Kwanting project.

Southeast of Mukden, on the railroad to Antung and Korea, is the city of Penki. Its municipal district, which actually exceeds that of Mukden or Fushun, has an area of almost 2,000 square miles and a population of 500,000. Penki is Manchuria's second iron and steel center after Anshan. It is distinctive because of its high-grade coking coal and iron ore, both low in phosphorus, which yield China's only low-phosphorus pig iron suitable for Bessemer converters. The pig iron is used in the production of special steels, both at Penki and elsewhere. Penki's low-phosphorus coke is shipped to Anshan and as far as the blast furnaces of Süanhwa and Maanshan. Penki arose as a metallurgical center in 1915, when two 200-ton blast furnaces went into operation. Two large blast furnaces, each of 500-ton capacity, were added by the Japanese in 1939 in the southern suburb of Penki, called Miyanohara in Japanese and Kungyüan in Chinese. One of the large furnaces was restored in 1948, the other in 1955. During the Second World War, Penki accounted for about 20 per cent of Manchuria's pig iron output, including both ordinary and low-phosphorus iron. The iron ore comes from Penki itself, from Miaoerhkow on a rail spur twenty miles south of Penki, and from Waitowshan, twenty miles northwest of Penki. All mines are within the Penki municipal limits. Also within the urban district are the coking coal mines. These mines, which lie along a rail spur going east from Kungyüan, include Niusintai, Siaoshih, Tienshihfu and Chienchang, thirty-five miles east of Penki. The coal deposit continues west of Penki in the Yentai mine. Both Yentai and Niusintai have alunite. Other industries at Penki are refractories and cement.

West of Penki, on the Mukden-Dairen railroad, is Anshan, Manchuria's and China's leading iron and steel center. The first two blast furnaces were built here in 1919, a third one in 1930. Initially high-grade local ore, containing 50 to 60 per cent iron, was used. However, supplies were limited and iron-mining operations moved to Kungchangling, a deposit twenty-five miles east of Anshan, with 800 million tons of reserves and an iron content of 35 to 40 per cent. Under the Japanese-dominated Manchukuo regime, the Anshan works were greatly expanded, two steel plants being added in 1935 and 1940 and six modern blast furnaces between 1937 and 1943. At the peak of production during the Second World War, Anshan contributed 843,000 tons of steel and 1,325,000 tons of pig iron to the Japanese war effort. Soviet dismantling at the end of the Second World War reduced the plant to a mere shadow of its former self. Pig iron and steel output in 1949 was of the order of 100,000 tons. During the following years reconstruction proceeded at a rapid pace. In the blast furnace department, the three oldest blast furnaces were the first to be restored in the early years of the Communist regime followed by the modern No. 7 and No. 8 furnaces in 1953, No. 6 in 1954, No. 5 in 1955, and No. 9 in 1956. (See Table 14, p. 59). By the end of 1954, Anshan produced 1,500,000 tons of pig iron. In the open-hearth department, one reconstructed steel plant working at full capacity produced 980,000 tons of steel in 1954. Other key installations that went into operation in 1953 included a heavy rolling mill for rails and shapes and a seamless steel tubing mill for oil-drilling pipe. Expansion of Anshan is scheduled to be continued and by 1960 the production of pig iron is to reach 2.5 million tons and that of steel 3.22 million tons. In addition to Kungchangling iron ore, Anshan also proposes to use increasingly the iron ore of Talitze and other mines of the Tungpientao district in Kirin Province. For its coke, Anshan relies chiefly on a mixture of Fushun bituminous coal and a good coking coal, such as that from Penki. In connection with its industrial expansion before the Second World War, Anshan reached a population of 280,000 by 1945, a hundredfold increase from 1930. The city declined during the civil war and rallied at 190,000 in 1949. Since then, as a result of continued expansion and reconstruction, the population has risen to 600,000.

North of Anshan, along the railroad to Mukden, is the fifth provincial city of the Mukden urban complex, Liaoyang. One of the oldest of Manchuria's cities, Liaoyang has been greatly surpassed in size and importance by the new industrial centers in the area. It has only light industries, such as cotton mills, and is the center of a cotton-growing district. A connecting railroad leads east to the Kungchangling iron mines and to Penki.

In the southeastern part of Liaoning Province lies Antung, gateway to North Korea. Situated on the right bank of the Yalu River opposite the Korean city of Sinuiju, Antung owes its development largely to the construction (1907) of the railroad from Mukden to Korea, which here crosses the Yalu on a half-mile-long bridge. One of the oldest industries of Antung is the milling of the wild silk produced in the area. This was followed by the establishment of sawmills and match factories to process the timber floated down the Yalu River from the East Manchurian uplands. Increasing settlement of the Yalu basin and agricultural expansion introduced flour and soybean mills into the city. The most recent development has been the establishment of power-oriented industries following the construction of the Shuifeng (Supung) hydroelectric station, upstream on the Yalu River. This station, whose power output is shared by China and North Korea, was originally built by the Japanese in 1941. Its projected capacity was six turbines of 100,000 kilowatt each, but by the end of the Second World War only four had been installed. The plant was damaged by aerial bombings during the Korean war and partly dismantled by the Russians. It was scheduled to reach its full planned capacity of 600,000 kilowatt by 1956. Construction of an aluminum plant was started but not completed by the Japanese at Antung. The city has a population of about 300,000. Although situated near the mouth of the Yalu River on Korea Bay, Antung has not developed into a port of any importance. Ocean-going vessels of ten-foot draught can reach Antung at high tide. At other times, ships anchor off Tatungkow (officially Antung hsien), the outer port of Antung city.

Three provincial cities in the western part of Liaoning are Fusin, Chinchow and Yingkow.

Fusin is a rapidly developing coal-mining center likely to overtake Fushun in the future. Already in 1957 Fusin is scheduled to produce 8.45 million tons, compared with 9.3 million tons at Fushun. In 1936 only 80,000 tons of coal were mined at Fusin. In the following year, the railroad came and output began to soar. It reached 6 million tons by the end of the Second World War. Coal-mining capacity was expanded in 1953 with the completion of a giant open pit at Haichow, just southwest of Fusin. Fusin's coal, whose reserves are estimated at about 4 billion tons, is not of coking grade, but can be mixed with coking coal in by-product ovens. The city's population rose from 50,000 in 1949 to 240,000 in 1953.

Chinchow, at the entrance to the Liaosi corridor leading to Shanhaikwan and the North China plain, is an old Manchurian city. It is situated on the Peking-Mukden railroad at the junction of branch lines to Jehol and to Fusin. It is thus a natural outlet for the products of the Jehol uplands and the coal of Fusin. The Japanese built plants for the extraction of synthetic fuel, chemicals and gas from Fusin coal. Other Chinchow industrial products are textiles, paper and food products. Southwest of Chinchow is the Chinsi (formerly Lienshan) industrial area. From Chinsi, on the Peking-Mukden main line, a spur leads east into the hills to the molybdenum and lead mines near Yangkiachangtze. Another spur leads east to the port of Hulutao. Hulutao is an artificial icefree port built by the Japanese from 1930 to 1934. Because of its sheltered site, year-round navigability and thirty-foot channel, Hulutao was pictured as Manchuria's port of the future, rivaling even Dairen. No such development has yet taken place. The port lies off the main Manchurian rail lines and has only the Jehol uplands as its hinterland.

Another Manchurian port whose traffic lags far behind that of Dairen is Yingkow, at the mouth of the Liao Ho. However, unlike Hulutao, Yingkow once was Manchuria's leading seaport prior to the coming of the railroads. From 1836, when Yingkow replaced the original silted Liao port of Newchwang, until the turn of the century, when Dairen became the chief Manchurian outlet, Yingkow was the gateway to Manchuria. It handled the growing agricultural production of the Liao plain and received the increasing numbers of Chinese settlers. It declined not only because of the rise of Dairen, but also because of its own inadequacies as a port. It is frozen three to four months. The Liao Ho is navigable only for small vessels, and its sediments moreover silt up the approaches to Yingkow. The city maintained some importance as a local trade port and industrial center. Rail spurs approach it from Tashihkiao (officially Yingkow hsien), on the Dairen-Mukden railroad, and from Kowpangtze, on the Peking-Mukden line. Only the first spur was again in operation after the Second World War. A city of about 200,000, Yingkow has a major soybean-processing industry. A plant designed to extract magnesium from the near-by magnesite deposits was projected here by the Japanese.

At the southernmost tip of the Liaotung peninsula is the Port Arthur–Dairen municipal district. It is known as Lüta in Chinese, for the Chinese names of Port Arthur (Lüshun) and Dairen (Talien). The urban district has an area of 1,300 square miles and a population of 1,200,000. The successor of the Japanese-leased Kwantung territory, the district was set up in 1945 as a joint Soviet-Chinese naval base area. Soviet troops were withdrawn in 1955. The urban district includes not only the two cities of Port Arthur and Dairen, but the two hsiens of Kinhsien, on the peninsula, and Changhai, in the Changshan Islands east of the peninsula.

Dairen began to be developed in 1898 by the Russians, who called it Dal'niy. It passed to the Japanese in 1905. As the southern terminus of the Manchurian main line and the principal outlet for Manchuria's agricultural products, Dairen boomed under Japanese rule, its population rising from 386,000 in 1931 to 873,000 in 1945. The city is Manchuria's leading soybean-processing center and rivals Mukden as a machinery manufacturer. It produces rolling stock and street cars, cranes, electrical and mining machinery, machine tools, precision instruments, chemicals, cement and textiles. It is the site of the No. 7 petroleum refinery and large shipyards. Situated on the sheltered south shore of the Bay of Dairen, the city consists of the modern former Japanese administrative and commercial Chungshan section adjoining the port and the former Chinese residential Sikang quarter in the west. The port, sheltered by a 2.5-mile-long mole, can accommodate vessels up to 20,000 tons along a total of three miles of piers. South of the city are the residential resort towns of Laohutan and Singpu.

Port Arthur is twenty-five miles southwest of Dairen at the very tip of the Liaotung peninsula. The city is situated on the north shore of a land-locked bay accessible through a 1,000-foot-wide strait. The old Chinese city and the new section are respectively east and west of the railroad station. Port Arthur is a major naval base dominating the entrance to the Po Hai.

The only autonomous unit in Liaoning Province is the Mongol Tumet banner, which has its headquarters at Fusin hsien, just east of Fusin city. The banner adjoins the Jerim League of Inner Mongolia.

KIRIN PROVINCE

Capital: Changchun; area: 70,000; population: 11,290,073

Like Liaoning Province, Kirin also falls into a western lowland section and eastern uplands, each occupying roughly one-half of the total area. The lowland, the most important agricultural part of the province, lies astride the low divide separating the Liao and Sungari plains. The eastern hills, extending as far as the borders of Korea and the USSR, are part of the East Manchurian uplands. They include the Changpai Mountains with the lake-topped volcanic peak Paitow Shan culminating at 9,000 feet. Lumbering and mining are the principal branches of the upland economy.

Soybeans occupy about 30 per cent of the sown area and constitute the leading commercial crop, especially in the valleys of the east branch of the Liao Ho and the upper Sungari River. Among the food grains, kaoliang and corn predominate in the western lowland, with wheat increasing northward. In the eastern upland valleys, rice and millet are cultivated chiefly by the Korean population. The 1955 plan for all food crops, which include soybeans, was set at 6.54 million tons.

Lumbering has assumed two specialized aspects in Kirin Province. In the upper Sungari basin, the emphasis is on construction timber, with the principal sawmills at Kirin city. In the extreme eastern part of the province, timber of the upper Mutan and Tumen valleys is largely converted into pulp and paper.

Mineral resources are less important than in Liaoning. Coal is found again along the zone separating the lowland from the eastern uplands. The largest production comes from Liaoyüan (formerly called Sian). Other coal mines are at Kiaoho, east of Kirin, and in the Tungpientao district near Tunghwa. The Liaoyüan and Kiaoho coals are subbituminous types. The Tungpientao district, on the other hand, yields good bituminous coking coal of Permian age, similar to the Penki coal. The principal coal center in this district is Pataokiang.

The Tungpientao district, a potential metallurgical center, also has large iron ore reserves of up to 60 per cent iron. The iron ore is in close proximity to the coking coal. The most important producing center, which ships its iron ore to Anshan, is Talitze, just southwest of Linkiang, on the Yalu River (Korean border).

Among other metallic deposits are gold lode sites near Hwatien and Yenki, copper-lead-zinc at Tienpaoshan, twenty-five miles west of Yenki, and near Panshih.

Transportation in Kirin relies primarily on the Mukden-Changchun-Harbin railroad and its branch lines. Most important among these are the Mukden-Kirin line, running roughly parallel to the main line on the east, and the Szeping-Tsitsihar railroad, on the west. Two transverse lines—from Szeping via Meihokow to Tsian and from Changchun via Kirin to Tumen—cross into North Korea. A third transverse route from Changchun via Paicheng crosses into Inner Mongolia. The only navigable waterway is the upper Sungari, which is accessible to small vessels.

Six provincial cities are under the direct jurisdiction of the Kirin government. They are Changchun (the capital), Kirin, Szeping, Liaoyüan, Tunghwa, and Yenki, capital of the Yenpien Korean Autonomous Chou.

Changchun ("long spring") occupies a central position in Manchuria and under the Manchukuo regime it was selected as the country's capital under the name of Hsinking ("new capital"). The city's development was closely tied to the railroad construction program. As the junction (after 1905) of the wide-gauge Chinese Eastern and the standard-gauge South Manchuria railroads, Changchun became a major transshipment point between northern Manchuria and the southern port cities. The city's first industries were concerned with the processing of the agricultural products of central Manchuria. In 1912, the Changchun-Kirin railroad linked the city with the lumbering areas of the East Manchurian uplands and Changchun acquired a sawmilling and match-making industry. As the capital of Manchukuo from 1932 to 1945, Changchun was greatly enlarged and reconstructed, gaining broad avenues, parks and modern public buildings. As the administrative and educational center of Manchuria, the city expanded from 133,000 persons in 1931 to 862,600 in 1945. The city suffered a sharp decline after the Second World War with the departure of the Japanese, who had made up about one-third of the population, and the effects of the civil war. By June, 1953, the city's population had again risen to 800,000. The most important industrial project initiated since 1949 is the No. 1 Automobile Plant. Construction was started in July, 1953, and by 1957 annual production of Tzefang (Liberation) trucks is to reach 4,000. The No. 1 plant is expected to produce 30,000 trucks a year when operating at full capacity. A large locomotive and car shop is to be completed by 1957.

Kirin, the province's second largest city, is head of navigation on the upper Sungari River. Founded in 1673 as a Chinese fortress and administrative center, Kirin was the capital of the province until its transfer to Changchun in 1954. Kirin is a major lumber center, with sawmills and match factories. It also has an active grain and tobacco trade. During the Second World War, it acquired a number of power-oriented industries, including calcium carbide. Power was supplied by the Fengman hydroelectric station, 15 miles southeast of Kirin. This station, built at the point where the Sungari leaves the East Manchurian uplands in a rapids-strewn section, has a dam 0.7 mile long and 300 feet high. The projected capacity was eight turbines of 70,000 kilowatt each, but by the end of the war only two turbines were in operation as a result of Soviet dismantling. Construction proceeded after 1949 and the projected capacity is to be attained by 1959. In March, 1954, a 220,000-volt transmission line, designated the No. 506 line, was inaugurated, linking the Fengman station with the Mukden industrial complex over a distance of 230 miles. The Fengman station is also known as Siaofengman (Little Fengman) for a settlement on the left bank of the river and Tafengman (Great Fengman), a settlement on the right bank.

Szeping, formerly called Szepingkai, is a major railroad center on the Changchun-Mukden railroad. From here, branch lines go west to Tungliao, railhead in Inner Mongolia, northwest to Tsitsihar, and southeast to Tsian, on the Korean border. Szeping is primarily a transportation and food-processing center.

Southeast of Szeping, on the railroad leading to Korea, are the mining centers of Liaoyüan and Tunghwa. Liaoyüan, called Sian until 1950, is Kirin's principal coal producer. The reserves, estimated at 270,000,000 tons, yielded 2 million tons annually during the Second World War. The coal is of subbituminous rank. The name Liaoyüan was formerly applied to a rail junction (now called Shwangliao) west of Szeping.

Tunghwa is the center of the so-called Tungpientao district. Tungpientao contains both rich iron ore resources, such as those at Talitze, and coking-coal deposits, such as those at Pataokiang. The proximity of iron ore and coking coal make Tungpientao a potential iron and steel district. The Japanese had high hopes for its development as the

Second World War ended. The plans have not been further implemented by the Chinese Communists.

Aside from one Mongol banner—the South Gorlos Banner on the Sungari River, opposite Fuyü—Kirin Province has one major autonomous unit: The Yenpien Korean Autonomous Chou.

The Yenpien Korean Autonomous Chou was set up in September, 1952, in the easternmost part of Kirin long settled by Koreans. The chou borders both on North Korea and on the Soviet Union. It is drained by the Tumen River and its left tributaries. Rice and millet are leading crops. Lumbering and paper and pulp milling are major industries. The chou has a population of 763,000, of which 73 per cent is Korean. Its capital is Yenki, center of an agricultural district. The name Yenpien consists of the characters for "yen" (as in Yenki) and "pien" (the Chinese word for frontier). Prior to establishment of the chou, the area was known as Chientao.

HEILUNGKIANG PROVINCE

Capital: Harbin; area: 180,000; population: 11,897,309

Heilungkiang Province borders in the north on the Amur River, which the Chinese call the Heilung Kiang (Black Dragon River), and in the east on the Ussuri. The province is drained by the Sungari River and its chief left tributary, the Nun Kiang. Most of the population and economic activities are concentrated in the lowlands of these two rivers.

The cultivation of spring wheat plays a far more important role in Heilungkiang than in southern Manchuria. Both soils (largely chernozem and dark chestnut) and climate (relatively cool summers) favor wheat growth. The leading areas are the lowlands of the Sungari and its tributaries, the Lalin and Hulan rivers, south and north of Harbin, and the Nun Kiang. Harbin itself is the center of the flour-milling industry. Oats and barley have been traditionally concentrated in the northwestern part of the province, along the old cattle trail from Tsitsihar to Aigun on the Amur River. The total food crop is due to rise from 6.7 million tons in 1954 to 9 million by 1957. The yield per unit area is planned to increase from 1.18 tons per hectare in 1954 to 1.5 in 1957.

Soybeans are a major crop along the Sungari and Hulan rivers, where they take up about 30 per cent of the sown area. The 1955 plan for soybean production was 1.7 million tons, about double the 1949 output.

Two distinctive industrial crops in Heilungkiang are sugar beets and flax. Sugar beet production has been pressed in recent years. Output rose from 470,000 tons in 1952 to 700,000 tons in 1954, when yields were 14.5 tons per hectare. An increase of one-third in the sown area to 77,000 hectares was planned for 1955. Four sugar refineries were either built or expanded in 1953 and 1954, including mills at Harbin and Kiamusze. A fifth was under construction in 1955. The Harbin mill has a capacity of 18,000 tons of sugar a year, that at Kiamusze 24,000 tons.

Flax production has also been spurred. In 1954 flax output was 53,000 tons, representing a yield of 1.4 tons per hectare. The growing of flax was introduced into the area by Russian settlers who came into Manchuria following the construction of the Chinese Eastern railroad. The crop supplies raw material to a linen mill at Harbin.

Heilungkiang's vast virgin lands, estimated at 10 million hectares, offer a major potential of agricultural expansion. About 3,000,000 hectares are to be put under cultivation by 1957. This would raise the crop area from its present 6 million to 9 million hectares. Perhaps the most spectacular project is the establishment of the Soviet-equipped state farm at Santaokang, seventy miles east of Kiamusze. The Santaokang farm is charged with the development of the vast lowlands between the lower Sungari and Ussuri rivers, as yet virtually uninhabited. According to Chinese estimates, about 2 million hectares can be made arable there. Reclamation of idle land is being speeded by mechanized state farms, of which Heilungkiang has thirty-two, more than any other province.

Lumbering plays a major role in the economy of the East Manchurian uplands and the Little Khingan. The major centers of the eastern uplands are Mutankiang and Ilan, at the mouth of the Mutan River in the Sungari. The lumbering industry in the Little Khingan has been expanded in recent years, notably in the vicinity of the new lumber town of Ichun. Ichun developed after 1948 on a rail spur built northward into the virgin forest from Nanyi, rail junction on the Kiamusze-Suihwa railroad. Timber production at Ichun more than quadrupled from 1951 to 1955.

Coal and gold are the principal mineral resources of Heilungkiang Province. There are three major coal basins: Hokang, Shwangyashan and Kisi, all producing coal of coking grade. Hokang, the most important basin has reserves estimated at 5 billion tons. It was developed largely by the Japanese and yielded 2.7 million tons of coal in 1944. The large Tungshan mine was opened there in 1955. Hokang, which was formerly called Hingshan, is linked by a railroad with Lienkiangkow, coal-lading station on the Sungari River opposite Kiamusze.

The Shwangyashan coal-mining district was known as Tsienshan until 1954. It is situated on a rail branch going fifty miles east from Kiamusze. The development of this basin dates largely from the end of the Second World War and the post-war period.

The third coal basin, around Kisi, is also known as the Mishan basin, for a near-by town. Kisi, the center of this coal basin, has a mining machinery plant. The coal mines are situated at Lifuchen, southwest of Kisi; Titao, west; Pingyang, east, and Hengshan, southeast. The Kisi coal-mining area was developed as a result of Japanese rail construction, linking the mines with existing railroads.

Gold is mined predominantly in placer deposits along left-bank tributaries of the Amur River. There are three major districts: the Argun River district, with major producers at Kilalin, Kileimutu, and Moho; the Amur River district, with major placers near Aigun and Lopei, and the lower Sungari district, exploited between Ilan and Fuchin. The gold is found in recent alluvial placers at a depth of ten to twenty feet, with the gold-bearing layer ranging in thickness from three to six feet.

The main railroad of Heilungkiang is the old Chinese Eastern, which traverses the southern part of the province from northwest to southeast. It enters from Inner Mongolia, crosses the Nun Kiang at Lungkiang (former Fularki) and the Sungari River at Harbin, passes through the Mutankiang lumbering district and crosses the Soviet border at Tungning (former Suifenho). Major branch lines go north from the main line near Tsitsihar, at Harbin and in the Mutankiang area.

During the ice-free navigation season, the Sungari River has an active traffiic below Harbin for ships up to 500 tons. Smaller vessels can ascend the upper Sungari as far as Kirin and the Nun Kiang as far as Tsitsihar. The navigation season is about six months, from April to October.

Five major industrial cities are under the direct control of the provincial government. They are Harbin, the capital, Tsitsihar, Mutankiang, Kiamusze and Hokang.

Harbin, a city with a population of 1,200,000, is the product of the railroads. Prior to the construction of the Chinese Eastern in 1897, it was an insignificant village. It became the transportation hub of northern Manchuria and rapidly rose to second position among Manchuria's cities (after Mukden). It is Manchuria's leading food processing center, with a vast complex of flour mills, tobacco and soybean-processing plants, sugar, flax and linen mills. Among machinery plants that are being promoted by the Chinese Communists are installations producing electrical goods, power generators, measuring instruments and cutting tools. Of marked Russian physical appearance, Harbin has long had a Russian minority population, estimated in 1945 at 40,000. The city consists of several sections, sharply differentiated in their functions. Along the Sungari bank and opposite the left-bank winter harbor is the commercial Taoli district, the industrial and port district at the foot of the Sungari bridge and the old Chinese residential Fukia section with consumer industries. Farther inland and adjoining these riverside districts is the new city of Harbin, which developed largely after the First World War. The population of the city increased eightfold from 40,500 in 1911 to 332,000 in 1931 and then doubled to 661,000 by 1940. The city was officially called Pinkiang under Manchukuo rule. Its present official Chinese name is Harbin, which is rendered phonetically by means of the characters Ha-erh-pin.

Tsitsihar, the province's third largest city, is the metropolis of the Nun Kiang valley at the foot of the Great Khingan Mountains. Founded in 1691 as a Chinese fortress among Mongol tribes, it developed largely in a spread-out Mongolian pattern around the central walled Chinese city. With the near-by stations of Lungkiang and Angangki on the Chinese Eastern railroad, Tsitsihar developed into the transportation hub of the Nun Kiang plain. Soybeans and grain from the plain are processed here. The city's population is about 200,000.

Mutankiang, the second city of Heilungkiang, is the industrial center of the East Manchurian uplands. It developed as a station on the Chinese Eastern railroad and rapidly supplanted the old Manchu city of Ninguta (Ningan), situated to the south. The position of Mutankiang at the junction of railroads and the Mutan River have made it the center of the lumbering industry of the surrounding forested uplands and of the farming of intermontane valleys and basins. The city has a population of about 250,000.

Kiamusze is the chief city of the lower Sungari River. Until the building of the railroads under Japanese control, Kiamusze was dependent on the Sungari River trade. The improved transportation links led to a rapid increase in population, which rose from 20,000 in 1931 to 128,000 in 1940. Kiamusze has food-processing industries based on the surrounding farm production, including soybeans, grain and sugar beets. There is a paper mill producing kraft paper.

Kiamusze is also the supply center for the near-by coal centers of Hokang and Shwangyashan. Hokang, on a branch railroad north of Kiamusze, has a population of 90,000.

Heilungkiang Province includes a number of small non-Chinese minorities. Two Mongol banners are the only two autonomous administrative units at the hsien level. They are the Durbet Banner at Taikang, on the Chinese Eastern railroad southeast of Tsitsihar; and the North Gorlos Banner at Chaoyüan, on the Sungari River northeast of Fuyü.

Daurs, a sedentary nationality related to the Mongols, are settled in the Tsitsihar area, where they number about 5,000. The total Daur population of Heilungkiang, including settlements near Aigun and Fuyü, is about 24,000.

Three Manchu-Tungusic tribes live in the remote mountain and lowland areas of the province. They are the Orochon, Solon and Gold tribes.

The Orochon, known in Chinese as Olunchun, are hunters and herders related to the Evenki (Tungus) of the Soviet Union. They are found in small numbers in the northernmost part of the Great Khingan, in the Ilkhuri connecting range, where they are known as Manegir, and in the Little Khingan, where they are called Birar.

The Solon tribe, known in Chinese as Solun, are found generally in the same areas as the Orochon. The Solon engage in hunting and agriculture.

In contrast to the Orochon and Solon tribes, the Gold are lowland dwellers living in the marshy lowland between the lower Ussuri and Sungari rivers. The Gold are known as the Nanay in the Soviet Union. Their Chinese name is Hoche or Hochih. The Gold, who are more properly Manchu than the related tribes of the Khingan Mountains, engage in fishing and number about 2,000 persons.

CHAPTER 13

INNER MONGOLIA

INNER MONGOLIAN AUTONOMOUS CH'Ü

Capital: Huhehot; area: 450,000; population: 7,000,000

Inner Mongolia is not being treated here as a natural region with more or less homogenous physical characteristics. In fact, it is a region of great physical diversity ranging from the Gobi desert lands to the coniferous forests of the Great Khingan Mountains. Inner Mongolia is discussed here rather as a region of political unity, one of the major autonomous units of the Chinese People's Republic.

Topographically, Inner Mongolia represents essentially part of the Mongolian plateau, lying at an average elevation of 3,000 feet. Four major physical divisions may be distinguished: the Great Khingan Mountains in the east, the Yin Shan mountain system in the southwest, the great Yellow River bend with the Ordos plateau south of the Yin Shan, and the Mongolian plateau proper.

The Great Khingan Mountains, known in Chinese as Ta Hsing-an Ling, are the eastern edge of the Mongolian plateau, separating it from the Manchurian plain. The mountains trend roughly NNE-SSW, rising to about 6,000 feet in its middle section. The Great Khingan has steep slopes on its eastern side and merges more gently westward into the Mongolian plateau.

The Yin Shan system, a continuation of the Holan (Alashan) Mountains in Kansu Province, trends generally east-west on the north side of the Yellow River bend. Its ranges enclose the Hotao irrigated plain north of the Yellow River and the Huhehot plain, an eastern continuation. The Yin Shan has an average elevation of about 4,500 feet, with individual heights rising to nearly 9,000 feet. Like the Great Khingan, the Yin Shan has one steep-sloped side (on the south) and gentle slopes on the plateau side.

The Yellow River on entering Inner Mongolia describes a vast rectilinear bend. Irrigated plains along the river are major agricultural districts. They include the Hotao plain and the Huhehot plain, to the east. The Hotao plain is an alluvial lowland of clayey soils of high fertility. About 100 miles long and forty miles wide, the Hotao plain is crisscrossed by a dense network of irrigation canals dating from the late Manchu dynasty. The Huhehot plain, between Paotow and Huhehot, is irrigated in part by the Minsheng Canal, originally built in 1918. The canal subsequently fell into disuse and is now being rehabilitated. South of these irrigated lowlands lies the Ordos plateau, enclosed west, north and east by the Yellow River bend and sloping gently from south to north. In the south, hill ranges crowned by the Great Wall separate the Ordos from the loess uplands of northern Shensi. It is a desert covered with a veneer of gravel or small stones that rest directly on the hard eroded rock floor.

North of the Yin Shan and west of the Great Khingan is the Mongolian plateau proper. The plateau, at an average elevation of 3,000 feet, is underlain by a complex of hard rock formations eroded to an essentially flat surface and covered with a gravel veneer. It ranges from the Gobi desert to steppes along the foothills of the enclosing mountains, with steppe and semi-desert landscapes most prominent. Major physical subdivisions of the Mongolian plateau are the Hulunbuir (Barga) steppe, west of the Great Khingan, the drier Silingol steppe, and the Olanchab semi-desert.

In addition to the four major subdivisions, the Inner Mongolian Autonomous Ch'ü also includes the upper Liao plain on the east side of the Khingan system and (since 1956) part of the adjoining Jehol uplands. The upper Liao plain, centered on the city of Tungliao, lies on the western margins of the Manchurian plain and has many of its physical characteristics.

The variety of topographic forms in Inner Mongolia is also reflected in the region's climate. In general, Inner Mongolia is distinguished by extreme continentality, which expresses itself in a great annual temperature range and low precipitation. During the winter the region is under the influence of the Siberian high, which produces dry, extremely cold and windy weather. Mean January temperatures vary from –22° F (–30° C) in the extreme north to 18° F (–8° C) in the south. In contrast to the great range of January temperatures within Inner Mongolia, summer temperatures are fairly uniform throughout the region. Average temperatures in July are 68 to 72° F (20 to 22° C), with generally cooler temperatures in the northern Great Khingan.

About 80 to 90 per cent of the precipitation occurs from May to September, when the region comes under the influence of a Central

Asian low-pressure area. In the extreme east, on the seaward slopes of the Great Khingan, a large part of the precipitation comes from the southeasterly summer monsoon. Annual precipitation ranges from 20 inches in the east near Tungliao to less than 2 inches in the western desert. Most of the rainfall occurs on the eastern slopes of the Great Khingan and in the mountains themselves. Through most of Inner Mongolia, rainfall is inadequate for farming and irrigation is essential. Precipitation is subject to great variability, typical of continental conditions. For example, Huhehot, which has an annual average precipitation of 16 inches, received 33 inches in 1919 (a record year) and only 2 inches in 1928.

Climate and topography combine to restrict agriculture to a few areas of adequate rainfall or available irrigation. Only about 3 per cent of the total area is under cultivation. Adequate rainfall occurs on the eastern slopes of the Great Khingan, where the Tungliao and Ulanhot lowlands are the major agricultural areas. Irrigated farming is practiced on the Yellow River bend, in the Hotao and Huhehot plains. Leading crops are spring wheat, kaoliang, millet and corn, linseed, soybeans and sugar beets. Wheat and oats yield best results on irrigated land, where they are sown in April and harvested in August. Millet and kaoliang, which are drought-resistant crops, are cultivated on nonirrigated land in early May and harvested in early September. Soybeans are grown especially on the western margins of the Manchurian plain. Linseed is cultivated chiefly for its oil, which is used for lighting purposes. Sugar beets, a new crop, are being introduced in the irrigated land of the Yellow River belt. In 1955, 8,000 hectares were to be planted in beets and were expected to yield 20 tons per hectare. The beets are to be processed in the new Paotow sugar refinery, with a capacity of 22,000 tons of sugar a year. The refinery, completed in the fall of 1955, was built with East German assistance.

The total output of food crops was planned at 3.35 million tons in 1954 and 3.5 million tons in 1955. The bulk consisted of millet and kaoliang, while spring wheat made up only about 10 per cent of the crop. Oilseeds covered about 330,000 hectares in 1954. One-half of this area was in sesame, the rest in rapeseed, castor beans and sunflower.

Outside of the limited farming areas, livestock herding is the leading economic activity on the Mongolian plateau. There are three types of animal husbandry in Inner Mongolia: (1) nomadic herding with year-round maintenance of the livestock on the open range, as practiced by the Mongols; (2) summer herding and winter stall feeding, common in livestock and crop-raising areas with mixed Chinese-Mongol population, and (3) stall feeding of livestock, chiefly draft animals, in Chinese agricultural areas. About 50 per cent of the herds in the pasture areas are sheep and goats, 25 per cent are cattle, and the rest, horses, camels and other stock. The total livestock population has developed as follows in recent years (within Inner Mongolia's present area):

1949	8 million head
1952	14.1
1953	16.8
1954	19.49
1955 Plan	21.7
1957 Plan	24

The rich timber resources of the Great Khingan have made Inner Mongolia one of China's leading lumbering areas. The forests of the Great Khingan, which cover 7 million hectares, make up 12 per cent of the total area of Inner Mongolia and one-sixth of China's total forest area. Reserves of timber have been calculated at 1 billion cubic meters. About 75 per cent of the stands are made up of the Daurian larch, with an admixture of Siberian stone pine and Asiatic white birch.

Timber stands of commercial importance are found along the upper reaches of the Hailar River on the western slopes of the Great Khingan, and along the Yalu and Chor (Chol) rivers on the eastern slopes. Forests covering 720,000 hectares along the Hailar River offer the greatest potentialities. Yakoshih is the center of the main lumbering district. From this station on the Chinese Eastern, a branch railroad was driven 100 miles northeast to Tuliho, a town on the Tuli River, a tributary of the Argun. Yakoshih lumbering operations, which produced railroad ties by hand as late as 1950, were 90 per cent mechanized by 1952. Construction of a paper mill was begun at Yakoshih in 1953.

Inner Mongolia has still been little studied from the point of view of mineral resources. However, ample reserves of coking coal and iron ore in the vicinity of Paotow are providing the basis for a major iron and steel industry in the area. The coal center is Shihkwaikow, twenty miles northeast of Paotow. The Japanese developed a mine there during the Second World War and produced 100,000 tons a year. The only other active coal producer is Chalainor, in the far north of Inner Mongolia. Chalainor was developed at the time of the construction of the Chinese Eastern railroad. Its deposits are estimated at 3.9 billion tons, but its production was limited to satisfying the needs of the railroad. Under the Japanese, output reached a peak of 300,000 in 1944. In 1950, almost 200,000 tons were produced. In addition to supplying the needs of the railroad, Chalainor coal also furnishes the fuel for small power plants at Manchouli, Hailar, Chalainor and Chalantun, all situated along the Chinese Eastern.

The precise location of the iron deposits in the Paotow area is unclear. Iron ore has been mined at Paiyünopo (Bayin Obo), thirty-five miles westnorthwest of Pailingmiao and ninety miles north of Paotow. Early investigation disclosed reserves of 34 million tons. The ore lies close to the surface and can be mined by stripping methods. The Chinese Communists have reported the discovery of a large iron ore deposit, but it is not clear whether they refer to the site at Paiyünopo or an eastward continuation. After the completion of the Tsining–Ulan-Bator railroad, it was reported that large iron ore deposits could now be worked along the line. The railroad runs 160 to 170 miles east of Paiyünopo.

The seasonal lakes of the Mongolian plateau proper and the Ordos plateau abound in salt and soda deposits. Soda is most important in the Hulunbuir League and the Ordos plateau, common salt in the Silingol League. Asbestos and mica are mined in the Yin Shan north of the Huhehot plain.

Inner Mongolia is penetrated by a number of railroads, but has no transportation lines linking the north and southwest sections. The railroads either cross Inner Mongolia or penetrate the region as feeder lines from adjoining Chinese provinces. In the far north, Inner Mongolia is served by the Chinese Eastern, which passes through Chalantun, Pokotu, Yakoshih, Hailar, Chalainor and Manchouli on its way from Harbin to the Soviet Union.

Farther south, Inner Mongolia is penetrated by a branch of the Manchurian railroad system from the junction of Paicheng (formerly called Taoan). This line passes through Ulanhot and Solun on its way to the hot spring resort of Arshan (Aerhshan) near the border of Outer Mongolia. Other branches of the Manchurian rail system serve Tungliao and Chihfeng in southeasternmost Inner Mongolia.

The southwestern part of the region is served by the line from Peking to Paotow via Tsining and Huhehot and, since 1955, by the Tsining–Ulan-Bator railroad. A continuation of the Peking-Paotow railroad is under construction to Lanchow via Yinchwan.

The rail lines are supplemented by a number of automobile roads, notably the Kalgan-Ulan-Bator highway. Kalgan, although situated outside of Inner Mongolia, is the hub of a number of roads serving the Chahar and Silingol leagues. In 1953, a bus service was inaugurated linking Kalgan with Silinhot, capital of the Silingol League.

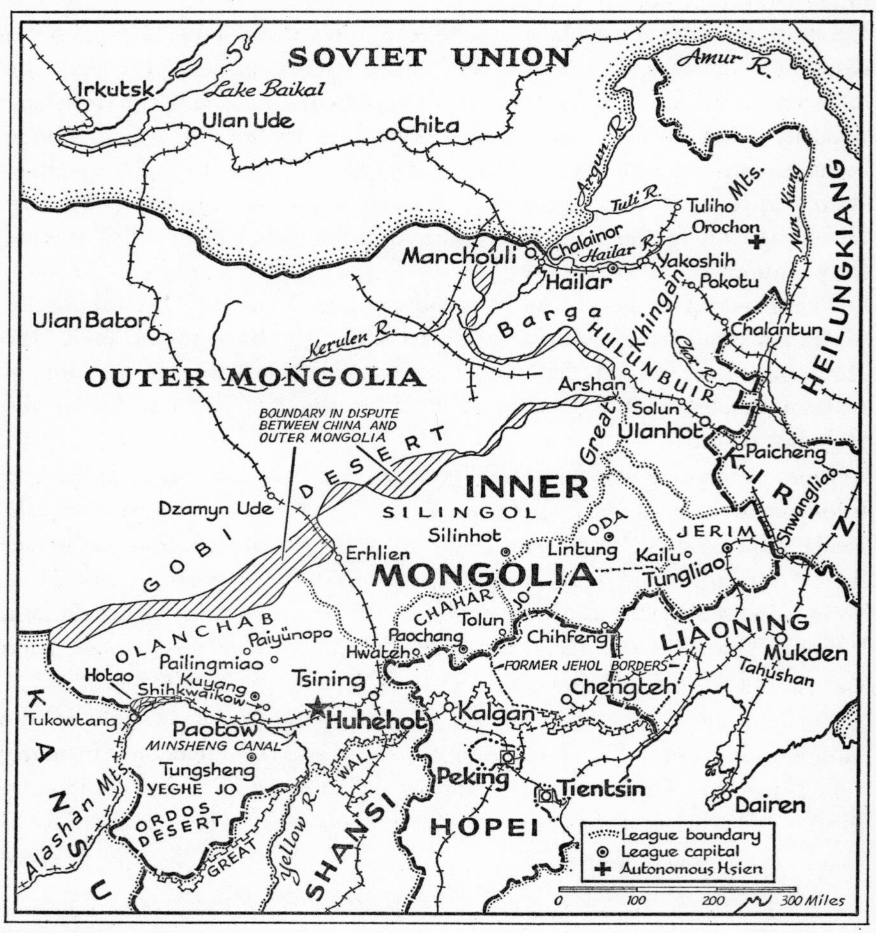

Inner Mongolia

The Inner Mongolian Autonomous Ch'ü was formally established May 1, 1947, including at first the leagues of Hulunbuir, Silingol and Chahar. In 1949, the area of Inner Mongolia was expanded through the incorporation of the Jerim League from Manchuria's former Liaopei Province and of the Jo-oda League from northern Jehol. In 1952, the region was further enlarged through the addition of the three hsien of Hwateh, Paochang and Tolun from partitioned Chahar. At this point, Inner Mongolia had an area of 255,000 square miles and a population of about 2,500,000, of whom 800,000 were Mongols. In March, 1954, Inner Mongolia absorbed Suiyüan Province. The annexation expanded Inner Mongolia's area to 425,000 square miles and its population to 6,100,104, of whom about 1,000,000 were Mongols. Then, in January, 1956, the region absorbed the northern part of partitioned Jehol Province, with an additional 1,000,000 persons, including 200,000 Mongols.

The initial capital of Inner Mongolia after its formation in 1947 was Ulanhot, in the eastern part of the region. In anticipation of further territorial annexations in the west, the seat of administration was moved westward in 1950 to Kalgan (Chahar Province) and in July, 1952, to Kweisui (Suiyüan Province). Kweisui has remained the capital of Inner Mongolia after the incorporation of Suiyüan Province and was renamed Huhehot in April, 1954.

Administratively, as of January, 1955, Inner Mongolia falls into seven Mongol leagues and two Chinese-majority special ch'ü. The Mongol leagues (and their administrative centers) are: Hulunbuir (Hailar), Jerim (Tungliao), Jo-oda (Lintung), Chahar (Paochang), Silingol (Silinhot, formerly called Peitzemiao), Olanchab (Kuyang), Yeghe Jo (Tungsheng). The two Chinese ch'ü, both in former Suiyüan Province, are Hotao (Shenpachen) and Pingtichüan (Tsining, also called Pingtichüanchen). Both the Mongol leagues and the Chinese ch'ü are further subdivided into Mongol banners and Chinese hsien.

Chinese, who make up about 80 per cent of the total population, live in the agricultural sections of Inner Mongolia, the Hotao and Huhehot plains of the Yellow River bend, the upper Liao plain around Kailu and Tungliao, and near Ulanhot. These are the areas of greatest population density (about 100 per square mile). Of the 1,200,000 Mongols, about 70 per cent are sedentary or semi-sedentary cultivators in Chinese-majority areas. Only 300,000 are nomadic herders, chiefly in the Silingol, Olanchab and Yeghe Jo leagues.

In northernmost Inner Mongolia live Tungus-Manchu tribes, such as the Orochon and Solon. Only the Orochon, known in Chinese as Olunchun, constitute an autonomous banner set up in November, 1951.

Hunting is the only means of livelihood of the banner population of 798. About 1,500 more Orochon live outside the limits of the banner, which was set up on the eastern slopes of the forested Great Khingan Mountains.

Seven cities of Inner Mongolia are above the hsien level of administration. They are: Hailar, Manchouli, Ulanhot, Tungliao, Paotow, Tsining and Huhehot.

Huhehot, the capital of the Inner Mongolian Autonomous Ch'ü, was called Kweisui until April, 1954, when it reverted to its traditional Mongolian name meaning "blue city". Huhehot consists of two sections, about one mile apart. They are the old Mongol city with commercial enterprises and the new Chinese administrative city, which developed around the railroad station after 1921. The Chinese combined the names of the old city (Kweihwa) and the new city (Suiyüan) to form the name Kweisui. Huhehot, which has a population of 200,000, is the center of one of Inner Mongolia's farming districts.

Paotow, railhead at the western end of the Huhehot plain, is the site of a major projected iron and steel center based on near-by coking coal at Shihkwaikow and iron ore at Paiyünopo. Preparatory construction work was under way in 1955. Paotow developed as a major trade center after the coming of the railroad in 1923, shipping hides and wool from the surrounding area. Highways lead from here north into the Olanchab League, south into the Ordos desert and west into the Hotao irrigated plain. A railroad leading west and southwest to Yinchwan and Lanchow is under construction.

Tsining has become a major Inner Mongolian city as a result of the construction of the new trans-Mongolian railroad to the Soviet Union. During the period of construction (1953-1955), the city's population rose from 30,000 to 80,000. Situated at the junction of the wide rail gauge of the trans-Mongolian route and the standard-gauge Chinese rail net, Tsining has become a major freight transshipment point. This is also the place where the wheel trucks of passenger through cars are changed from one gauge to the other. As a growing regional center, Tsining has also acquired a meat-packing plant and a wool-washing factory to process the livestock products of the surrounding area.

Tungliao, known in Mongol as Bayantala ("rich plain"), is the center of an agricultural island of Chinese settlement surrounded by Mongol pastoral areas. The center of the Jerim League, Tungliao is reached by two railroads of the Manchurian system: the line from Shwangliao (completed in 1921) and the railroad from Tahushan (on the Peking-Mukden main line; completed in 1927).

Ulanhot ("red city") is the former capital of Inner Mongolia. Known as Wangyehmiao until 1947, Ulanhot is also the center of an agricultural district inhabited by Chinese settlers. The city is served by a railroad going northwest to the hot springs resort of Arshan. The city developed rapidly while it was the capital, reaching a population of 35,000 in 1950, and continued to be a major center of eastern Inner Mongolia as the capital of the Khingan League. In the summer of 1954, the Khingan League was merged with the Huna League to form the present Hulunbuir League and most of the administrative functions of Ulanhot passed to Hailar.

Hailar is the former capital of the Huna League and since 1954 administrative center of the Hulunbuir League. Formerly known by the Chinese name of Hulun, Hailar consists of an old and a new city. The old section, founded in 1734, is a typical Chinese city, with closely built-up, narrow streets. The new city, south of the Chinese Eastern, developed with the construction of the railroad along a rectilinear street pattern. Hailar is the processing center for the surrounding livestock district. The city has a population of about 50,000 persons.

Manchouli, the Soviet-Chinese border city on the Chinese Eastern railroad, is another center for the processing of livestock products of the Hulunbuir district. Until the completion of the Tsining–Ulan–Bator railroad virtually all the trade between China and the Soviet Union passed through here. The name Manchouli is a Chinese phonetic rendering of the original Russian name Man'chzhuriya (Manchuria).

CHAPTER 14

THE KANSU CORRIDOR

KANSU PROVINCE

Capital: Lanchow; area: 300,000; population: 12,928,102

Like Inner Mongolia, the Kansu corridor cannot be considered a physically homogeneous region. It is treated as a separate division, partly because of its political unity, partly because of its traditional importance as a routeway linking China proper with central Asia. In September, 1954, Kansu absorbed the adjoining province of Ningsia, thus nearly doubling its area but gaining only about 1,000,000 persons in population.

The enlarged province can be divided into five major physical regions: the Ningsia irrigated plain and the Alashan desert in former Ningsia province, and the eastern Kansu loesslands, the Lanchow basin and the Kansu corridor proper.

The eastern Kansu loesslands are actually part of the northern Shensi loess plateau, which adjoins on the east. The loess area, which is drained by the King Ho, a tributary of the Wei Ho in Shensi, lies at an average elevation of 2,500 to 3,000 feet. Pingliang is the chief city of the loesslands, which are bounded in the west by the Liupan Mountains.

West of the Liupan Mountains lies the Lanchow basin, a mountain-ringed region situated at the focal point of transportation routes. From this heartland of Kansu, historic routeways lead west onto the Tibetan high plateau, northwest through the Kansu corridor to Sinkiang, northeast along the Yellow River to the Ningsia plain and Inner Mongolia, and southeast to China proper. The basin is traversed by the upper Yellow River, which descends from the Tibetan high plateau in the west and receives here the Tao Ho, on the right. The Lanchow basin is the leading agricultural area of Kansu Province. It is also known as the Lungsi basin ("west of the Lung Shan"), named for the Lung Shan, another name of the Liupan Mountains. The main cities of this subregion are Lanchow, Tienshui and Linsia.

Northwest of the Lanchow basin, and separated from it by the Wukiao Mountains, is the 600-mile-long Kansu corridor, historic route-way to central Asia. The corridor extends along the north foot of the towering Kilien Mountains, a section of the great Nan Shan system. From these mountains, rising to nearly 20,000 feet, streams feed water to oases before disappearing into the desert sands of the Mongolian plateau. The leading oases are those of Wuwei, Changyeh, Kiuchüan and Tunhwang. The Changyeh and Kiuchüan areas are watered by two branches of the Jo Shui (known in Mongol as the Edsin Gol). The Jo Shui penetrates deep into the Gobi desert, terminating in two salt lakes on the border of Outer Mongolia. Another mountain stream, the Shuleh or Sulo River, waters northwesternmost Kansu, including the Yümen and Tunhwang areas.

Northeast of the Lanchow basin lies the irrigated Ningsia plain, the heart of former Ningsia Province. Separated by the Alashan Mountains from the desert to the west, the Ningsia plain extends along the Yellow River between Chungwei (in the south) and Shihtsuishan. Irrigation canals diverted from the Yellow River bring much-needed water to about 160,000 hectares, including the cities of Yinchwan and Wuchung.

The Alashan desert extending west from the mountains of the same name is part of the Gobi desert. Mountain springs support a few small oases on the western slopes of the Alashan range, including Bayinhot, capital of the Kansu Mongol Chou. Farther west, the sandy desert is virtually lifeless, except for pastures along the lower Edsin Gol.

Kansu's climate, like that of Inner Mongolia, is classified as a middle-latitude dry climate, including both the steppe and desert varieties. The climate is characterized by interior continental location, far from oceans, resulting in very low precipitation and a great annual temperature range. Monthly mean temperatures range from 15 to 20° F (–10 to –6° C) in January to 70 to 80° F (21 to 26° C) in July. In general January temepratures increase from north to south, while summer averages are more or less uniform throughout the region.

Most of the region receives insufficient precipitation for the growing of crops. Annual precipitation, most of which occurs in the summer, ranges from 20 inches in the southeast (Lanchow basin) to less than two inches in the northwestern desert.

Irrigation is developed especially in the Ningsia plain along the Yellow River and along streams descending from the Kilien Mountains into the Kansu corridor. The Shuleh River in northwestern Kansu, for example, is expected to irrigate 66,000 hectares, mainly in state farms. Irrigation is to be greatly expanded along the Yellow River after completion of the Liukia reservoir on the Tsinghai border and the Tsingtung reservoir in the Ningsia plain south of Wuchung during the second five-year plan.

In accordance with its physical differentiation, Kansu Province falls into three distinct agricultural regions: the winter wheat-millet area, the spring wheat area, and the area of oasis agriculture. The winter wheat-millet area coincides with the loesslands of easternmost Kansu. Here January temperatures just below freezing still permit the cultivation of winter wheat, while millet leads kaoliang as the summer grain. Cotton and tobacco are the chief cash crops. The spring wheat area includes the Lanchow basin, while irrigated agriculture is the rule in the Ningsia plain and the oases of the Kansu corridor.

Before the merger of Kansu and Ningsia provinces, food crop figures were as follows for the year 1953: Kansu produced 2.6 million tons, while Ningsia produced only 325,000 tons. The ratio clearly reflects the physical conditions and lack of agricultural development in the former desert province. Food output of the merged provinces rose to 3.9 million tons in 1954. Livestock raising, on the other hand, plays a more important role in the arid parts of Kansu. Livestock holdings in former Ningsia Province, outside of the irrigated plain along the Yellow River, rose from 450,000 in 1949 to 1,320,000 in 1953.

Kansu Province contains China's most important oilfield. This is the Yümen field in the Kansu corridor at the north foot of the Kilien Mountains. The oilfield, situated forty miles southeast of Yümen hsien at Laochünmiao, was made a special oil-producing ch'ü in 1954. Production began here in 1939 and during the Second World War two small refineries were constructed. The oilfield provided virtually all China's wartime needs of gasoline, kerosene and Diesel oil. The field was rehabilitated and expanded after the Communists took over in 1949. Pending the construction of the Sinkiang railroad from Lanchow, which is expected to reach the Yümen field by 1956, production remains limited for lack of transportation. In the meantime, tanker trucks take the refined products of the Yümen refineries toward the steadily advancing railhead for transshipment to tank cars.

Kansu has a local coal source in the Akanchen mine south of Lanchow, and in near-by Shihmenkow. Salt and soda are obtained in a number of desert lakes, chiefly in former Ningsia Province. One of the principal producers of salt is the salt lake Shara Burdu (Chi-lan-t'ai) in the Alashan desert, linked by a road with Shihtsuishan on the Yellow River. Salt is also shipped from the Yenchih area east of the Ningsia plain.

Since ancient times, Kansu has been the routeway between China and central Asia. Here passed the Silk Road, used by caravans loaded with silk, tea and other Chinese goods. In modern times, the Silk Road became an automobile highway that played a particularly important role during the Second World War as one of China's lifelines. At the present time railroad construction is proceeding along this highway from the direction of Lanchow. The line is scheduled to reach Yümen in 1956 and then continue on into Sinkiang and the Soviet Union. Lanchow itself was reached by the railroad in 1952, when the Lunghai line was extended to the provincial capital from Tienshui. Another railroad, the line from Paotow to Lanchow via Yinchwan, will link the Lanchow basin with the irrigated Ningsia plain and Inner Mongolia.

Lanchow, transportation hub of southeastern Kansu, is linked by highways with Sining, capital of Tsinghai, with Yinchwan, center of the Ningsia plain, and with the Tibetan autonomous areas of southern Kansu and Szechwan. The southern Kansu road leads from Lanchow to Jo-erh-kai (until 1953, called Langmusze), just across the Szechwan border. The road is to be linked with the Chengtu-Ahpa highway in the Ahpa Tibetan Autonomous Chou of Szechwan.

The Yellow River, Kansu's only potential waterway, is to be made navigable through the long-range Yellow River reclamation project. Navigation is expected to be opened in a 500-mile section below Yinchwan after completion of the project's first phase in 1967. Only after completion of the entire project, expected to last about fifty years, would Lanchow be accessible for 500-ton vessels. At the present time, shallow-bottomed junks and sheepskin rafts are able to travel with salt loads between Shihtsuishan and Paotow.

Kansu has five cities under provincial jurisdiction. They are Lanchow, Tienshui, Pingliang, Linsia, and Yinchwan. With the exception of Yinchwan, all are situated in the southeastern part of the province where agriculture and population are concentrated and transportation routes are best developed.

Lanchow, the provincial capital, is situated on the south bank of the Yellow River. Here routes converge from the loesslands in the east, the Kansu corridor in the northwest, the Ningsia plain in the northeast, and the Tsinghai and Tibetan highlands in the west. Historically the chief crossing of the upper Yellow River on the way to central Asia, Lanchow has developed into a major transportation center. The Yellow River, here 700 feet wide, was bridged in 1910 for road traffic and in 1954 for the new railroad to Sinkiang. Its excellent transportation position has made Lanchow the natural supply and distribution center for China's

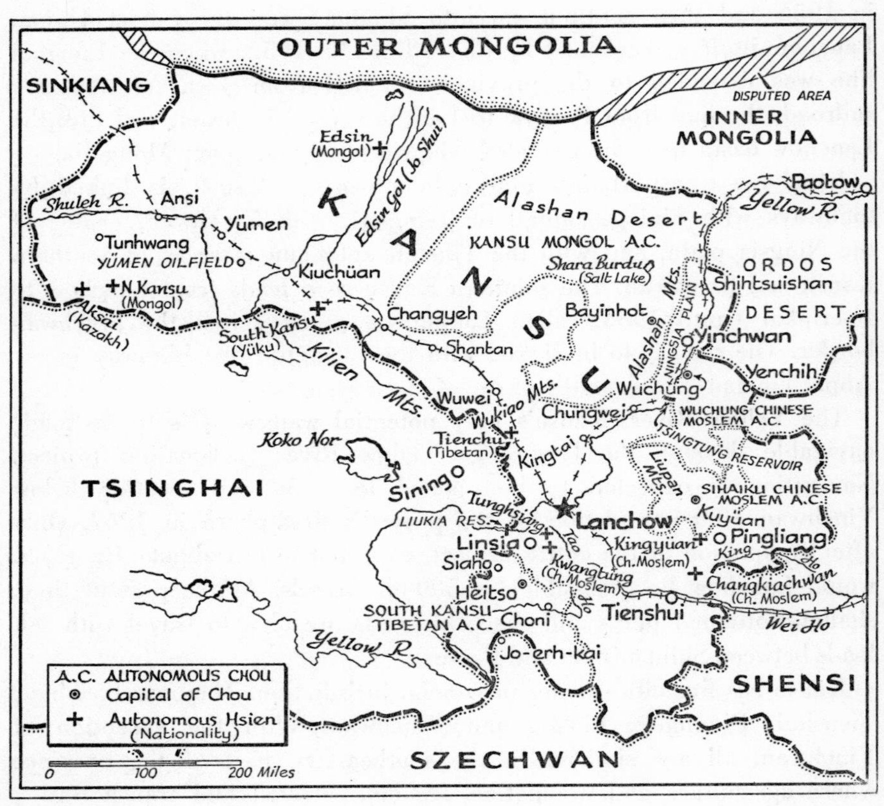
OUTER MONGOLIA
SINKIANG
DISPUTED AREA
INNER MONGOLIA
Edsin (Mongol)
Edsin Gol (Jo Shui)
K A N S U
Paotow
Yellow R.
Shuleh R.
Ansi
Alashan Desert
Yümen
Tunhwang
YÜMEN OILFIELD
Kiuchüan
KANSU MONGOL A.C.
Shara Burdu (Salt Lake)
ORDOS
Shihtsuishan
DESERT
N. Kansu (Mongol)
Aksai (Kazakh)
Changyeh
Bayinhot
Alashan Mts.
NINGSIA PLAIN
Yinchwan
South Kansu (Yüku)
Shantan
Kilien Mts.
Yenchih
Wuwei
Wukiao Mts.
Wuchung
Chungwei
WUCHUNG CHINESE MOSLEM A.C.
TSINGTUNG RESERVOIR
Koko Nor
Tienchu (Tibetan)
Kingtai
Liupan Mts.
TSINGHAI
Sining
SIHAIKU CHINESE MOSLEM A.C.
Kuyüan
Tunghsiang
Lanchow
LIUKIA RES.
Linsia
Tao
Kingyüan (Ch. Moslem)
Pingliang
King Ho
Siaho
Kwangtung (Ch. Moslem)
Changkiachwan (Ch. Moslem)
Heitso
Tienshui
SOUTH KANSU TIBETAN A.C.
Choni
Wei Ho
Yellow R.
Jo-erh-kai
A.C. AUTONOMOUS CHOU
Capital of Chou
Autonomous Hsien (Nationality)
0 100 200 Miles
SHENSI
SZECHWAN

Kansu

Northwest. Livestock products are processed here into woolens and leather goods. Among the new industries developed in recent years are factories producing oilfield equipment (for Yümen), cement (for the growing construction program), and chemicals. Trucks used widely in the highways of the Northwest come to Lanchow for repairs and parts. Spurred by the new economic activity in the area, Lanchow's population has risen from about 200,000 in 1949 to 500,000 in 1954. Construction began in 1956 on a large oil refinery designed to process crude from the Yümen field.

Tienshui, in the eastern loesslands, was the head of the Lunghai railroad before its extension to Lanchow. The city was originally planned to be the junction of the railroad from Chengtu, before revised route alignments made Paoki the new rail center. Tienshui is the center of irrigated agriculture in the upper Wei Ho valley. Its population is about 100,000.

Pingliang, another loessland city, lies on the Sian-Lanchow highway. Its importance has partly declined since the completion of the railroad link between the two cities. Pingliang is the agricultural center of the upper reaches of the King Ho, tributary of the Wei Ho.

Linsia, situated southwest of Lanchow, is the gateway to the Tibetan districts of southern Kansu and concentration point for such livestock products as hides and wool.

Yinchwan, the center of the irrigated Ningsia plain, was formerly also known as Ningsia. It lies on the projected railroad from Paotow to Lanchow and ships wool and hides.

Thus far none of the cities in the Kansu corridor has been raised to the status of provincial city. However, it is expected that their importance will greatly increase as they are progressively reached by the railroad from Lanchow. The leading corridor towns are Wuwei (former Liangchow), Changyeh (former Kanchow), and Kiuchüan (former Suchow). The last two former designations gave Kansu its provincial name. All three centers are situated in oases of irrigated agriculture and serve as distribution points for the near-by nomadic districts.

Beyond Kiuchüan lies the Yümen oilfield. In northwesternmost Kansu are the two road centers of Ansi and Tunhwang. Ansi lies on the projected route of the railroad to Sinkiang and will presumably develop into the regional center. Tunhwang is noted chiefly for the locality of Tsienfotung, ten miles southeast, site of ancient caves containing stone Buddhas, murals and writings of the Tang and Sung dynasties.

Chinese speaking the northern Mandarin constitute 88 per cent of the population of the province. They are settled in the agricultural areas of the southeast, including the loesslands and the Lanchow basin, and in the irrigated oases of the corridor and the Ningsia plain.

Among the eleven minorities that make up 12 per cent of the total population are Chinese Moslems, Tibetans, Mongols, Tunghsiang, Yüku and Kazakh. These six ethnic groups are organized in a total of thirteen autonomous areas at the hsien level or higher. Lesser minorities include the Paoan, Salar and Uigur.

The Chinese Moslems, who constitute the largest minority, number about 700,000. They are organized in two autonomous chou and three autonomous hsien. The Wuchung Moslem Autonomous Chou, situated east of the Yellow River in former Ningsia Province, was called the Hotung ("east of the river") chou until April, 1955, when it was renamed for its capital. The Wuchung chou has a population of 230,000, 62 per cent of whom are Moslems. The Wuchung chou includes the east-bank section of the Ningsia irrigated plain, adjoins the Ordos desert and passes southeastward into the loesslands. The autonomous chou was set up in April, 1954.

Adjoining it in the south is the other Chinese Moslem autonomous chou, set up in October, 1953, within Kansu Province. The chou, which has a population of 220,000, is called the Sihaiku Moslem Autonomous Chou for its three hsien—Siki, Haiyüan and Kuyüan, the capital. The chou is situated astride the Liupan Mountains on the western edge of the loesslands.

Of the three Chinese Moslem autonomous hsien, two are situated in the loess area, the third in the Lanchow basin. The two loess hsien are Kingyüan (formerly called Hwaping), established in 1953 just southwest of Pingliang, and Changkiachwan, set up also in 1953 northeast of Tienshui on the Shensi border. The Changkiachwan hsien has a population of 134,000, of whom 77 per cent are Moslem. The third Moslem hsien is at Kwangtung (formerly called Ningting), just east of Linsia. The Kwangtung hsien, set up in the fall of 1953, has a population of 90,000, of whom 72 per cent are Moslem.

The second most numerous minority in Kansu are the Tibetans, who are settled predominantly in highland areas southwest of Lanchow on the Tsinghai and Szechwan borders. The first Tibetan autonomous unit to be established here was the Choni autonomous hsien set up in 1951 just southwest of Lintan. Other autonomous units were established subsequently, notably at Siaho, site of the great Labrang monastery. These original autonomous units were merged in the fall of 1953 to form the Kannan (South Kansu) Tibetan Autonomous Chou. The chou has a population of 302,000, of whom about 50 per cent are Tibetans,

43 per cent Chinese, and 6 per cent Chinese Moslems. The headquarters, at first established at Siaho, was moved in 1954 to Heitso, site of the Tohusze lamasery, 35 miles southeast of Siaho. In addition to its autonomous chou in southern Kansu, the Tibetan minority also has the Tienchu Autonomous Hsien, situated on the railroad to Sinkiang 100 miles northnorthwest of Lanchow. The headquarters of the hsien, which is situated in the Wukiao Mountains, is at the railroad station of Anyüanyi.

Mongols, the third largest minority group, number no more than 40,000 in Kansu Province. They are constituted in three autonomous units, two in former Ningsia Province, one in the original territory of Kansu. The most important is the Alashan Banner, set up in 1949 or earlier in the Alashan desert of former Ningsia Province. The banner covers about 50,000 miles of desert, about half of the former province, and has a population of 60,000, of whom 30 per cent are Mongols, largely of the Olot tribe. Its capital was set up in the town of Tingyüanying, at the west foot of the Alashan range. Tingyüanying, subsequently renamed Bayinhot ("rich city"), is linked by road with Yinchwan in the Ningsia irrigated plain on the other side of the mountains. At the time of the merger of Ningsia and Kansu in September, 1954, the Alashan Banner was transformed into the Kansu Mongol Autonomous Chou.

Adjoining the Alashan Banner in the west is the Edsin Banner, situated astride the Edsin Gol and inhabited by the Torgot tribe. Since the creation of the autonomous banner about 1949, its administrative headquarters has shifted repeatedly within the Edsin Gol plain, the main source of water within the desert. Headquarters was set up originally at Pu-ho-lan-ta (Buhelanda) south of the ruins of Kharahoto, on the east branch of the lower Edsin Gol. Subsequently, it migrated to Erh-li-ho-tze, on Gashiun Nur, one of the two terminal lakes of the Edsin Gol. As of January, 1955, the seat of the Edsin Banner was at Hsi-miao ("western temple"), on the western branch of the lower Edsin Gol. The Chinese phonetic transcription of Edsin is O-chi-na or Ngo-chi-na.

In northwestern Kansu is the Supei (North Kansu) Mongol Autonomous Banner, with another migrating headquarters. This banner, set up about 1951, was originally centered at Tsiangküntai in the Kansu panhandle north of Yümen. In 1953, the administrative seat was reported at Chihkinpu, on the main highway between Yümen and Kiuchüan. Finally, as of January, 1955, it was in the upper reaches of the Tang Ho, southsoutheast of Tunhwang.

The Tunghsiang, Yüku and Kazakh minorities have each one autonomous unit at the hsien level. The Tunghsiang Autonomous Hsien was set up in 1950 in the area southwest of Lanchow. The hsien, which has a population of about 160,000, has its seat at Sonanpa, 15 miles northeast of Linsia. The Tunghsiang are Moslems speaking the Mongor language, related to Mongolian.

The Sunan (South Kansu) Yüku Autonomous Hsien is situated halfway between Changyeh and Kiuchüan in the foothills of the Kilien Mountains. The hsien, which was set up in March, 1954, has its seat at Hungwansze, 50 miles southeast of Kiuchüan, near the Tsinghai border. The hsien has a population of 6,600, of whom half are of the Yüku nationality, a Turkic group of Lamaist religion.

In northwesternmost Kansu is the Aksai Kazakh Autonomous Hsien, established in April, 1954, at the junction of the Tsinghai and Sinkiang borders. The hsien, which has a population of 3,000, has its administrative seat 50 miles southsouthwest of Tunhwang and west of the Supei Mongol hsien.

CHAPTER 15

SINKIANG

SINKIANG UIGUR AUTONOMOUS CH'Ü

Capital: Urumchi; area: 660,000; population: 4,873,608

Sinkiang is China's largest political unit. It is situated north of the Tibetan highlands and borders on three Central Asian republics of the Soviet Union—Kazakhstan, Kirghizia and Tadzhikistan. Aside from the highland margins that penetrate into Sinkiang from the south, the region can be divided into three major subregions: the rugged Tien Shan mountain system in the center, separating the Dzungaria basin in the north from the larger Tarim basin in the south.

The Tarim basin is bounded in the north by the Tien Shan, in the south by the Kunlun system, and extends from the Pamirs in the west to Kansu in the east. With a length of 850 miles from west to east and a width of 350 miles, the basin occupies about 55 per cent of all of Sinkiang. The oval-shaped basin can be visualized in the form of a series of concentric belts, proceeding from the outer mountain barriers, past the foothills and alluvial fans, a string of oases, the sandy desert and the playa lakes at the center.

The Kunlun system, which towers at 20,000 feet above the Tarim basin, is the northern edge of the Tibetan highlands. It extends from the Pamir mountain knot, branching out eastward where subsidiary ranges enclose the Tsaidam basin of Tsinghai. Beyond the zone of foothills, rising to an average elevation of 3,000 feet, semi-permanent mountain streams spread their water in irrigation ditches over their alluvial fans. Each oasis thus formed commands a piece of Sinkiang, including a bit of desert, some irrigated land with a chief town, and the well-watered mountain valleys upstream. The principal oases of the Tarim basin are Khotan, Yarkand, Kashgar and Aqsu. Between the oases and beyond stretches the desert, taking up about half the area of the entire Tarim basin. This is the nearly rainless Taklamakan, filled with great sand dunes, more developed here than anywhere else in

China. Sinkiang's main river, the Tarim, is fed by major mountain streams, such as the Khotan, Yarkand, Kashgar and Aqsu rivers. These rivers have the greatest flow in the late spring and early summer, when they are fed by the melting snow and glacier ice. A large part of their water evaporates, is used for irrigation or disappears in the desert sands before reaching the Tarim. Having skirted the northern edge of the Taklamakan, the Tarim River in turn reaches its terminal lake, the Lop Nor, a salt lake with a unique history. According to ancient Chinese sources, the lake was at 90° E and 41° N 2,000 years ago. Alternate sedimentation and wind deflation gradually diverted the lake basin southward and the Russian explorer Przhevalski found it at 40° N in 1876. The Swedish explorer Sven Hedin found subsequently that the Tarim had returned to its earlier course and that the Lop Nor occupied its original site. That is where the lake is shown on current Chinese maps.

The Tien Shan mountain system consists of a series of parallel ranges extending from Soviet Central Asia eastward into Sinkiang for 1,000 miles. Elevations reach 24,500 feet on the Soviet-Chinese border in the Pobeda (Victory) Peak and 23,600 feet in the Khan Tengri, just to the north. The ranges of the Tien Shan system enclose intermontane basins and valleys, where population and economic activities are concentrated. In the extreme west, the Borokhoro and Ketmen ranges enclose the Ili River valley, centered on the city of Kuldja and oriented toward the Soviet Union. Between the main Tien Shan and the Kuruk Tag lies the Yenki (Qara Shahr) depression occupied by the salt lake Bagrach Kol. Between the Bogdo Ula and the Chol Tag lies the Turfan depression. The bottom of the depression, at 427 feet below sea level, is the lowest point in China. At the eastern end of the Tien Shan are the twin Hami and Barkol depressions, respectively south and north of the Barkol Tag.

The Dzungarian basin, situated north of the Tien Shan, extends to the Altai Mountains on the Soviet and Mongolian borders. West of the Dzungarian basin, the Tarbagatai and Dzungarian Ala-Tau ranges enclose the Dzungarian Gates, main routeway between Dzungaria and the steppes of Kazakhstan. Like the Tarim basin, the Dzungarian subregion includes a zone of oases at the foot of the enclosing mountains and a steppe and desert belt in the center of the depression. Major oases along the north foot of the Tien Shan are Kitai, Urumchi and the Manass and Wusu oases; on the northern side of the Dzungarian basin are Tahcheng (Chuguchak) and Altai (Chenghwa or Sharasume).

Unlike the Tarim basin, Dzungaria has no unifying river. Dzungaria is slightly less arid than its neighbor to the south, its sand dunes are less developed and its grassland belt more ample. The main rivers are the intermittent Manass River, which sometimes reaches its terminal lake, the Telli Nor; and the upper Irtysh River, which flows west into the Soviet Union.

No part of China is as far removed from the moderating influence of oceans as is Sinkiang. The high mountains that enclose the region on all sides cut off maritime air masses and produce a continental arid steppe and desert climate throughout the region. Internal climatic differences are largely caused by the Tien Shan, which separates the exceptionally dry Tarim basin from less arid Dzungaria. The Tien Shan acts, in particular, as a climatic barrier against the continental polar air that enters Dzungaria from Siberia during the winter. As a result, average January temperatures in the Tarim basin are about 20° F (–7° C) compared with 5° F (–15° C) in many parts of Dzungaria. In the summer also, average temperatures north of the Tien Shan are generally lower than south of the mountains. In Dzungaria, July averages vary from 70° F (20° C) in the north to 75 F (24 C) in the south. In the Tarim basin, July averages in the neighborhood of 80° F (27° C) are more typical. The hottest point is the Turfan depression, where adiabatically heated air descending from the surrounding mountains produces a July average of 93° F (33.7° C).

While Dzungaria is exposed to the northern air masses, it is also accessible to Atlantic maritime polar air, especially during the spring. At that time of the year, weak cyclonic storms occasionally reach Dzungaria from the west. These storms, to be sure, have lost most of their moisture in their long overland route but they are the major factor in the slightly moister climate of northern Sinkiang. Urumchi, in the steppe belt along the northern foot of the Tien Shan, has an annual precipitation of nearly 10 inches. The Tarim basin, by contrast, is effectively barred from most moisture sources. It receives less than four inches a year. Charkhliq (Chohchiang), near the lower reaches of the Tarim River, has the reputation of being the driest point in China. Its average annual precipitation is one-fifth of an inch. In contrast to the spring storms in Dzungaria, whatever little moisture reaches the Tarim basin is of Pacific origin and occurs during the summer.

The mountain climate of the Tien Shan reflects the conditions of the adjoining basins. Greater precipitation and generally lower temperatures are characteristic of the northern slopes, where the snow line is at

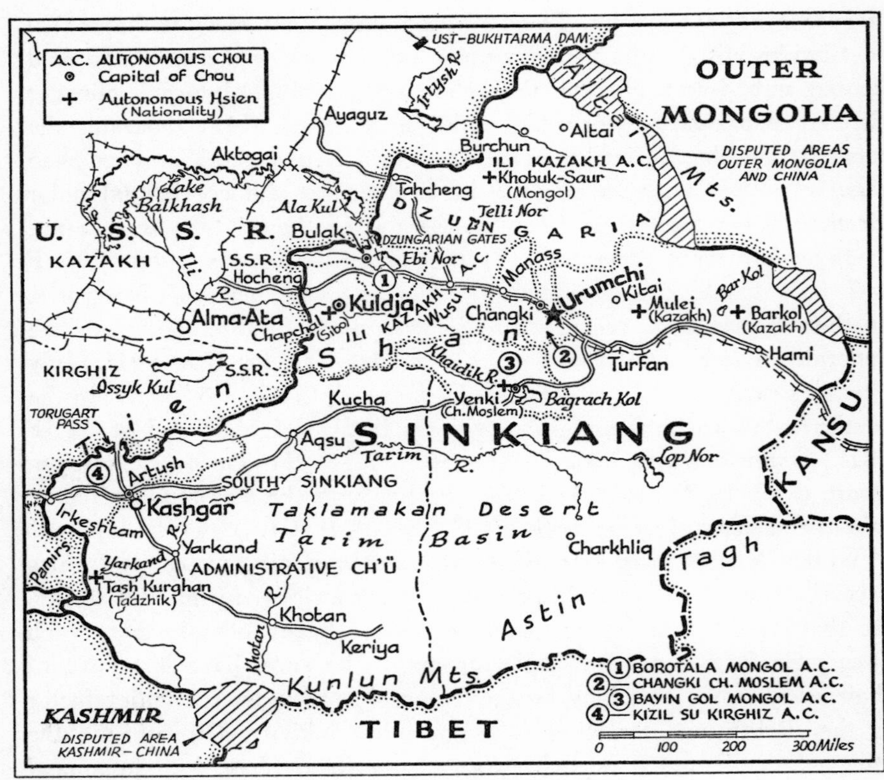
A.C. AUTONOMOUS CHOU
Capital of Chou
Autonomous Hsien (Nationality)
UST-BUKHTARMA DAM
Irtysh R.
OUTER MONGOLIA
Ayaguz
Altai
Burchun
Aktogai
ILI KAZAKH A.C.
Khobuk-Saur (Mongol)
DISPUTED AREAS OUTER MONGOLIA AND CHINA
Lake Balkhash
Ala Kul
Tahcheng
Telli Nor
Mts.
U. S. S. R.
KAZAKH S.S.R.
Bulak
DZUNGARIAN GATES
DZUNGARIA
Ebi Nor
Hocheng
Ili R.
Manass
Urumchi
Kitai
Bar Kol
Alma-Ata
Kuldja
ILI KAZAKH A.C.
Wusu
Changki
Mulei (Kazakh)
Barkol (Kazakh)
Chapchal (Sibo)
Shan
Tien Shan
Turfan
Hami
KIRGHIZ S.S.R.
Khaidik R.
Issyk Kul
Kucha
Yenki (Ch. Moslem)
Bagrach Kol
TORUGART PASS
SINKIANG
Aqsu
Tarim R.
Lop Nor
KANSU
Artush
SOUTH SINKIANG
Irkeshtam
Kashgar
Taklamakan Desert
Tarim Basin
Charkhliq
Tagh
Yarkand
Yarkand R.
Pamirs
ADMINISTRATIVE CH'Ü
Tash Kurghan (Tadzhik)
Khotan
Khotan R.
Keriya
Astin
Kunlun Mts.
1 BOROTALA MONGOL A.C.
2 CHANGKI CH. MOSLEM A.C.
3 BAYIN GOL MONGOL A.C.
4 KIZIL SU KIRGHIZ A.C.
KASHMIR
DISPUTED AREA KASHMIR-CHINA
TIBET
0 100 200 300 Miles

Sinkiang

11,500 feet. Forests and alpine meadows are well developed. Higher temperature and greater aridity are typical of the south slopes, where the snow line is at 13,000 feet and vegetation is sparse.

In accordance with the moister climate, chestnut soils are developed on the fringes of the central Dzungarian desert. The associated steppe vegetation constitutes an important belt of grazing land. The Tarim basin has no such grasslands and the population and economic activity are limited to the oases.

Climatic differences between north and south continue to be evident in the distribution of the rural economy. Widespread oasis agriculture in the Tarim basin occupies about 40 per cent of the population, while only 2 per cent are engaged in animal husbandry. North of the Tien Shan, the grasslands support about 35 to 40 per cent of the population through the grazing of herds.

A seven-month growing season in the south makes possible the raising of two crops, provided ample irrigation water is available. The first crop is usually sown in February and harvested in June, the second planted in July and harvested in October. Only one crop is harvested in Dzungaria, which has a five-month season.

The semi-circular oasis belt of the Tarim basin, west of a line linking Kucha and Keriya (Yütien), contains about 95 per cent of all oasis land and 97 per cent of the population of southern Sinkiang. There are concentrated the major towns of the Tarim basin, including Khotan, Yarkand, Kashgar and Aqsu.

Efforts have been made in recent years to expand the area under cultivation through the construction of new irrigation systems and the expansion of old ones. One of the major projects is the Hungyenchih reservoir, completed in the spring of 1953 in a gorge just south of Urumchi. The reservoir was designed to place an additional 6,000 hectares of desert under cultivation. The campaign to expand the sown area has resulted in an expansion of cultivated land from 1,050,000 hectares in 1949 to 1,400,000 hectares in 1955. Long-range plans call for the investigation of further expansion during 1955-1957. It is hoped to increase the sown area threefold to 4,000,000 hectares through appropriate irrigation works in the areas of Urumchi, Manass, Turfan and Aqsu.

Most of the reclamation work has been handled by Army personnel in Sinkiang. Acreage cultivated by the Army increased from 65,400 hectares in 1950 to more than 100,000 hectares in 1952. During the same period, Army-grown grain rose from 35,000 to 110,000 tons. The project that has been given the most publicity in recent years is the

Manass project, where reclamation personnel have brought large areas under cultivation. By 1954, 26,400 hectares had been won from the desert. Of the total arable land, 9,240 hectares were in winter wheat and 5,410 in cotton. By 1957, 79,200 hectares are to be reclaimed in the Manass area.

About 85 per cent of the total sown area is in grains. In 1954, for example, grains covered 1.2 million hectares out of a total cultivated area of 1.4 million hectares. Almost 40 per cent of the sown area is in wheat, with spring wheat predominating in the Dzungarian area and winter wheat in the Tarim basin. Rice, which covers 12 per cent of the cultivated area, is grown chiefly in the Aqsu valley, but also in the Ili River basin and along the north foot of the Tien Shan. Corn, another important grain occupying 21 per cent of the total crop area, predominates in southern Sinkiang. Total grain production in recent years has varied as follows (in million tons):

1949	1.1
1952	1.602
1953	1.6
1954	1.8
1957 Plan	2.175

Cotton and silk growing are important in the Tarim basin. Sinkiang's cotton is long-staple and the fiber grown in the Turfan depression is generally regarded as the finest. Total cotton output in 1954 was 16,200 tons. Silk growing occupies a large part of the population in the oases of Khotan, Aqsu and elsewhere. The oases of the Tarim basin are major producers of dried fruit, including raisins, pears and apricots. Hami is noted for its melons.

Outside of grain, the Chinese Communists publish production statistics for cotton and oil crops. Output in Sinkiang has fluctuated as follows in recent years (in tons):

	Cotton Lint	*Oil Crops*
1949	5,100	no data
1952	12,200	74,200
1953	12,500	no data
1954	16,200	69,600
1957 Plan	53,000	85,500

About 575,000 nomads, or 12 per cent of the total population, are engaged in animal husbandry, the great majority in the Dzungarian steppes. The herders are predominantly Kazakhs and Mongols in the north, Kirghiz and Tadzhiks in the south. As elsewhere in central Asia, transhumance is practiced, with herds moving to summer pastures in the mountains and winter pastures in the lowlands. About 60 per cent are sheep, with cattle, camels and horses making up the balance. Sheep and camel wool, hides and horse hair are major export items, shipped partly along the main road through Kansu to China or directly to the Soviet Union.

Sinkiang's livestock population has increased as follows in recent years (in million head):

1949	12.0
1952	13.815
1953	15.6
1954	17.04
1955 Plan	19.0
1957 Plan	23.124

The nature of Sinkiang's mineral resources was stressed in 1950 and 1951, when Soviet-Chinese joint stock companies were set up to exploit petroleum and nonferrous and rare metals. Mineral production sharply increased during the subsequent years and as of January 1, 1955, control over mineral exploitation passed entirely into Chinese hands.

The principal oilfield is at Tushantze, fifteen miles southeast of Wusu. Drilling began here in 1935 and the first petroleum was obtained in 1938. Daily output thereafter reached 100 tons a day. Crude oil production in 1954 was 25 times the output in 1951. The oilfield has a local refinery producing gasoline and a coking plant. Asphalt and barite plants were to be added in 1955.

Among nonferrous metals, Sinkiang has deposits of copper, lead, zinc and silver. Copper is found in the Paicheng-Kucha area on the south slopes of the Tien Shan. Complex lead-zinc-silver ores occur mainly in the Wukia area west of Kashgar and at Nilki (formerly Kungha), east of Kuldja. Molybdenum deposits are found near Tsingho and tungsten has also been exploited. Details of the exploitation of these minerals have not been disclosed, but gross output of the rare metals company rose 3.2 times from 1951 to 1954.

Coal, which is exploited in small amounts throughout the region, is mined especially near Urumchi. Together with near-by iron ore it forms the raw material base for a small metallurgical plant in operation at Urumchi.

Sinkiang is an important gold producer, yielding the precious metal both on the south slopes of the Altai Mountains and the north slopes of the Kunlun system. Virtually all the output stems from lodes. Other minerals are jade, obtained near Khotan and a major trade item since ancient times, as well as salt and gypsum found in recent and and ancient lake deposits.

Pending the completion of the Sinkiang railroad, the region is served by a number of major land routes that have been transportation links since ancient times. They are the North Road (north of the Tien Shan) passing from Kansu through Urumchi and Wusu, where it bifurcates into two routes going to the Soviet Union. The northern branch reaches the Turksib railroad at Ayaguz, the southern branch passes through the Ili valley to Alma-Ata. The South Road skirts the south foot of the Tien Shan, serving the major oases of the Tarim basin. It circles the Taklamakan desert and joins the little-frequented North Kunlun road passing south of the Lop Nor.

Several routes link Sinkiang and the Soviet Union. In the far north, the Irtysh is navigable in the summer for small vessels below Burchun (Puerhtsin). After the completion of the Ust-Bukhtarma dam in the Soviet Union the level of the Irtysh River will be raised, facilitating navigation in the upper course. South of the Irtysh are the two branches of the North Road, crossing the Soviet border in the Tahcheng-Bakhty and Hocheng (Hoerhkwosze or Horgos)–Panfilov areas. Between the two branches lie the Dzungarian Gates, an ancient routeway unused in recent times by modern transportation. In April, 1955, a Soviet railroad survey team began to study a route for the Soviet end of the Sinkiang railroad, proceeding from Aktogai on the Turksib railroad to the Dzungarian Gates.

From Kashgar, in southwestern Sinkiang, two routes cross the border into the Soviet Union. One proceeds north across the 12,155-foot-high Torugart Pass into the Kirghiz SSR and the Issyk-Kul area. The other, west of Kashgar, crosses the Soviet line at Irkeshtam (Ierhkoszetang), continuing toward the Fergana Valley.

Three cities are directly under the jurisdiction of the Sinkiang government. They are Urumchi, the capital, Kuldja and Kashgar.

Urumchi was officially known as Tihwa, its Chinese name, until February, 1954. Situated at the north foot of the Tien Shan, the 180,000-population city is the center of one of Sinkiang's agricultural districts in the Dzungarian steppe belt. Urumchi's industries include a small iron and steel plant named "August 1." The plant had two small blast furnaces and a third larger furnace, exceeding the previous two in combined capacity, was completed in 1954. Other factories make auto repairs, manufacture cotton textiles (the "July 1" mill), and produce cement, chemicals (acids, dyes) and flour. Industries are powered by a coal fed electric plant and the near-by Ulabai hydroelectric station built between 1951 and 1955. The Liutawan coal mine is near Urumchi.

Kuldja, Sinkiang's second largest city, is officially known by its Chinese name Ining. The city, with a population of 100,000, is the center of the Ili valley, which is enclosed by high ranges of the Tien Shan and opens toward the Soviet Union, 40 miles westward. Kuldja is linked by road with Alma-Ata in the Kazakh SSR and with Urumchi.

Kashgar is the largest city of the Tarim basin, situated also near the Soviet border. Its Chinese official name is K'o-shih, an abbreviated form of K'o-shih-k'a-erh, the phonetic rendering of Kashgar. Prior to 1950, Kashgar was known in Chinese as Shufu. The city has a population of about 75,000, predominantly Uigur in ethnic composition. It is a center for trade in cotton, silk and sheepskins. Just southeast of Kashgar is the Chinese hsien town of Shuleh or Sulo. known in Uigur as Yangi Shahr ("new city"). By analogy, the Uigurs sometimes apply the name Kona Shahr ("old city") to Kashgar proper.

As might be expected from the predominantly settled rural economy of southern Sinkiang, 75 per cent of the population of Sinkiang is concentrated in the oases fringing the Tarim basin. Since the oases cover a total area of only 5,500 square miles and the mountains and deserts are virtually unpopulated, the average population density in the settled areas of southern Sinkiang can be estimated at about 500 persons to the square mile. Of the total population of about 1,200,000 in the Dzungarian section of Sinkiang, about 40 per cent are nomadic herders who graze their livestock in the steppes. The rest is settled along the fringes of the enclosing mountain ranges, chiefly the north foot of the Tien Shan.

Ethnically, the Sinkiang region is 75 per cent Uigur. It was on the basis of the predominant Uigur population that Sinkiang was transformed from a province into an autonomous ch'ü in September, 1955. The Uigurs live predominantly south of the Tien Shan in the oases of the Tarim basin, where they engage in agriculture and commerce.

The Kazakhs are the second largest ethnic group, comprising about 10 per cent of the total population. They are chiefly nomadic herdsmen in the steppes of Dzungaria, north of the Tien Shan. Third are the Chinese, with about 6 per cent, living in the cities and towns, both north and south of the Tien Shan. Chinese Moslems, who number 2.5 per cent of the total population, are settled chiefly in the area around Urumchi. Lesser minorities are the Kirghiz, Mongols, Tadzhiks and Sibo.

Administratively, these minorities are constituted in five autonomous chou and six autonomous hsien within the Sinkiang Uigur Autonomous Ch'ü as a whole. Of the eleven autonomous units, nine are situated in and north of the Tien Shan. This illustrates the greater ethnic diversity of Dzungaria compared with the more homogeneous and predominantly Uigur Tarim basin.

The Kazakh minority has one chou and two hsien in Dzungaria. The Ili Kazakh Autonomous Chou includes virtually all of Dzungaria, except for the southeastern section. It was set up in November, 1954, and has a population of 770,000, of whom the Kazakhs are a bare majority. The capital of the chou was set up in Kuldja, in the Ili valley; other major towns are Tahcheng and Altai. The two Kazakh hsien, situated in southeastern Dzungaria, were both created late in 1954. They are the Mulei Kazakh Autonomous Hsien with its headquarters at Muleiho, 130 miles east of Urumchi, and the Barkol (Palikun) Kazakh Autonomous Hsien, with its seat at Barkol (former Chensi), situated northwest of Hami across the Barkol range. The Barkol hsien has a population of about 10,000 Kazakhs.

The Ili Kazakh Autonomous Chou includes within its territory a Mongol autonomous chou, a Mongol hsien and a Sibo hsien. The Borotala Mongol Autonomous Chou occupies the valley of the Borotala River, between the Borokhoro Mountains and the Dzungarian Ala-Tau, and its terminal lake Ebi Nor. The chou was formed in 1954 and has a population of 41,100, of whom 24,600 are Mongols. The administrative seat is Bulak (Polo), west of the lake Ebi Nor.

The Khobuk-Saur Mongol Autonomous Hsien is situated 140 miles east of Tahcheng. It occupies the Khobuk valley at the south foot of the Saur Range. The hsien was established in 1954 with its seat at Hofeng.

The Chapchal Sibo Autonomous Hsien is situated on the southern side of the Ili valley at the Soviet border. The hsien, established in March, 1954, is named for the Chapchal Pass in the Ketmen range. The total population of 35,000 includes 9,100 Sibo. The administrative seat is at Ningsi, westsouthwest of Kuldja.

Outside of the Kazakh chou, in the Urumchi agricultural area, is the Changki Chinese Moslem Autonomous Chou, with headquarters at Changki, northwest of Urumchi. The population of 98,000, of whom 37 per cent are Chinese Moslems, is engaged in mixed farming and animal husbandry in a territory that extends from the Tien Shan down the northern slopes into the Dzungarian desert. At the time of the formation of the chou in July, 1954, it had 26,000 hectares under crops and 280,000 head of livestock.

On the south slopes of the Tien Shan, in the drainage of the lake Bagrach Kol, lies the Bayin Gol Mongol Autonomous Chou, set up in May, 1954. The name Bayin Gol, rendered phonetically in Chinese as Pa-yin Kuo-leng, means "rich river" and may refer to the Khaidik River, the area's principal stream emptying into the Bagrach Kol. The chou, centered at Yenki, has a population of 57,000, of whom 20,000 are Mongols. The economy combines animal husbandry in the upland steppes–there were 670,000 head of livestock in 1954—with irrigated agriculture around Yenki and fishing and salt collection in the lake Bagrach Kol. About half the population of the entire Mongol chou is concentrated in Yenki hsien, which was set up as a Chinese Moslem autonomous hsien in March, 1954. Its population is 28,000, including almost 10,000 Chinese Moslems engaged in irrigated farming.

The southwestern section of Sinkiang contains nearly 75 per cent of the total population and is at the same time far removed from Urumchi, the administrative capital of Sinkiang. To facilitate the administration of this economically important, yet remote, section, the Sinkiang government set up in August, 1954, a special South Sinkiang Administrative Ch'ü, with headquarters in Kashgar. The South Sinkiang Ch'ü includes the entire Tarim basin west of Long. 84 degrees E., with most of the great oases and a population of about 3,000,000. Ethnically, the population is predominantly Uigur and there are only two autonomous units: the Kizil Su Kirghiz Autonomous Chou and the Tash Kurghan Tadzhik Autonomous Hsien.

The Kizil Su Kirghiz Autonomous Chou lies along the border of the Kirghiz SSR of the Soviet Union. It is named for the Kizil Su, rendered in Chinese as K'o-tzu-le Su, the Kirghiz designation of the Kashgar River. The chou, which was created in July, 1954, has its headquarters at Artush, rendered in Chinese as A-t'u-shih, 15 miles northwest of Kashgar. The chou extends for 300 miles along the south slopes of the Tien Shan and has a population of 135,000. Of these about 50,000 are Kirghiz, the others Uigur, Chinese, Tadzhik and Uzbek. In 1954, the chou had 20,000 hectares under irrigated cultivation and livestock holdings of 600,000 head.

The Tash Kurghan Tadzhik Autonomous Hsien, set up in 1954, lies at an elevation of 10,000 feet on the eastern fringes of the Pamir highlands. It is situated on the Tash Kurghan, a headstream of the Yarkand River. The total population is 10,000, of whom 78 per cent are Sarikoli Tadzhiks. The hsien seat is Puli, known by the Tadzhiks as Tash Kurghan ("stone fort").

CHAPTER 16

THE TIBETAN HIGHLANDS

The Tibetan highlands are a unique part of China. Extending over an area of 900,000 square miles in the heart of Asia, this region lies for the most part above 10,000 feet. Within its largely desolate highland plains live 3 million persons who carry on a precarious existence with animal husbandry and marginal agriculture. As treated in this chapter, the Tibetan highlands are taken to include the province of Tsinghai and Tibet proper.

In broad strokes the Tibetan highlands can be divided into four major regions bounded on the north by the Kunlun and Nan Shan mountain systems, on the south by the Himalayas and on the east by the longitudinal ranges of western Szechwan. The four regions are: the Tsinghai plateau, the Tsinghai-Sikang canyon country, the Chang Tang plateau of northern Tibet and the great valley of southern Tibet.

The Tsinghai plateau lies between the Nan Shan in the north and the Bayan Kara Mountains in the south. On the eastern side of the plateau, which takes up the northern part of Tsinghai Province, rises the Yellow River. Rising at an elevation of 13,000 feet, this great northern Chinese stream flows through the two lakes Kyaring and Ngoring and then describes a zigzag course between the Bayan Kara, Amne Machin (Kishih) and Tasurkai (Sitsing) mountains. In the northern part of the plateau are the Tsaidam and Koko Nor basins. The former is an oval-shaped, mountain-ringed desert swamp at an elevation of 9,000 feet. The latter is occupied by the lake Koko Nor or Tsing Hai, Mongol and Chinese designations that mean "blue sea." The lake, which lies at an elevation of 10,000 feet, is the largest of the Tibetan highlands with an area of 1,600 square miles.

The Tsinghai-Sikang canyon country lies south of the Bayan Kara Mountains. This land of great valleys and intervening high ranges is the source area of some of Asia's greatest rivers—the Yangtze, the Mekong, the Salween and the Irrawaddy. The valleys of these rivers, which have a general southeasterly trend, offer so little level land that most people live on the mountainsides between 9,000 and 13,000 feet.

The westernmost range of the canyon country is the Nyenchen Tanglha, separating the Brahmaputra and Salween valleys and continued southward by the Kaolikung Mountains on the Yünnan-Burma border. Toward the east follow in succession the Nu Shan, between the Salween and the Mekong, and the Ningtsing Mountains, between the Mekong and the upper Yangtze River. Beyond the Yangtze are the canyons and ranges of the dissected Sikang plateau, since 1955 part of western Szechwan.

The Chang Tang plateau forms the largest part of Tibet proper. Situated between the Kunlun system in the north and the Transhimalayan ranges in the south, this desolate upland consists of a series of desert playa basins and massive, low mountains, trending generally east-west. Situated at an average elevation of 15,000 feet, the Chang Tang is too cold and dry for grass or cultivated crops. Among the hundreds of lakes, both fresh and salt, the largest is the Tengri Nor, known as Nam Tso in Tibetan. The southern margin of the Chang Tang is formed by the massive Transhimalayan ranges, so described by the Swedish explorer Sven Hedin, but variously known as the Kailas in the west and the Nyenchen Tanglha in the east. On Chinese maps, the Transhimalayan ranges are designated as Kang-ti-szu Shan.

The great valley of southern Tibet extends for more than 1,000 miles between the Transhimalaya and the Himalaya. It is occupied by the upper Indus River in the west and the upper Brahmaputra in the east. In this trench, situated at 12,000 feet above sea level, are concentrated the population and economy of Tibet. The valley includes the chief cities of Tibet, including Lhasa, Shigatse and Gyangtse, and most of the meager agriculture and animal husbandry.

The climate of the Tibetan highlands is conditioned by its great elevation and by the encircling mountains. The high altitudes and the rarefied air combine with intense insolation and strong radiation to produce sharp temperature contrasts between night and day and between the dry winters and moist summers. Conditions differ widely, depending on elevation and exposure. In the northern Tsinghai plateau, for example, the winter lasts six months and the summer is characterized by a wide diurnal temperature range with frosts mornings and evenings and afternoon readings of up to 85° F (29° C). In the Chang Tang plateau the average annual temperature is 23° F (–5° C), with summers virtually absent. Only in a few months does the average temperature rise above 32° F and even during the warmest months water freezes at night.

By contrast, southeastern Tibet has a relatively mild climate, resembling the conditions of western Yünnan. Lhasa monthly averages range from 32° F (0° C) in January to 63° F (17° C). Lhasa is at an elevation of 12,200 feet, where intensive radiation and the long winter reduce the growing season to 140 days, from May to September. This is also the rainy season when the valleys of southeastern Tibet come under the influence of the monsoon from the Indian Ocean. Lhasa's average annual precipitation is 64 inches, most of it occurring in July and August. However, annual rainfall is highly irregular from year to year, ranging from 200 inches to 20 inches.

The high, nearly parallel ranges in southern Tibet operate as an effective rain barrier. Almost none of the moisture crosses the Transhimalayan ranges into the Chang Tang plateau and the Tsaidam basin. The average annual precipitation there is less than four inches.

Differences in climate, vegetation and agricultural land use are all conditioned by elevation. In the lowest valleys, below 5,000 feet, a very mild climate prevails making possible the cultivation of corn and tea. From 5,000 to 10,000 feet, the cultivation of corn, potatoes and grains is possible, with the first two crops dropping out above 10,000 feet. On rainy slopes, a slim forest growth is found below 11,500 feet, followed by highland steppe and meadows. The snow line is generally found at 16,000 feet in the Tibetan highlands.

Most of the population lives along the eastern and southern margins of the Tibetan highlands where lower elevations provide meager agricultural and grazing possibilities. Cultivators are settled in valleys and intermontane basins, while herdsmen migrate over the upland pastures.

The main agricultural districts are the Sining valley east of the lake Koko Nor and the Brahmaputra valley, especially in the neighborhood of Lhasa. Barley, buckwheat, rye and peas are the leading crops. Barley, the staple grain of the Tibetans, is made into tsamba, a national food made of parched barley, butter and tea. Barley grows at elevations up to 11,500 feet. It is sown in April and harvested in August.

Animal husbandry is the basic economic activity of the highlands. The main grazing lands are in the valleys of southern Tibet, the upper reaches of the Yellow and Yangtze rivers, and the Tsaidam basin. The stock is driven into the uplands after the melting of the snows. In the fall it is returned to the valleys and foothills. Yak, sheep, camels and horses make up the bulk of the herds. The yak is the typical Tibetan draft animal, whose endurance and surefootedness make it well suited for highland travel.

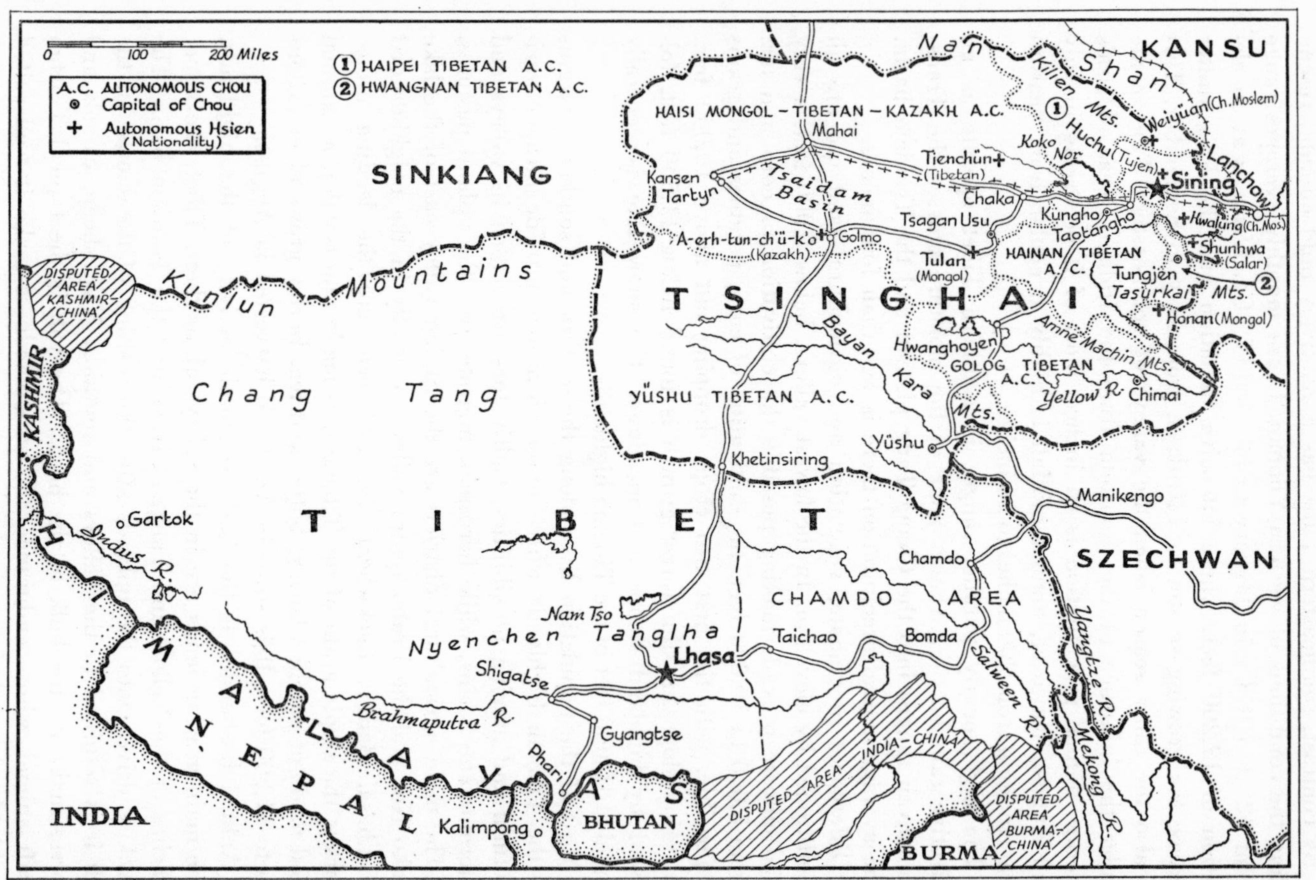

Tibet and Tsinghai

Mineral resources are still largely unexplored and unexploited. Gold has been found in the upper reaches of the major streams, including the Sining River near lake Koko Nor, the Yellow River and the Yangtze. Major efforts are being made to explore for petroleum in the Tsaidam basin, and salt is obtained in many of the upland lakes.

The main highways of the Tibetan highlands focus on Lhasa. They are the Tsinghai-Tibet road, linking Lhasa and Sining; the Sikang-Tibet road, linking Lhasa and Chamdo; the India-Tibet road, linking Lhasa and Kalimpong; and the West Tibet road, running up the valley of the Brahmaputra to Gartok, on the upper Indus River, and on into Ladakh. After years of construction in difficult terrain, the Tsinghai and Sikang roads were opened to truck traffic late in 1954.

The Tibetan highlands are inhabited predominantly by Tibetans. They make up about 60 per cent of the total population. Of the 1,700,000 Tibetans listed as of June, 1953, 450,000 live in Tsinghai and 1,250,000 in Tibet proper. The rest of the population includes Chinese, settled in the Sining area and around Chamdo; Mongols and Kazakhs in the Tsaidam basin west of lake Koko Nor, and Chinese Moslems, Tujen and Salar groups in the Sining area.

TSINGHAI PROVINCE

Capital: Sining; area: 320,000; population: 1,676,534

Out of Tsinghai's total population, more than 700,000 persons, or about 42 per cent, are members of national minorities. The Tibetans, with 450,000, are the leading minority group. Some of the minorities, such as the Tibetans, Mongols and Kazakhs, lead traditionally a pastoral mode of life. Herding is the chief occupation of 440,000 persons, or about 27 per cent of the total population. Other minorities, such as the Chinese Moslems, Tujen, and Salar, as well as the Chinese themselves are essentially cultivators.

The population and economy of Tsinghai are concentrated in the Sining area east of lake Koko Nor. This area, situated west of Lanchow, the capital of adjoining Kansu Province, is the northeastern gateway to Tsinghai and the Tibetan highlands. Here Chinese settlers have penetrated deeply into Tibetan ethnic territory.

Sining, the capital, is situated on the south bank of the Sining River, a left tributary of the Yellow River, at an elevation of 7,500 feet. It is the center of Tsinghai's agricultural district, producing mainly grains, such as spring wheat and barley. Sining is reached by highway from

Lanchow and is the focus of Tsinghai's transportation routes. From Sining highways go north across the Kilien Mountains into the Kansu corridor, west to the Tsaidam basin, and southwest to the Tsinghai plateau. Sining's excellent position makes it the natural marketing and shipping center for the province's products, which consist largely of wool, hides and salt.

Enclosed within the Chinese-majority area around Sining are three autonomous hsien based on the Tujen, Chinese Moslem and Salar minorities, all established in February, 1954. The Tujen Autonomous Hsien is situated at Huchu, 30 miles northeast of Sining. The hsien has a population of 160,000, of which 13.5 per cent, or almost 20,000 persons, belong to the titular Tujen nationality. The Tujen ("T'u people") are Lamaist in religion and speak Mongor, a form of ancient Mongolian.

Southeast of Sining, in the upper Yellow River valley, are the Chinese Moslem and Salar autonomous hsien. The Chinese Moslems have their seat at Hwalung, 45 miles southeast of Sining. The Salar have their headquarters at Shunhwa, on the south bank of the Yellow River and 70 miles southeast of Sining. The Shunhwa Salar Autonomous Hsien has a population of 42,000, including 22,000 persons of the Salar nationality which is a Turkic Moslem group.

In 1955, the total cultivated area of Tsinghai amounted to 370,000 hectares, nearly all of which was in the Chinese-populated Sining area. The expected agricultural output in that year was 425,000 tons of food crops (mainly grain) and 20,000 tons of oilseeds.

Livestock numbers have increased considerably in Tsinghai in recent years. Total holdings rose from 7.15 million head in 1949 to more than 12.4 million in 1954. The livestock goal for 1957 is set at 19.7 million head.

Outside of the Sining district extend the sparsely populated highlands of Tsinghai, inhabited by Tibetan herders, and the Tsaidam basin, where Tibetans are found next to Mongols and Kazakhs. The non-Chinese part of Tsinghai, which includes more than 90 per cent of the area, but only one-third of the population of the province, is divided (as of January, 1956) into five Tibetan autonomous chou, one joint Mongol-Tibetan-Kazakh chou, and one Mongol autonomous hsien.

The five Tibetan chou, which include nearly all of Tsinghai's Tibetan population of 450,000, are the Haipei Tibetan Autonomous Chou, north of lake Koko Nor; the Hainan Tibetan Autonomous Chou, south of the Koko Nor; the Hwangnan Tibetan Autonomous Chou, south of the Yellow River, on the Kansu border; the Golog Tibetan Autonomous Chou, in southeastern Tsinghai, astride the uppermost course of the

Yellow River, and the Yüshu Tibetan Autonomous Chou, in the uppermost reaches of the Yangtze River, in southwestern Tsinghai.

The Haipei ("north of the lake") autonomous chou was set up in late 1953 between lake Koko Nor and the Kilien Mountains in the Kansu border. It has a population of 70,000, including 24,000 Tibetans. The administrative center, Weiyüan, also is the seat of a Chinese Moslem autonomous hsien, situated on the northern margins of the agricultural area of Sining.

The Hainan ("south of the lake") autonomous chou was established about the same time (December, 1953) as its northern counterpart. The southern chou has a population of 100,000, of which 70 per cent are Tibetans. The chou capital, Kungho, is situated on the Sining-Yüshu highway, which traverses the chou from northeast to southwest. The name Kungho was applied before 1954 to the village of Chükow, just southeast on the Yellow River. In that year the Kungho hsien was moved to the present site, formerly called Kiapukia.

The Hwangnan ("south of the Yellow") autonomous chou was established in 1953 south of the Yellow River along the Kansu border. Its population is 72,000, including 64,000 Tibetans. Its administrative center is Tungjen, on a road southwest from Shunhwa.

The Golog (Kuo-lo) autonomous chou, named for a Tibetan tribe, was established in 1954. Its headquarters was initially named Ch'a-lang Szu (lamasery), on the Yellow River. In 1955, in connection with the establishment of four hsien within the chou, the administrative center was given as Chimai. It was not immediately clear whether Chimai was a new name for the lamasery or another location. The chou has a population of 110,000, of whom 90,000 are engaged in animal husbandry and the rest in crop tilling.

The Yüshu autonomous chou dates from February, 1952. Its administrative center is Yüshu, main town of southern Tsinghai. Yüshu was temporarily classified as a provincially administered city during 1952 and 1953, when it was officially called Chiehku, the Chinese rendering of the Tibetan name Jyeku (ndo). Yüshu is a major highway center, linked by an automobile road with Sining (since 1954) and by a route with Manikengo on the Sikang-Tibet highway. The chou, which is crossed in its western part by the Tsinghai-Tibet highway, has a population of close to 100,000, mainly Tibetan.

West of lake Koko Nor, in the Tsaidam basin, is the vast Haisi ("west of the lake") Mongol-Tibetan-Kazakh Autonomous Chou. This unit, officially established in January, 1954, has its headquarters at Tsagan Usu ("white water"), rendered phonetically in Chinese as

Ch'a-han-wu-su (until 1954, called Tulan), on the Tsinghai-Tibet highway. The chou was formed through the amalgamation of three autonomous hsien, one each of the Mongol, Tibetan and Kazakh nationality. The Mongol autonomous hsien has its seat at Shangko, also known as Hsiang-jih-t'e, on the Tibet highway southwest of the chou capital. The name Tulan, formerly applied to the chou center, is now applied to the seat of the Mongol hsien. The Tibetan autonomous hsien has its seat at Tienchün, on the Buhain Gol and 70 miles west of the lake Koko Nor. The Kazakh autonomous hsien is situated at the highway junction of Golmo (Chinese phonetics Ka-erh-mu), where the Tsinghai-Sinkiang highway joins the Tsinghai-Tibet road. The Kazakh name of the hsien is rendered on Chinese maps as A-erh-tun-ch'ü-k'o. The total population of the three-nationality chou was given as 20,000 in 1954, of whom 50 per cent were Kazakhs.

The desolate Tsaidam basin became the center of a major Chinese oil-exploration effort in 1955. Exploratory drilling is being pressed along the northern margins of the salt marsh that occupies the center of the basin. To insure transportation for the prospecting teams, two new highways were laid. One, about 540 miles long, traverses the northern edge of the Tsaidam from east to west. It links Kansen on the Tsinghai-Sinkiang road with Chaka on the Tsinghai-Tibet road west of lake Koko Nor. The other road traverses the basin from north to south, linking Tunhwang (Kansu Province) via Mahai with Golmo, road center on the southern edge of the Tsaidam. Food for the exploration parties is supplied by two state farms set up at Golmo and at Tehlingha, on the transverse east-west road. A newly opened coal mine supplies the required fuel. A railroad into the basin is projected.

Little information is available on the Honan ("south of the river") Mongol Autonomous Hsien, which first appeared on Chinese maps in 1952. Situated in the Sitsing Mountains on the right bank of the upper Yellow River, it is bounded on the north by the Hwangnan Tibetan chou, on the west by the Hainan Tibetan chou and on the east by the South Kansu Tibetan chou.

TIBET AUTONOMOUS CH'U

Capital: Lhasa; area: 580,000; population: 1,273,969

The physical and economic characteristics have been discussed in the general treatment of the Tibetan highlands and the following section will be devoted to the political and other changes that have occurred in Tibet proper since 1951.

Prior to the Chinese political and military seizure of Tibet in that year, Tibet had been under the supreme control of the 14th Dalai Lama, who was installed in 1940 and assumed full power in 1950 after a ten-year regency. The control of the Dalai Lama and his Tibetan Local Government extended over that part of eastern Tibet known as Kham, with its center at Chamdo (Chinese *Changtu*). Although the Tibetans were in effective control of the Chamdo Area, the Chinese had claimed the territory for several decades and had shown it on their maps as part of Sikang Province.

When the Chinese People's Liberation Army began its drive on Tibet in October, 1950, the Chamdo Area was the first to come under Chinese control. It was thought at first that the long disptued area would be made part of Sikang Province to conform with existing Chinese maps. However, when the Chinese announced the formation of the Kantse Tibetan Autonomous Chou in November, 1950, it was noted that the autonomous unit extended westward as far as the upper Yangtze River and did not include the Chamdo Area. The administrative status of the area remained in doubt as Chinese pronouncements referred to Chamdo in the context of both Tibet and Sikang. In the fall of 1953, a separate administration, the so-called People's Liberation Committee, was set up in the Chamdo Area. Three deputies from the Chamdo Area were listed separately, neither under Tibet or Sikang, among the delegations to the First Chinese National People's Congress in September, 1954. Finally, when the results of the 1953 census were released in November, 1954, the population of Chamdo (300,000) was listed as part of Tibet.

Meanwhile, the Chinese had signed in May, 1951, an agreement with the Dalai Lama Government for the peaceful occupation of Tibet and late in 1951, Chinese troops entered Lhasa, the Tibetan capital. The agreement provided for the return to Tibet of the Chinese-sponsored 10th Panchen Lama, traditional ruler of the Tashi Lumpo monastery at Shigatse, Tibet's second largest city. The Panchen Lama returned to Tibet in April, 1952, and organized a government, the so-called Panchen Kanpo Lija Committee. This body has exercised administrative control over the Shigatse area, while the Dalai Lama's Tibetan Local Government has had jurisdiction over the rest of Tibet. Both Tibetan bodies have operated under the supervision of representatives of the Peking Government.

In March, 1955, the Peking Government decided to take steps to set up a Tibetan Autonomous Ch'ü. A preparatory committee, including representatives of the Dalai Lama and the Panchen Lama governments, the Chamdo Area administration and the Peking Government, was charged with preparations aimed at the establishment of the autonomous ch'ü. The inclusion of the Chamdo representatives demonstrated officially that the Chamdo Area was to become part of autonomous Tibet.

Perhaps the most important single achievement of the Chinese since their occupation of Tibet has been the construction of the Tsinghai and Sikang highways for truck transportation. The highways, completed in December, 1954, put Lhasa within two weeks' truck travel of the railheads of Lanchow in Kansu and Chengtu in Szechwan. In the course of 1955 and 1956, a truck road was built from Lhasa to Shigatse and Gyangtse, and on to Phari on the Indian border, a total distance of 350 miles.

Economic projects scheduled for Tibet include the construction of small hydroelectric plants at Lhasa and Shigatse. A small tanning and leather-working factory is to be set up in Lhasa, and an ironworking plant will be built to produce farm implements and simple machine parts. In the field of agriculture, flood control and irrigation is planned in the Lhasa and Shigatse areas and an experimental agricultural station at Lhasa is to be expanded.

With the exception of Chamdo, in eastern Tibet, the major centers of Tibet are situated in the great east-west valley south of the Transhimalayan ranges.

Lhasa, the capital, is situated at an elevation of 12,000 feet, on a left tributary of the Brahmaputra. The city, dominated by the spectacular Potala, residence of the Dalai Lama, is the center of a small agricultural district and the political, religious and commercial center of Tibet. Its population is about 50,000.

Shigatse, Tibet's second city, is situated on the Nienchu River, a right tributary of the Brahmaputra. It also lies at the heart of a small farming area that comes under the control of the Panchen Lama, with residence in the Tashi Lumpo lamasery. Shigatse's population is estimated at 20,000.

Gyangtse, the third city in the central part of the valley, lies on the road to India and has a population of about 10,000.

Chamdo, the center of eastern Tibet, is six days' truck travel from Lhasa since the completion of the Sikang-Tibet road. It is situated on the upper Mekong in the great canyon country of the Tsinghai-Sikang borderlands.

The main town of western Tibet is Gartok, in the upper reaches of the Indus River. It is a major trade center on the route linking Tibet and Kashmir.

BIBLIOGRAPHIC NOTE

In writing this book, the author has based himself almost entirely on Communist sources, both Chinese and Soviet. Most of the information, moreover, was gathered from newspapers and periodicals. It must be remembered that under Communist regimes publishing is a state monopoly. The main newspapers, such as *Jen-min Jih-pao (People's Daily)* in Peking and *Pravda* and *Izvestia* in Moscow, are in effect official publications. In the language of researchers, they are primary source materials. It is this type of material, painstakingly gathered and collated over a number of years, that has furnished the basis for this volume.

The author has benefited from the mimeographed serial publications of the American Consulate General in Hong Kong, which were kindly made available by the External Research Staff of the Department of State. These publications include: *Current Background,* which reproduces major Chinese Communist documents and presents original research on selected topics; *Survey of China Mainland Press,* which reproduces the English-language daily news report of the New China News Agency and translates important articles from the Chinese; *Extracts from China Mainland Magazines,* which translates selected articles from Chinese Communist periodicals.

Of occasional value were the Chinese Communist English-language magazines *People's China,* a fortnightly, and the two pictorial monthlies, *China Reconstructs* and *China Pictorial.*

A surprising amount of information was gathered from Soviet newspapers and periodicals. In his continuing research on economic geographic developments in the Soviet Union, the author is scanning regularly seventeen daily newspapers published in Moscow and in the Soviet republics, as well as magazines in the geographic field. These sources have often supplied data not encountered in the Chinese press, or disclosed considerably later by the Peking regime. Examples of earlier Soviet disclosure are the location of the automobile plant at Changchun, printed in Izvestia as early as October, 1954, and the location of the tractor plant at Loyang, in May, 1955.

Because of the need for up-to-date economic information, monographs were of little use. However, a number of Soviet books on the geography of China and Russian translations from the Chinese provided useful background. These included:

Akademiya Nauk SSSR, Institut Geografii, *Vostochnyy Kitay* (East China), Moscow, Geografizdat, 1955.

Ch'u Shao-t'ang, *Geografiya Novogo Kitaya* (Geography of the New China), translated from the Chinese by L. S. Gingol'd and A. M. Ledovskiy, Moscow, Izdatel'stvo Inostrannoy Literatury, 1953.

Lesa i Pochvy Kitaya (Forests and Soils of China), symposium translated from the Chinese by B. A. Mitbreyt and Ya. M. Berger, Izd. Inost. Lit., 1955.

Murzayev, E. M., *Severo-Vostochnyy Kitay* (Northeast China), Moscow, Akademiya Nauk SSSR, 1955.

Nikitin, N., and I. Fedorov, *Tyan'tszin'* (Tientsin), Moscow, Geografizdat, 1953.

Ovdiyenko, I. Kh., *Vnutrennyaya Mongoliya* (Inner Mongolia), Moscow, Geografizdat, 1954.

Tambovskiy, A. M., *Mukden*, Moscow, Geografizdat, 1954.

A major part of the research that went into the present volume was concerned with the compilation of up-to-date economic statistics. The statistical framework of the first five-year plan was provided by the text of the plan, published in Peking in August, 1955. Its reference is as follows:

Chung-hua Jen- min Kung-ho-kuo Fa-chan Kuo-min Ching-chi-ti Ti-i-ko Wu-nien Chi-hua 1953-1957 (First Five-Year Plan for Development of the National Economy of the People's Republic of China in 1953-1957), Peking, Jen-min Ch'u-pan-she, 1955.

This book contains six documents. Of these, four brief statements concerning the preparation of the draft plan in the first half of 1955 and the report of Li Fu-ch'un, a Deputy Premier and chairman of the State Planning Commission, on the five-year plan had been published in the press. But the book also includes the actual text of the five-year plan (pages 7-156), not previously published.

The text of the plan supplied 1952 actual figures and 1957 plan figures for the statistical tables that appear in Part I of this book. Other figures were obtained by computation from the annual reports on plan fulfillment published in September of 1953, 1954 and 1955 for the preceding years. A large amount of regional statistical material was pieced together from countless isolated news items and other sources.

Detailed analysis of Chinese Communist maps and atlases supplied much valuable information. Comparison of several editions of the same map or atlas would frequently disclose data not otherwise available. The most important map sources were:

Chung-hua Jen-min Kung-ho-kuo Fen-sheng Ti-t'u (Provincial Atlas of the People's Republic of China), Shanghai, Ti-t'u Ch'u-pan-she, 1953.

Chung-hua Jen-min Kung-ho-kuo Hsing-cheng Ch'ü-hua T'u (Map of the Administrative Divisions of the People's Republic of China), Shanghai, Ti-t'u Ch'u-pan-she, first edition, January, 1954; third edition, April, 1955.

INDEX